Luisa Sweeney.

WRITING MEDICO-LEGAL REPORTS IN CIVIL CLAIMS

an essential guide

Best wishes
Giles Eyre

Giles Eyre and Lynden Alexander

Published by Professional Solutions Publications

This edition is published in 2015 by Professional Solutions Publications, 12 Bloomsbury Square, London WC1A 2LP

Professional Solutions Publications is an imprint of: Professional Solutions Learning and Development (www.prosols.uk.com)

Typeset in Minion Pro and Lato by
Karen Arnott, Graphic Designer, 14a High Street, West Wratting, Cambridge. CB21 5LU. (www.karenarnott.co.uk)

EDITORS' NOTE: The views set out in this text are those of the authors alone. Whilst great care has been taken in connection with the preparation of this work, no liability whatsoever can be accepted in respect of the material contained herein by the authors or publishers. The reader is directed to the legislation, case law and other primary materials referred to in the text. Medical opinion used in this book is provided only for the purpose of illustrating medico-legal principles and the authors do not put forward the medical opinions expressed as definitive of medical opinion.

ISBN 978-0-9569341-1-6

A Cataloguing-in-Publication record is available for this book from the British Library.

Authors

Giles Eyre

Giles Eyre is a barrister practising from 9 Gough Square, London (www.9goughsquare.co.uk). Giles has extensive experience in conducting and advising in personal injury, industrial disease and clinical negligence claims. He is a mediator and was appointed a Recorder in 2004.

Giles regularly presents seminars for lawyers on a wide variety of topics, and for medical practitioners and other expert witnesses on legal principles, effective report writing and giving evidence. He is a contributing editor of *Asbestos Claims: Law, Practice and Procedure* published by 9 Gough Square (3rd edition September 2015) and *Clinical Negligence Claims – A Practical Guide* published by 9 Gough Square (3rd edition September 2015).

Lynden Alexander

Lynden Alexander is a communication skills consultant who specialises in forensic communication. He leads the expert witness programme at Professional Solutions Learning and Development.

He began offering training to expert witnesses in 1996 and has since trained more than 6000 expert witnesses in forensic writing, preparing for court and courtroom presentation skills. He advises clients on forensic communication throughout all stages of the litigation process. He also presents workshops for the Expert Witness Institute and for other professional bodies.

Professional Solutions Learning and Development

Professional Solutions has been presenting workshops to expert witnesses since 1996. Its small group training workshops are targeted to the needs of the professionals attending each training session and it has established an excellent reputation for the quality of its training. The training is presented by highly experienced barristers and forensic communication consultants.

Lynden Alexander and Giles Eyre have been presenting workshops together for nearly 20 years and are knowledge leaders in the field of expert witness training. They have created a programme of seminars, practical workshops, e-learning and publications to support the learning of professionals who are seeking to achieve the highest standards of practice in expert witness work.

For further information about the workshop programme and other learning resources, please visit: www.prosols.uk.com.

Acknowledgements

We would like to thank James Badenoch QC and Dr Jan Wise for taking the time to provide forewords to the second edition of this text. That they have done so while on their summer holidays shows commitment beyond the call of professional duty and we are very grateful to them for their good-natured understanding. We are also grateful to Betty Doyle at the Expert Witness Institute for her continued interest in this project and for communicating the importance of this text to medical experts both within and beyond the Institute.

We would like to thank Rachel Bush (Bush and Company Rehabilitation) and Alison Somek (Somek Associates) for their enthusiasm for the first edition of this text and for their demands that the text expand to include the needs of quantum experts. We would also like to thank Amy Dooley of Bush & Company for the help she has given us in producing the outline template for Occupational Therapy and Care Reports – her expertise in the area of complex brain injury reporting has been an invaluable resource when addressing the pragmatic issues that arise in producing quantum reports. Dr Ken Gulleford has been similarly vocal about the importance of mental capacity and we hope that our inclusion of this topic in the second edition meets with his favour.

We would also like to thank the many readers of the first edition of this text who have taken the time and the trouble to recommend the book to fellow professionals. We need especially to mention Mr Michael Foy, Chairman of the Medicolegal Committee of the British Orthopaedic Association and Dr Joanna Iddon, Coordinating Editor for the Division of Neuropsychology Newsletter – thank you both for championing the text to professional colleagues. We would also like to thank Dr François Sestier, who as director of the bilingual program of Insurance and Medicolegal Expertise at the University of Montreal seems to have single-handedly promoted this text across Canada.

Finally, we would like to thank all of the readers of the first edition of this text. We have received so much warm and insightful feedback that has been both gratifying and encouraging in equal measure.

The text of this second edition has been much improved by the help we have received – it goes without saying that any mistakes to be found in the text are the sole responsibility of the authors.

Contents

Table of Cases

F

G

H

I

J

K

L

M

N

O

P

R

S

Foreword to the Second Edition

James Badenoch QC

Chairman Emeritus of the Expert Witness Institute

I said about the first edition of this book that no medical expert witness should be without it, and the same applies to this second edition. It is an essential and invaluable resource for all involved in medico-legal work as expert witnesses, whether dealing with negligence/causation or with quantum, and for the lawyers who enlist the experts.

The text provides a comprehensive update of the relevant law and procedure, with a clear exposition of the many changes in the Civil Justice System over the last four years, knowledge and understanding of which is essential to opinion evidence that meets legal requirements and fulfils its proper function in the litigation process.

The days of the "amateur" expert witness are gone. Lawyers who litigate claims, and the judges who hear them, demand increasingly high standards of enlisted experts, both in the practice of their professions outside the courts and in the opinion evidence they provide for the courts. The implementation of the "Jackson Reforms" has reinforced the importance of conformity with, and correct application of, the rules of court in each stage of litigation and in the production of evidence. The authors have responded by introducing a new chapter to explain and to emphasise the important current principles which govern expert witness work, and how these will apply to some of the practical issues which arise.

Avoidable errors in the litigation process can be very costly, and in an extreme case an aggrieved party may seek financial redress against an expert whose lapse from the required standards has led to irrecoverable loss. The conscientious expert will find the chapters on legal principles and court rules an important aid to compliance, and so to avoiding a damages claim for an inexcusable mistake.

The text has been expanded in respect of expert report writing for all phases and aspects of a claim for damages: liability, causation and, in this edition, establishing and quantifying the loss. It provides for experts an enhanced understanding of how the lawyers use their opinions in the pursuit of the damages claim, and additional insight into the interrelation of evidence in different disciplines, with particular help on the crucial distinction between recoverable and irrecoverable ("in any event") costs and losses.

Amongst their many additions, the authors have provided new guidance on reporting on causation, in particular in respect of future effects on the Claimant, have included recent important developments in the law of patient consent, and have now addressed reporting on mental capacity, all very welcome for experts who must tackle these difficult issues.

As in the first edition, the text illustrates key-points by giving examples of evidence that helps or hinders the lawyers and adds further emphasis by highlighting many of these points in stand-alone text boxes and in summary lists at the end of each chapter.

I am sure that readers, whatever their experience, will find this new edition an invaluable aid to legal understanding and to the enhancement of their practical skills as expert witnesses. It is accessible, interesting and informative, and will serve further to improve the quality of evidence they produce for the lawyers who instruct them and for the courts. I commend it most highly.

James Badenoch QC
Chairman Emeritus of the Expert Witness Institute
August 2015

Foreword to the Second Edition

Dr Jan Wise

Chair of the BMA Medico-Legal Committee 2004 - 2015

Expert practice has changed dramatically over the last 10 years, and as if mirroring the digital world, albeit at a slower pace, it continues to change.

Giles and Lynden have revised and expanded their book, keeping it up to date and nigh on indispensable to the medical expert. In some ways, their seven pillars of wisdom are the seven basic plots: the only stories that exist – the ones that every guide to report writing should cover – and they cover them well!

The authors identify the need to develop a 'medico-legal mind'. Just as the diagnostic and clinical skills of a doctor are neither innate nor inherent - they are nurtured, developed, honed - so too are the technical skills of the expert. If the principles in this book are absorbed, applied and reflected on, then the growth of your report writing skills and of that 'medico-legal mind' will be greatly accelerated.

One common misconception is corrected early on – the authors remind the medical expert that the claimant is not his or her patient. Another area of clarity leading to significant change, one I am sure is not aimed at forestry conservation, is the drive towards shorter and concise reports. For some, this is a real challenge, one which is made easier with their guidance.

The authors cover the roles and duties of experts; proof; causation and acceleration; quantum and costs; and negligence. The section on 'inconsistencies' is written in refreshing detail. They comment on the economic realities and pragmatics of litigation, shining a light on what is an opaque or unexplored arena for most.

In a fitting finale, as if Giles and Lynden had not provided enough worthy material to be digested amongst this feast of knowledge for the reader, is a comprehensive package addressing practical concerns, which often evade the budding medico-legal expert who has given insufficient consideration to the commercial aspects of the business of being an expert.

It is all very well producing a skilled report, complying with all the Court procedures, but if one has not established contractual terms and conditions or has failed to set oneself up properly the novice to the field will fail to flourish. Even those who are becoming long in the tooth would do well to review their own terms and conditions against the sample provided in the closing pages.

I have said before that cross examination is like being faced by a trained Rottweiler who wants nothing more than to discredit you. The foundation on which the 'edifice' of your opinion is presented is the expert report. Reading and applying the knowledge in this book will make that assault far less successful, making your report more 'earthquake resistant', and thereby enhancing your reputation. After more than two decades of report writing, this book proves to me that there is always something new to learn! In short, it is a must-have-manual for the new expert, a go-to-guide for the mature expert.

Dr Jan Wise
MBBS MSc FRCPsych IFAPA CCST
August 2015

Foreword to the First Edition

This is an important and admirable book. It is thorough, lucid and extremely practical and is a manual of all that medical expert witnesses need to know about their proper role in the justice system, and about the law and practice in civil litigation.

The overwhelming majority of medical experts are aware of their duty to the court and many regard their understanding as sufficient for the role of expert witness. In this guide, the authors ask experts to go further, by understanding the expert's duty to the court in the context of both the wider processes of the civil justice system, as codified by the Civil Procedure Rules (CPR), and the legal principles upon which the civil law is founded. They argue that such an understanding enables experts to offer opinions that are more pertinent and more precise in dealing with the issues in dispute and are therefore more helpful to the court and the overriding objective of the CPR, 'to deal with cases justly'.

There is little doubt that medical experts are often faced with very difficult medico-legal issues to address and do their honest best to deal with these issues in a manner that complies with their duty to the court. However, many experts feel that there is a paucity of detailed guidance that they can refer to when dealing with such cases. This book offers an impressive level of detailed and practical guidance on how to deal with cases properly, from applying basic principles such as proof, breach of duty and causation through to extremely complex cases that involve both evidential and legal difficulty - cases in which medical experts need to possess a high level of technical skill in medico-legal practice. Throughout the text there are practical examples of helpful and unhelpful expert evidence when addressing such matters and these will no doubt prove to be an extremely useful starting point when considering the best way to report to the court.

The authors' purpose, brilliantly achieved, is to create a user-friendly guide to the perils and pitfalls of expert witness work, and to the ways and the means of making expert evidence most useful and most effective. It will I believe become the standard reference, and should be compulsory reading for all medical expert witnesses, and also for all lawyers who enlist, instruct and call them – in short it will be an invaluable resource for all who are concerned with medico-legal work.

James Badenoch Q.C.
Chairman of the Expert Witness Institute
1 Crown Office Row, Temple, London EC4Y 7HH

Giles Eyre and Lynden Alexander have written this excellent book with the aim of helping medical practitioners to write better medico-legal reports, in the form and with the clarity that lawyers and judges need.

It is not only a very practical guide to best practice in report writing, but it also sets out the law and the procedure which apply to personal injury, industrial disease and clinical negligence cases. The text is always expressed in clear and accessible terms and offers useful practical guidance on many of the difficult issues that arise in medico-legal practice.

Having just written my last medico-legal report, some thirty five years after the first - for the form of which I had to rely on advice from my then consultant's secretary - I welcome this book for the invaluable help it gives. How helpful it would have been at the start of my 'career' as an 'expert' to have been able to read and refer to it.

Sir Roger Vickers, KCVO, FRCS.
Previously, Consultant Orthopaedic Surgeon to St George's Hospital, London.
Council Member, Medical Defence Union.

Authors' Note

The Origin of "Foot-Wearing"

A holiday snap taken many years ago by Giles while in Mandalay, Burma, is the source for an informal technical term, 'Foot-Wearing'. This term we have come to use when discussing extracts from medical expert reports that defy a proper legal interpretation.

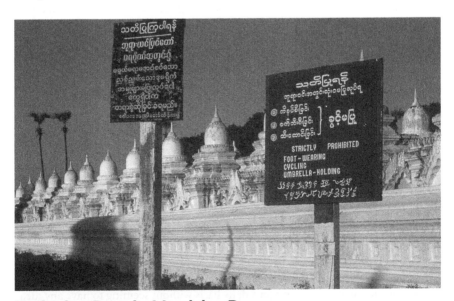

Kuthodaw Pagoda, Mandalay, Burma

Whilst most visitors to this particular temple complex are generally in awe of the sacred architecture, Giles found himself distracted by the sign at the entrance to the site. Intended to make clear to visitors unacceptable forms of behaviour, the sign became the subject of detailed lawyerly scrutiny and especially:

"Strictly Prohibited: Foot-Wearing"

Giles found this prohibition a little worrying. Glancing down to his feet, he found, sure enough, definite signs of Foot-Wearing. Unsure as to the proper interpretation of the prohibition and wary of local sensibilities, he decided to tread carefully and to remove his shoes (though not his feet). The visit passed without incident, not least because he had neither bicycle nor umbrella.

At this point, an analysis of the context for this attempt at communication is valuable. What to Giles appeared to be a succession of bubbles, would, to a Burmese, have made clear the writer's interdict. To the translator, bridging the expanse between the language of Burma and the language of the native English speaker, the prohibition was also clear. However, for Giles, comfortable only in his native English, guesses or assumptions had to be made as he sought to avoid causing offence.

Time passes and Giles is now to be found in chambers reading his daily dose of medico-legal reports:

> 'He should make a reasonable recovery from the effects of his injury over the next few years.'

> 'Although it is likely that there was some congenital weakness, the hernia was most probably the result of the heavy lifting in which he was involved.'

> '30% of his current symptoms are the result of his underlying condition and would have been present in any event, while 70% are attributable to the injury sustained in the accident'

> 'The accident has made symptomatic previously asymptomatic degenerative disease. The period of acceleration is about 3 to 5 years. As a result of these symptoms he has been unable to work.'

> 'His heavy cigarette smoking may be aggravating the extent and severity of his episodic finger whitening. I cannot rule out the possibility that this may be contributing to the neurological symptoms that he describes.'

Giles, in his role as a personal injury lawyer, finds these paragraphs as meaningful as 'No Foot-Wearing' when he was a tourist in Burma. These medico-legal paragraphs communicate to a lawyer that there is an issue to be considered, but beyond this, the interpretation relies heavily on guesswork. Yet, medical experts produce evidence of this quality on a daily basis without seeming to have any idea as to how defective this evidence actually is in medico-legal terms.

This poor standard of evidence has led to the frequent exhortation being made to medical experts (at least by Giles!) that in evidence, there should be "No Foot-Wearing!"

The medical expert must ensure that the medical evidence is expressed in language that a lawyer can understand, without the need to make guesses or assumptions as to its meaning or its application to the case.

Introduction to the Text

Over the last 24 months, the civil justice system has seen a vast array of changes to the way litigation is conducted in England and Wales. The report of Lord Justice Jackson into the conduct of civil litigation together with Government action against the so-called 'compensation culture' have led to a series of reforms, often less than competently implemented. These reforms have changed the environment in which cases are managed and as a consequence the way expert evidence is produced.

The reforms have created both opportunities and risks for new and established expert witnesses producing evidence in civil claims and has created the paradoxical situation of demands from lawyers for higher quality expert reports that need to be produced at a more competitive (that is, a lower) fee. All experts now need to be technically competent, medico-legally competent and business savvy.

The New Commercial Environment

The new emphasis upon and the importance of the principle of proportionality[1] in the conduct of litigation and recent changes to bring more civil claims into fixed fee regimes have meant that there has been a reduction of fees payable to the lawyers running a claim. This reduction in fees has made lower-value claims and claims requiring more investigation – and therefore more input from the lawyers involved – uneconomic. Many solicitors' firms have withdrawn from the lower value personal injury claims market, while others have pushed the caseload on to very junior lawyers or paralegals to run. At the time when the lawyers are seeking higher-quality expert reports, the quality of the legal minds dealing with the claims is falling away.

---

1   See Section 3.2.1

This means that experts now need a higher level of professional skill than ever before. Except in the lowest value cases, the expert who dabbles in expert witness work (unless such dabbling is a consequence of a particularly specialised area of expertise where instructions are in any event rare) seems destined to be eased out of the marketplace. It is likely that those experts who begin the task of producing each expert report 'as if for the first time' will quickly find the work required too onerous to maintain their interest.

Experts will find that the fees that they can charge for their expert reports do not allow them to approach instructions without a systemized, efficient and effective process for producing the evidence. Developing such a process inevitably relies on a flow of instructions that allows the expert to develop the most effective approach to producing the evidence, while spreading the fixed costs involved in an expert witness practice over a larger number of instructions.

For those experts who are willing to embrace the commercial demands of the marketplace, there are new opportunities for developing a successful practice as an expert witness. For example, for experts involved in soft tissue injury claims, lawyers can now access expert witnesses directly through MedCo[2], which will (we are promised) allow experts to be identified by Post Code and so will create the opportunity for experts to establish a commercial presence amongst local solicitors without having to use Medico-Legal Agencies as intermediaries.

There is also an expanding need for 'Advisory Reports' (a.k.a. 'Limited Screening Reports' or 'Desktop Reports') to advise lawyers on the prospects of a clam before the lawyer takes the risk of committing financial resources to progressing it. These reports allow experts to produce a large number of short reports relatively quickly, while establishing relationships with the solicitors who instruct them.

The Challenge of Writing Expert Reports in Civil Claims

Amongst the many professionals who are instructed to provide expert evidence in civil claims, the role of the medical expert is particularly challenging: every injured person responds differently to a trauma; every person heals and recovers in a different way; and the consequences of a trauma are unique to each person. Where clinical negligence is claimed, the complexity of medical practice is combined with the difficulty of predicting what the outcome would have been had the clinical care been adequate. In all such cases, the lawyers look to medical experts for answers, even when answers that are soundly based on medical proof are difficult or even impossible to establish. Once the lawyers are satisfied that the claim is economic to pursue, the medical evidence may then be the basis for care and therapeutic reports that are essential to establishing the quantum (the financial value) of the claim.

---

2   See Section 3.4.3

Civil Procedure Rules 1998

The Civil Procedure Rules 1998 (CPR) - the rules that govern the conduct of litigation in the civil courts - place specific requirements on the form and content of expert reports. Each requirement is intended to help experts to deal with the difficult and complex issues that often arise in disputes and to do so in a manner comprehensible to the lawyers and to the courts. However, the CPR cannot and never sought to address the legal principles and legal tests that an expert has to encounter or confront when producing an expert report. Gaining such insight is the sole responsibility of the expert and gaining an understanding of these legal principles and tests remains a fundamental need of experts reporting in civil claims.

It is perhaps a little unfair to hold expert witnesses solely responsible for the difficulties they have in understanding what lawyers actually require of their evidence. A communication void continues to exist between the medical and legal professions - even as each profession recognises that it does not understand the other, neither seems able to grasp quite why this is so and how to bridge the divide. The present standard of medical expert evidence seems to indicate that somewhere in the midst of professional life two socio-economically equivalent groups, with similar standards of education, have lost the ability to communicate meaningfully with each other.

Improving Medico-Legal Communication

This guide is written to bridge this communication void and to provide medical experts and those who rely on medical expert reports in reporting on quantum issues with the practical help needed to deal with what can often be very difficult evidential issues.

Writing Medico-Legal Reports in Civil Claims: An Essential Guide will seek to achieve seven aims:

1. to help experts to understand the legal principles and legal tests that are the basis for all expert evidence in personal injury claims[3] and for the resolution of which the evidence is obtained;

2. to understand the nature and extent of the duties imposed on experts providing evidence in civil claims;

3. to explain the framework or procedural rules that govern the actions of all participants in the litigation process;

4. to introduce the technical discipline of evidential writing, by offering skills and techniques to ensure that reports are written to the highest standards;

---

3   The term personal injury includes claims for accidental injury, clinical negligence, industrial disease and illness and supporting quantum reports.

5. to provide detailed expert report templates for personal injury, industrial disease, clinical negligence and care reports;

6. to provide examples of good and poor expert report writing, with explanatory notes; and

7. to bring experts up to date with the law as it affects medico-legal reports produced in civil claims.

The first edition of this text proved popular not only with medically qualified experts and lawyers, but also with care and therapeutic experts – the 'quantum experts'. In response, we have included a section setting out the basics of the law in relation to this area of expert reporting.

It is also very pleasing to discuss medico-legal issues with users of the book. These experts tell us that they have found for the first time an explanation for much that they are required to provide in their expert reports, an understanding of what it is that the lawyers need from them and perhaps most important of all, the way to provide that information to the satisfaction of the lawyers and the court.

In the past 15 years, we have delivered workshops on writing medical expert reports to over six thousand expert witnesses – a majority of whom were in the early stages of developing their expert witness practices, with a significant minority being highly experienced. Since the publication of the first edition of this text, it has been gratifying to see how many experts arrive at these workshops with a copy of the book. We have taken on board all of the generous feedback from these experts and have listened carefully to constructive criticism of the text.

Reading the Text

We have always intended this book to serve both as a training manual and as a useful and practical reference whenever the expert comes into contact with a civil claim. This guide can be read from beginning to end, providing a step-by-step approach to the process of producing expert evidence or it can be used for reference whenever an expert is faced with a difficult issue and needs guidance on the best way to report on the matter or how to approach a difficulty. We hope that you will find this guide an essential update on the present state of civil litigation and a useful ally as you seek to develop your skills as an expert witness.

Giles Eyre and Lynden Alexander
14 September 2015

Second Edition: What's New?

In this second edition of the text, we have introduced new information to:

1. highlight recent developments in the medico-legal marketplace, especially the impact of the 'Jackson Reforms';

2. identify the most recent trends in expert evidence and provide a basis for understanding the changes that are unfolding in civil litigation;

3. revise and update the chapters dealing with the Civil Procedure Rules, in respect of the conduct of litigation and progressing claims;

4. address the revised Pre-Action Protocols for the Resolution of Clinical Disputes and for Personal Injury Claims;

5. explore the impact of the extension of on-line portal claims and the limiting of medical reports and fees in the Fast Track portal, and the new method of selecting experts in soft tissue RTA claims through MedCo;

6. discuss the extensive revisions in the expert's duties required by the new Guidance for the Instruction of Experts in Civil Claims 2014, as well as new sections on an expert's terms of appointment, the provision of estimates, sequential reporting and withdrawal by an expert;

7. add further guidance on the drafting of joint statements;

8. provide further updated essential case law, including in relation to the new law on obtaining consent, as well as issues regarding causation and the status and basis of 'acceleration' of symptoms as a concept in the light of recent authority;

9. discuss reporting on mental capacity;

10. develop further consideration of the application of the *Bolam* test;

11. highlight the link between the reports of medical experts and those of quantum and care experts who need to use the medical reports as a basis for their own reporting;

12. address the writing of quantum reports and to provide advice on the issues that commonly arise in quantum and care reporting (an important area of work that we did not address in detail in the first edition);

13. address the increasing requirement for shorter and more focussed expert reports and the skills needed to achieve this;

14. explore some of the practical issues that experts commonly do not address adequately in running their expert witness practice; and

15. create a new legal case index, extend the use of "call out" boxes to emphasise key-points and increase the number of cross references within the text.

We hope the reader finds that the text remains, as before, practical and full of explanation and is the best guide available to assist in achieving the medico-legal mind, which every medical expert in litigation should be seeking to develop.

1

Essential Qualities of Medical Experts

Introduction

The skills needed to produce clear, concise and reliable expert evidence are fundamentally different from the skills needed to be successful in professional practice. When producing expert evidence, expert witnesses must apply specific legal standards and tests to the opinions they express and must produce evidence that fulfils the requirements of the litigation process. They must also write for an audience with no medical expertise and only limited technical knowledge. The vast majority of expert witnesses in practice today do not fully understand what the lawyers and the court require of their evidence and so consistently produce evidence that does not meet the requirements of the litigation process.

Chapter Outline

In this chapter, we will provide an overview of the key issues that experts have to understand before they begin to write expert reports. As all civil claims for damages in personal injury litigation require expert medical evidence, we will introduce the concept of the 'medico-legal mind' and explore the specific abilities that developing this mind enables. We will introduce the role of expert witnesses within the litigation process and the status of their evidence. We will then discuss medical expert reports and how these differ from pure medical reports before moving on to explain the dissatisfaction that lawyers have with the quality of medical expert reports. Finally, we will explain the commercial realities that underpin the litigation process and the often unforeseen consequences that result when experts produce reports that do not meet the requirements of the litigation process.

1.1 'Medico-Legal Mind'

All expert witnesses give opinions within a legal context. It is, therefore, essential that experts understand the legal principles and precedents that show how the court will assess and evaluate their evidence. They must also learn the analytical and evidential writing skills necessary to communicate effectively with both their instructing lawyers and with the court. An expert witness will only achieve a sufficient level of competence when this knowledge and these skills have been properly developed.

To achieve professional competence as a medical expert, a medical practitioner has to develop ways of thinking that are beyond the purely medical – to develop what we term a 'medico-legal mind'.[1]

There are seven key-qualities that distinguish experts who have developed a medico-legal mind. These experts are able to:

1. understand the duties of an expert witness and the specific requirements of expert evidence within the litigation process;

2. adopt an appropriate methodology to provide reliable evidence dealing with the medico-legal issues in dispute;

3. identify the factual matters relevant to a dispute and apply medical expertise to these facts in a logical and medically supportable way;

4. address all relevant medical issues that arise by providing opinions and conclusions that a lawyer can understand and engage with;

---

1   A *Google* search, limited to the UK, for "medico-legal mind" now produces a handful of results all of which refer back to or are echoes of this book, save for a reference to one work of fiction – this expression was unique to the first edition of this book and is not in common usage.

5. understand and apply, in every case, the civil standard of proof and the appropriate legal tests to the evidence;

6. understand how to assess and report on the consequences of an injury; and

7. recognise that the fundamental purpose of medical expert evidence is to help the court to assess the validity of a compensation claim and the level of damages to be awarded – known as the quantum of the claim[2].

In essence, competent medical experts are able to assess each medico-legal issue in a case, first applying their medical expertise or 'medical mind' to each issue and then placing their medical findings within a legal context by applying their medico-legal expertise or 'medico-legal mind'. This approach of combining the medical and the legal helps the court to more easily resolve a compensation claim.

Medical experts who have developed a medico-legal mind know that the strong medical emphasis on an evidence-based approach is important[3], but also understand that conclusive medical evidence is only useful and relevant if it can be gathered without incurring disproportionate cost and without the demand of invasive tests and procedures. Experts must also be able to work effectively knowing that in many cases no conclusive medical evidence or medical certainty will ever be established and must understand that medical certainty is never required for a civil case to be proved and for damages to be recovered.

Experts who have developed a medico-legal mind also know that in performing the role of an expert, they are required to express a clear and firm opinion on any issue where the evidence is capable of being assessed to the civil standard of proof, 'on the balance of probabilities'. This requirement holds even when no conclusive medical evidence is available to decide issues to a medical or scientific standard of certainty.

1.2 Role of the Expert Witness

The role of an expert witness is to help the court to decide issues that are beyond its technical knowledge or expertise. An expert has an overriding duty to the court to be independent and objective, no matter what pressure he/she may face from any party in the litigation.

The prevailing level of medical knowledge amongst lawyers and judges is at best rudimentary. Even in high-value and complex personal injury and clinical negligence claims, judges hearing cases are extremely unlikely to have any formal medical training or knowledge. The most carefully constructed and erudite medical expert evidence from a leading expert in his/her field will be of little practical

---

2   Care and Occupational Therapy reports are often referred to as 'quantum reports' for this reason.

3   Any conclusive evidence that a medical expert is able to present is likely to lead to a rapid settlement of a case.

use in the litigation process, unless it can be readily understood by an educated adult with a legal rather than a medical background. The ability to communicate complex technical matters in a clear manner to a lay audience is an essential skill for an expert to develop.

Expert evidence has an elevated status when compared with the evidence of factual witnesses. Once an expert has established his/her right to give expert evidence – by placing before the court details of his/her qualifications and relevant experience in respect of the issues in dispute – he/she can then give opinion evidence. Other witnesses, who are not experts, are not permitted to give opinion evidence and the court will stop any such witness who attempts to do so. With the elevated status an expert witness has in the litigation process and because the lawyers and the court have only a rudimentary knowledge of medical matters, lawyers and judges alike frequently surrender crucial elements of their decisions to the evidence of witnesses – and it has to be said, particularly to medical expert witnesses.

In general, what is said by a medical expert (whether in an expert report or in oral evidence) will be accepted by a court - and everyone involved in the litigation process knows it. It is essential, therefore, that medical experts remain within their specific area of expertise as doctors and that they should never adopt the attitude of a 'quasi-lawyer'. Medical experts can be assured that there will be enough qualified lawyers already involved in the litigation without their trying to join in as well.

The fundamental reason for instructing a medical expert is to bring medical expertise to the case, so it is essential that the medical expert always seeks guidance from the lawyers on any legal question or issue that may arise. This important distinction is perhaps most easily seen at the pre-trial meeting of experts, where the medical experts' role is not to achieve an acceptable compromise of the claim – this being the lawyers' role – but rather to identify whether any agreement on any of the medical aspects of the claim can be reached. Where this is not possible, the medical experts need to explain as clearly as possible the differences in opinion and, most importantly from the point of view of the lawyers, the reasons for these differences[4].

A fundamental issue for medical experts to fully understand and engage with is that a claimant should never be regarded as being a patient. A medical expert does not owe a medical duty of care to a claimant, and is not meeting the claimant in order to treat him/her or to recommend appropriate treatment. The medical expert does not have the same professional relationship with a claimant as he/she has with a patient. In a doctor-patient relationship, the doctor owes an express duty of care to the patient. However, when reporting to the court the expert owes an overriding duty to assist the court beyond any contractual duty to the claimant or to the lawyers who have instructed the expert. This need for professional detachment from the injured claimant applies to all experts instructed in the case.

---

4   See Section 4.7 'The Joint Discussion'

1.3   Medical Expert Reports

Medical expert evidence is provided to the court in the form of a written report, known as an 'expert report'. Expert reports are an essential component of claims for personal injury, industrial disease, and clinical negligence and have a unique status within civil litigation. The maker of the expert report is assumed by the court, whether justifiably or not, and unless proved otherwise, to be giving objective unbiased opinion evidence. The court will also assume that the expert has assessed all material facts and has complied with the duties and responsibilities set out in the *Civil Procedure Rules 1998 (CPR)*[5].

Medical expert reports are fundamental in enabling the court to assess:

1.   the injury, damage and loss caused by an accident, injury or other adverse event;

2.   the damages claimed for pain and suffering and loss of amenity;

3.   the damages for financial loss, both past and future; and

4.   in clinical negligence cases, the duty of care owed to a patient by the medical practitioners involved in his/her care.

1.3.1   Functions of Expert Reports

In personal injury cases, medical expert reports dealing with condition and prognosis serve four functions:

1.   to identify the factual basis relevant to the medical aspects of the claim;

2.   to identify the nature of the injury;

3.   to provide expert opinion on the causation of the claimant's injuries; and

4.   to provide expert opinion on the consequences arising from the claimant's injuries.

In industrial disease cases, in addition to the functions of a personal injury report, the expert may also be required to address whether the injury was 'reasonably foreseeable' or whether exposure to a substance made a 'material contribution' to the injuries or condition that is the subject of the claim[6].

---

5   In particular, CPR 35, Practice Direction 35 and the Guidance for the Instruction of Experts in Civil Claims 2014. See Chapter 4 for detailed discussion of the rules and guidance applicable to expert evidence.

6   See Section 6.3

In clinical negligence cases, the parties need to obtain medical expert reports on breach of duty and causation to establish whether there is a basis for a claim for damages. Medical expert reports dealing with breach of duty and causation serve three functions:

1. to identify the factual basis relevant to the medical aspects of the claim;

2. to establish the duty of care owed by the defendant to the claimant and whether this duty of care has been breached; and

3. to establish the causation of the medical injuries sustained[7].

In valuing claims, care and therapeutic reports draw from the expert medical reports and their own assessment of the injured person's domestic situation. The evidence of care and therapeutic specialists is often essential in enabling the loss consequent on the identified injury to be properly assessed and communicated to the lawyers. These experts provide a detailed breakdown of all the relevant items that form part of the claim for compensation.

Expert reports need to fulfil these functions within the litigation process in a clear, concise and reliable manner. Only then can the lawyers involved in the case make high-quality decisions about pursuing or settling the case and, should the case reach court, allow the judge to weigh up the evidence appropriately.

1.3.2 Writing the Report

It is essential that the expert understands how the report will be used by the lawyers and the court, and what specific issues the report needs to address. The expert must also be clear on the standard of proof and the legal test that the court will apply to each opinion, so that the expert can express his/her opinion in language that the lawyers and the court can accurately interpret and assess. The expert report needs therefore to:

1. establish the facts relevant to the medical aspects of the claim;

2. give clear opinions on all relevant issues;

3. support these opinions with clear and informed reasoning; and

4. apply to each opinion the civil standard of proof and the appropriate legal test.

Most experts are aware of their responsibilities in respect of identifying the medical aspects of a claim, but continue to have problems with the medico-legal aspects that the report needs to address. In personal injury reports, difficulties commonly

---

7   Clinical negligence reports dealing with causation are often obtained by the parties first, as this is where most clinical negligence actions founder. Reports on breach of duty are obtained once the causation issues have been considered and the viability of the claim assessed. Reports on condition and prognosis are usually obtained at a later stage in the litigation process.

arise when dealing with causation, prognosis and the consequences of the injuries, while in clinical negligence reports, issues arise with causation, breach of duty and factual conflicts in the evidence. In industrial disease claims, causation and the legal tests to be applied create most difficulty. Problems in the reports of the medical experts can create difficulties for other experts instructed later in the litigation process and often leads to confusion and misunderstandings that affect the quality of the evidence produced by these experts.

1.3.3 Comparison of Medical Reports and Medical Expert Reports

The duties of an expert are fundamentally different to those of a treating clinician and the differences between the medical expert report and the medical report reflect this difference in duties.

A medical expert report is not a medical report about a patient, addressing the health of a patient and appropriate treatment. A medical expert report about a claimant is prepared for the purposes of litigation to address whether or not the claimant is entitled to recover damages and if so, how much. It is also a report that may be subjected to close analysis and criticism – rarely the case with a medical report – and which must comply with and show understanding of numerous legal rules.

Let us summarise the differences between a medical report and a medical expert report:

	MEDICAL REPORTS	MEDICAL EXPERT REPORTS
1	Written about a patient	Written about a claimant
2	Written for a medically qualified readership	Written for a non-medically qualified readership
3	Used in medical treatment	Used in litigation to assess the validity of a compensation claim
4	Deals with clinical issues	Deals with medico-legal issues
5	Supportive of a patient	Independent assessment of a claimant
6	Emphasises positive or potentially positive outcomes	Assesses likely outcomes objectively
7	Supportive of clinical colleagues	Willing to criticise clinicians (if required to do so)

A similar distinction can be made in relation to all other court experts – between their role in their 'day job' and their role as an expert providing their opinions for the purposes of the litigation. A care and therapeutic expert will have no difficulty in identifying a similar list of differences between their court and non-court related work and in particular his/her assessment of what provision is reasonable within the restrictions of the NHS and what is reasonably required to put the claimant back in the position he/she would have been in, in the absence of the accident.

A high-quality expert report that deals fully with all of the relevant issues is easier and quicker to write than an inadequate report. Struggling to deal properly with the relevant medico-legal issues takes far more time than dealing with them accurately, clearly and concisely - a well-written report is often half the length of an inadequate report.

> The vast majority of civil cases are settled based on the written evidence of one or more medical experts. The accuracy and clarity of the expert report are critical to the litigation process. The quality of the communication – "the words on the page" – really matters.

1.4 Dissatisfaction with Medical Expert Reports

Ask any lawyer involved in personal injury litigation about the quality of the expert evidence they receive and you will find a high-degree of dissatisfaction with the quality of expert reports. Amongst lawyers, experts and the expert reports they produce are frequently criticised for their lack of forensic understanding. It is a common occurrence for a lawyer to be asked by a colleague to recommend a "good expert" in a particular field and to be unable to provide even one name. Even seeking an expert who can deliver an acceptable standard of report elicits the names of a very few. The recent review of medical reporting in whiplash claims[8] was in considerable part precipitated by what was seen to be the poor quality of medical reports and the unsupported opinions they contained.

Based on 30 years of professional practice, reading medical expert reports on a daily basis, we assess that 90% of these reports at least in part are not written to an acceptable professional standard. The vast majority of medical expert reports do not deal accurately or clearly with the matters that the lawyers need to have addressed and that the legal process requires to be addressed. This includes reports written by medical experts who believe themselves to be familiar with the process and who have much experience of writing expert reports.

---

8   Which began with the Ministry of Justice consultation document *Reducing the number and costs of whiplash claims* in December 2012

1.4.1   Consequences Arising from Inadequate Reporting

The consequence for the parties to the litigation of inadequate medical evidence is that a claim will ultimately be settled or decided at an incorrect value, whether it is the claimant who gets less than a fair level of compensation or the insurance company or health care provider that has to pay out too much. A failure by an expert to comply with the CPR may also result in the instructing party being penalised in costs, and in extreme cases, may result in the court refusing to allow the medical evidence to be given in evidence at all and even striking out the whole claim or the defence of it – with disastrous results for the instructing party.

The consequence for the medical experts of inadequate reports is that their expectations of repeat instructions may fail to be realised. Questions of clarification may also arrive many months or even years after they have examined claimants and filed case papers and reports away. With little memory of the case, experts are then required to address issues they had not previously considered to be relevant, or are asked to re-address issues in a manner they had not previously thought to be necessary or even appropriate.

The professional consequences for medical experts of providing inadequate medical evidence are also potentially serious. Apart from failing to provide a proper professional standard of service to their clients, experts may face possible complaints before their professional bodies[9]. The expert is at risk of being sued by the instructing party for damages resulting from an unacceptable standard of practice[10] or of being made liable for wasted costs[11]. Where an expert has provided an inadequate report to an unsuccessful party in litigation, that party may be required to pay additional costs to the winning side if the expert has been severely criticised for failing to address his/her responsibilities or to conduct him/herself properly as an expert witness[12]. If an inadequate report is provided to a successful party in litigation, then that party may be denied recovery of all or some of its costs. In the last of these situations, there would be a consequent potential claim against the medical expert for the resulting loss.

It takes only one instance of judicial criticism of an expert's performance in court or of an expert's failure to comply with his/her duty as a medico-legal expert to destroy a reputation and therefore a medico-legal practice. Judgments are frequently available on the internet and those that are not are often shared between lawyers through various professionally directed websites or more informally through their own databases. Examples of such judgments are referred to throughout this book.

---

9   *GMC v Meadow* [2006] EWCA Civ 1390; *Pool v General Medical Council* [2014] EWHC 3791

10   See Section 4.1.3

11   See *Phillips v Symes* [2004] EWHC 2330 in which an expert who caused significant expense to be incurred in 'flagrant and reckless disregard' of his duties to the court was penalised by paying costs so wasted.

12   *Williams v Jervis* (Costs)[2009] EWHC 1837

> If an expert is unwilling to go to court to defend his/her opinion under cross-examination, then he/she should not be performing the role of expert witness at all. Having expert evidence tested in court is a fundamental part of the litigation process.

1.4.2   Common Problems with Medical Expert Reports

A medical expert report must address those matters that the law and the legal process require to be addressed, applying those legal tests that the law requires to be applied and directed towards the legal principles relevant to the issues in the case.

Let us now identify the issues that commonly cause difficulties for medical experts, and ultimately for the lawyers who instruct them, when writing expert reports:

1. applying clearly, unambiguously and comfortably the civil standard of proof and appropriate legal tests to the evidence;

2. identifying and explaining the nature of the injury sustained and, where appropriate and necessary, explaining the interrelation between physical and psychological symptoms or causes;

3. identifying what injuries have been suffered or caused by the accident and explaining what difference this accident or injury has made to the claimant (i.e. causation);

4. describing and explaining complex progression or recovery from injuries following an accident and the symptoms and effects[13] experienced by the claimant during each stage of the progression or recovery;

5. dealing with the range of expert opinion on a matter;

6. dealing with a claimant's inconsistent, non-organic or exaggerated symptoms;

7. addressing the 'restrictions on activities' consequent on the injury - since the accident, at present and for the future;

8. addressing prognosis and future risks and relating these to potential future consequences;

9. distinguishing appropriately between the consequences of more than one accident or incident;

---

13   We discuss the medico-legal use of the terms 'injuries', 'symptoms', 'effects' and 'consequences' in Section 6.1.

10. providing a measured balance between explaining the medicine and overwhelming the lawyer with medical terminology;

11. (in clinical negligence) explaining clearly, in terms that a lawyer can understand, what constitutes an appropriate standard of medical care; and

12. using the English language in a way that enables the lawyers to understand a clear and precise message – No Foot-Wearing![14]

In the chapters that follow, we will address the knowledge and writing skills needed to resolve each of these issues.

1.4.3 Writing Concise Reports

The authors' longstanding call to write concise reports has been amplified by a recent judgment in the High Court. Competent experts understand that the lawyers and the court must be able to understand as quickly as possible the basis on which opinions are reached and the details of the reasoning process, in order to assess the strength of the opinions of the experts in the case. This process allows the court to give appropriate weight to the evidence when deciding the case. What the court requires are the key-evidential issues to be addressed, not for every piece of available evidence simply to be reproduced, whether relevant or not, by the experts in the case.

In far too many reports 'the trees' (the important facts) are lost in 'the forest' (the entire factual narrative). While the expert must do the necessary work of sifting through the available facts, the court is only interested in the results of the sifting process, and whether it has been conducted appropriately.

A 'succinct, focused and analytical'[15] report will be much more useful for the court and will be more proportionate in terms of the time spent reading and analysing the report for the lawyers, for other experts and for the court.

1.5 Criticism of Expert Witnesses

A sensible and cautious approach to a solicitor's instructions should enable an expert to practice without undue concern. However, when things go wrong, it is important to be aware that professional criticism of the expert involved can follow. When a professional makes fundamental errors while performing the role of expert witness, the consequences can be severe.

A useful definition of being an expert is found in *Dole v Johnson*:

> 'An expert witness is someone who has made the subject upon which he/she speaks a matter of particular study, practice or observation; he/she must have a particular and special knowledge of the subject.'[16]

---

14   For an explanation of "Foot-Wearing" see the Authors' Note and the Introduction to the Text

15   *Harman v East Kent Hospitals NHS Trust* [2015] EWHC 1662 at 32 and Section 11.1.

16   *Dole v Johnson* 50 N Hamp 454

A medical practitioner providing expert evidence in court (or professional regulatory) proceedings may subsequently have to justify that status – as being an expert – to the practitioner's own "fitness to practise" regulatory panel.

1.5.1 Qualifications and Relevant Experience

In *Pool v General Medical Council* [17] the Administrative Court on an appeal upheld the findings of a GMC "fitness to practise" panel in considering what amounted to being "an expert".

A psychiatrist ("P") had been instructed to provide an expert opinion on the fitness to practise of a paramedic in the light of her psychiatric condition (a diagnosis of personality disorder and PTSD following abuse in childhood). The Health Professions Council ("HPC") refused to admit P's expert evidence at the hearing and P was subsequently referred to the GMC.

P was on the specialist register for Psychiatry in Learning Disability, but not for Adult Psychiatry. He had experience of general adult psychiatric issues when a senior houseman, but subsequently had worked in secure hospitals where patients included females who had suffered sexual abuse and had been diagnosed with personality disorders and PTSD. He claimed sufficient expertise from his experience in his work to be regarded as an expert in this context and asserted that relevant expertise can come either from formal training or from experience gained in the course of work. Against him it was argued that he lacked day-to-day clinical experience in treating or researching such patients, and that the problems with which he would have had to deal in his practice would be very different from the current issue of assessing the ability of the paramedic to function in a job.

While the GMC panel accepted that a person might be equipped to act as an expert either by reason of training or by reason of day-to-day experience, it concluded that P was not an expert in general adult psychiatry for the combined reasons that he was not on the relevant specialist register, had not completed any higher professional training and had not worked in a relevant setting for the type of patient about whom he was providing an expert opinion.

Specifically, the GMC panel concluded that P had no direct experience of working with patients with personality disorders in the context of "fitness to practise" proceedings, did not have the relevant knowledge or experience to assess fitness to practise, did not take appropriate steps to ensure that he understood what was required in that context, and did not assess whether he was in fact competent to undertake this assignment. He could not therefore put himself forward as expert in the field of assessment of fitness to practise of an individual carrying out a particular role in the workplace.

---

17   [2014] EWHC 3791

1.5.2 Report Writing Skills

The structure of the written report he produced was also criticised, the panel finding that an important explanatory paragraph *"was not clear, not sufficiently logically argued and was disjointed [and] that it was not linked to your description of A's symptoms and behaviour earlier in the report"*. The suggestion that the report was adequate because any such lack of clarity could reasonably have been clarified by questions from the tribunal panel was firmly rejected.

The GMC panel observed that:

> *"to put oneself forward as an expert witness requires more than clinical experience and knowledge. It also requires the ability to produce an adequate report and to give oral evidence in an authoritative and convincing manner [whereas P's] evidence at the HPC hearing regarding your experience and expert status was confusing and unclear. The panel does not consider that you conducted yourself at the HPC hearing as an expert witness should when giving evidence. In your evidence to this panel you were also very unclear and often gave long, rambling, answers that did not address the question you had been asked. This panel concludes that, whilst you had some experience in General Psychiatry, you cannot be considered to be an expert."*

1.5.3 Understanding of Role

The panel noted that an expert at a tribunal hearing had a duty to be able to explain his role, and that an inability to do so was a significant failure. Instead, when asked at the HPC to give his understanding of his role as an expert, P *"gave rambling and unclear answers"*. P sought to excuse this before the GMC panel as being the result of his being shocked by being asked such questions and feeling *"disorientated"* by the nature of the questioning he received, but the tribunal noted that *"an expert witness must expect to be questioned closely and be subject to robust examination"*.

1.5.4 Seriousness of Failings

Although the GMC panel was concerned with only one occasion when P's competence as an expert was questioned, it held that this was sufficiently serious to amount to misconduct, and therefore to amount to impairment of fitness to practise, for which a sanction would be imposed, because:

> *"there is clearly a strong public interest in ensuring that doctors do not act outside their competence and do not put themselves forward as experts in areas in which they do not have adequate knowledge and expertise."*

1.5.5 Lessons to be Learnt

Although this case was concerned with expert evidence in the context of a "fitness to practise" tribunal, and specifically with expertise as a psychiatrist, it is highly relevant to expert evidence whenever and wherever it is given in proceedings.

These criticisms act as a timely reminder of the questions that any professional instructed as an expert in proceedings should ask him/herself, and any lawyer instructing the expert should also have in the forefront of his/her mind:

1. What is the purpose for which the expert is being instructed?

2. Does the expert have sufficient qualifications, training and experience to be put forward as an expert for this purpose?

3. Does the expert understand clearly the role and responsibilities of an expert in the proceedings in which the expert is instructed?

4. Does the expert have the ability to explain and justify all opinions on the issues for which the evidence is required to a professional, but non-expert, tribunal clearly, logically and succinctly both in writing and in answer to oral questions?

5. Does the expert have adequate report writing skills for this purpose?

6. Does the expert have adequate skills to explain him/herself and to answer challenging questions from trained advocates at a hearing?

These are questions which should be asked more than once – and at a minimum when instructions are first given, on completion of the report, on receipt of any opposing report and prior to any hearing.

An expert must be able to establish the appropriate professional credentials as an expert in the context in which instructions are being sought. An expert must also be able to demonstrate proper understanding of the expert's role and responsibilities, and of the skills necessary for effective report writing, through adequate training.

A failure on even just one occasion to demonstrate adequate expertise to justify a professional's role as an expert in the case, to show an adequate understanding of the role and its responsibilities, and to have competence in report writing may not only result in injustice within the proceedings and claims for damages for professional negligence but also the sanctioning of the "non-expert" for impaired fitness to practise.

1.6 Commercial Realities of Litigation

The vast majority of personal injury claims in which medical reports are obtained are settled by negotiation before they arrive at court – perhaps 98% of all claims that are intimated. In the year 2010/11, just under 50% of litigated claims in the County Court (where the majority of proceedings are issued) were for damages under £5,000 and just over 80% were for under £15,000[18]. Fewer than 4% of issued claims were stated to be for over £50,000.

---

18   Judicial and Court Statistics 2011. Statistics are recorded differently thereafter, but indicate a reduction in the total number of claims.

Most personal injury claims settle on the basis of the untested written word of one or more medical experts. This may be because there is only one expert dealing with a particular area of expertise or because the parties compromise in relation to the differences between two similar experts. Medical evidence will be necessary in all such claims in order to assess their value, but in a majority of cases, the time that can economically be justified by the lawyers for careful analysis of these reports will be minimal. Most personal injury claims are therefore processed quickly in something akin to a production line. The financial pressures on solicitors mean that this production line is often manned by trained but legally unqualified staff. With most claims settling prior to trial, it is rare for a medical expert in a personal injury claim to have a report scrutinised under cross-examination.

Similarly, most clinical negligence claims are settled without a court hearing[19]. Many such claims resolve around the issue of whether it can be proved that any claimed negligence has made a difference to outcome. Although by the nature and value of these claims there is an increased opportunity to give close attention to the expert reports (compared with most personal injury claims), it is still unusual for the evidence of the medical experts to be tested in court.

1.6.1 Imperative for Developing Evidential Skills

Medical expert reports are written in a communication void in which it can be readily – but wrongly – assumed that the lack of comment from the lawyers arises from their satisfaction with the report. Medical experts rarely receive comments on difficulties with their reports, such as a difficulty with understanding the content of the report or a difficulty applying the report to the required legal principles relevant to the claim. Rarely will medical experts receive notification from the lawyers on the settlement of a claim and the role in that settlement that their evidence played. As with any process that exists without feedback, mistakes will be repeated and dysfunctional aspects of professional practice soon become 'the way it is done'.

An unforeseen consequence of the solicitors' economic imperatives and the court's desire that parties settle rather than come to court is that the medical expert – even an expert who is not achieving an appropriate level of professional practice – has been given what is frequently an unassailable and pivotal role in the legal process. The legal profession has unwittingly surrendered much of the task of assessing the strength and the value of a claim to medical experts who often have little understanding of what is actually required. Currently, much of the responsibility for achieving a just settlement in medical cases has been placed upon the medical expert and it is an urgent imperative that medical experts develop their forensic skills in order to ensure a professional approach to meeting that responsibility.

---

19   The experience of the National Health Service Litigation Authority (NHSLA) is that typically less than 4% of claims where a formal letter of claim is received "go to court" – NHSLA Annual report and Accounts 2009/10

1.6.2   Imperative for Developing Commercial Skills

The reduction in the fees lawyers can recover for bringing a claim means that instructing solicitors are looking for ways to increase their margins. One approach has to been to push the work on to more junior lawyers, allowing legal firms to cut the costs involved in running the claims, another has been to seek to reduce the fees paid to experts, either by negotiating with the expert before instruction or by attempting a renegotiation of fees after a settlement has been achieved and a decision on costs has been made by the court.

Clearly, it is more important than ever before that expert witnesses know what their own commercial approach to the business of providing expert evidence actually is. The expert must be clear about the terms and conditions under which he/she is prepared to provide services and the work he/she is prepared to carry out in delivering each report.

In this present period of uncertainty, there are is a small minority of solicitors who are actively seeking out commercially naïve experts to obtain high-value services at an inappropriately low price or who are seeking to pass on functions that the solicitors themselves should carry out, such as sorting and paginating voluminous medical records.

Expert witnesses need to understand that at the preliminary investigatory stage a claimant solicitor is expending time and money on most cases in the knowledge that if the claim does not proceed or if the claim proceeds and is not successful, the solicitor will receive no payment for the work done or any expert advice obtained.

It is understandable that some solicitors in this situation would seek to share this risk with the expert who provides preliminary advice. The expert may agree to provide an advisory report free of charge in the expectation of receiving more instructions from the solicitor should this or other cases proceed. There is nothing wrong with such an approach, so long as the expert is treating these free services as a 'loss leader' – in essence, a form of relationship marketing. There is, however, a minority of experts offering advisory services to solicitors without charge, who rather than treating the cost of these free services as a loss leader simply build the cost of these free services into the fees they charge for court reports.

Experts should be in no doubt that disguising the cost of advisory reports unrelated to a claim within the fee charged for a court report is unethical, as the increased fees charged for the court report are then claimed on a false basis (i.e. that the fee is a reasonable one for the work carried out on the court report), whether this is paid eventually by the defendant, the claimant or by the solicitor. This is a highly unsatisfactory position for professionals to place themselves in. The fee charged for a court report should be a reasonable fee for the work involved in providing the court report in that case and that case alone.

Conclusion

An expert has to express his/her expertise within the context of the litigation process. This involves developing knowledge and skills beyond ordinary professional practice in order to engage with the medico-legal aspects of a claim for compensation. It is also essential that the expert understands his/her role and duties as an expert witness and the specific requirements of expert evidence. Being able to produce high-quality expert reports is fundamental to the expert's role in the litigation process, as the commercial realities of litigation have placed greater importance on the role of the experts instructed in the case

Key-Point Summary

1. Medical experts need to develop (medico-legal) knowledge and skills beyond those that are required in medical practice.

2. The overriding duty of an expert is to the court, not to the instructing party.

3. Expert witnesses must produce objective and unbiased evidence and must act as professionals who are independent of the parties.

4. There is great dissatisfaction amongst lawyers at the quality of medical expert evidence - an absence of feedback is not the same as client satisfaction.

5. The lawyers and the court give great weight to the evidence of expert witnesses, particularly the evidence of medical experts.

6. Experts must be confident that they can establish that they have appropriate and adequate expertise in relation to the matters on which they are asked to report and to the duties and responsibilities of an expert before accepting instructions.

7. Expert witnesses need to understand the commercial realities of the marketplace and must be able to deliver high-quality evidence to meet the instructions they have received, including the deadline for the production of the expert report.

Next Steps

In the next chapter, we will explore the essential legal principles that underlie a compensation claim for damages.

2

Legal Context of a Civil Claim for Damages for Personal Injury

Introduction

The foundation of a high-quality expert witness practice is having a clear understanding of the relevant legal rules and procedures applicable to a claim. Yet experts often admit to having only a vague understanding of the legal rules and procedures that are essential to bringing a civil claim for damages for personal injury. These legal rules and procedures not only affect the instructions that experts receive from their instructing solicitors, but also the nature of the evidence that experts need to provide to the court. It is essential when performing the role of expert witness that the expert understands the fundamental issues facing the lawyers in bringing or defending a claim and ensures that the expert report deals fully with all relevant issues. In the last two years, civil litigation has been transformed by the 'Jackson Reforms' and experts need to understand the impact on the conduct of litigation and the professionals who participate in it.

Chapter Outline

In this chapter, we will place the role of the expert witness within the context of a civil claim for damages for personal injury, which includes claims in clinical negligence and for industrial disease[1]. We will see how such claims are made, what the claim consists of and the issues that are of concern to the parties and their lawyers. We will also explore how medical expert evidence plays an essential role in the litigation process.

2.1   Purpose of a Civil Claim for Damages

The purpose of a civil claim arising out of personal injury suffered as a result of an accident, clinical negligence or from industrial disease is to achieve financial compensation – known as 'damages'. Claimants use civil litigation as a method of recovering damages, while defendants actively seek to absolve themselves of responsibility or to limit the level of damages they may be required to pay.

Sometimes, there are non-financial issues at stake, particularly from a claimant's viewpoint, such as seeking:

- an apology or acceptance of responsibility by a defendant;
- a change of working practice in businesses or hospitals (or wherever) to ensure that no one else suffers in the same way;
- an acknowledgement that the claimant's injuries and physical complaints are real;
- the re-education or retraining of the person seen as at fault; or even
- retribution and revenge.

Although these non-financial issues may be a key to what fires the litigation for the claimant, and may make achieving a settlement more difficult, these issues will never be resolved in court or by the direct act of legal proceedings. The only instrument of civil justice is the award of money[2]. In most cases, the claimant is

---

1   The term 'personal injury' is widely used in two different ways. Technically, every compensation claim that arises from an injury to a person gives rise to 'a personal injury claim' – there is no differentiation of injuries arising from an industrial disease, an act of clinical negligence or even a 'slip and trip'. However, lawyers and doctors also commonly refer to 'a personal injury claim' to specify a claim that deals with an accident, rather than industrial disease or an injury arising from clinical negligence. We use the term in both of these ways throughout this book and offer explanation where the sense we intend is unclear.

2   Although a stated objective of the Pre-Action Protocol for the Resolution of Clinical Disputes seeks to encourage the defendant to make an early apology to the claimant in appropriate circumstances (para 2.2(c)).

interested in what money can be recovered and the more the claimant recovers, the more satisfied with the system the claimant tends to be.

The defendant is normally an insurer, or in a clinical negligence claim, an NHS Trust or medical defence organisation. For sound commercial and ethical reasons, defendants are concerned to ensure that the award of damages is the lowest that can reasonably be made, so as to protect their own interests. Defendants may also occasionally have an ulterior motive, perhaps where the view is taken at an early stage that the claim is fabricated or exaggerated or that it is necessary to discourage the particular type of claim that is being made. In such circumstances, commercial reasoning (the balance of risk against cost) may take a backseat to a desire to expose a fraud or to send a clear message to other potential claimants.

The parties' lawyers will have interests similar to those of the parties themselves, although in the case of the claimant's lawyers, with less emphasis on the non-financial issues (i.e. apology, acceptance of responsibility, change in systems for the future etc.). Generally, the party seen as the loser at the conclusion of the claim has to pay the costs incurred in the claim by both parties[3]. Given the very considerable sums likely to be incurred in costs – court fees[4], the costs of the lawyers, the costs of the medical experts, and all of the ancillary costs in making a claim – winning is vital.

Winning generally means that a party recovers its own costs and is not liable for the costs of the other side. However, it is possible to recover damages, but in particular circumstances still be regarded as the loser because the liability for costs outweighs the damages recovered[5].

2.2 Legal Basis of a Claim

Suffering an injury does not provide an automatic right to recover compensation. Damages will only be awarded to compensate for provable loss caused by a breach of duty of care – a legally imposed duty of care or a statutory duty – owed to the claimant by the defendant. To succeed in a claim for damages for personal injury, it is necessary for the claimant to prove:

1. that the defendant is in breach of a duty owed to the claimant;

2. that injury, loss or damage has been caused to the claimant (sufficient to form the basis of a claim in law) as a result of the breach of duty; and

3. the nature and extent of the injury, loss or damage sustained.

---

3   But see the impact of Qualified One-Way Costs Shifting for claims after 1st April 2013 at Section 2.8.1

4   Recently increased by up to 600%

5   See the discussion of Part 36 offers at Section 2.8.5

In response, the defendant may deny:

1. the existence of a legal duty;

2. the duty has been breached;

3. any breach has caused injury, loss or damage; and

4. the damage sustained is as great as that claimed.

The defendant may assert any one or more or even all of these points. In addition, the defendant may allege that the claimant is partly to blame for the injury as a result of his/her acts or defaults (contributory negligence) or that the claimant has failed to take reasonable steps to minimise his/her loss or damage (or both).

2.2.1   Breach of Duty

In the areas of personal injury, clinical negligence and industrial disease claims, a breach of duty will normally arise because of:

1. negligence or a breach of statutory duty (or both); or

2. a breach of a term of a contract.

Negligence is the failure to take reasonable care to prevent foreseeable injury to a person whom the law regards as being within a category of persons to whom such a legal duty is owed. For example, the motorist owes such a duty to other road users; the employer owes such a duty to employees or others over whose work he/she has sufficient control; a medical practitioner owes such a duty to patients.

Statutory duties exist in many areas. They are created by primary legislation (Acts of Parliament) and secondary legislation (Statutory Instruments). For example, occupiers of land owe a duty to take reasonable care of visitors under the Occupiers' Liability Act 1957 and a more limited duty to trespassers under the Occupiers' Liability Act 1984.

Employers are required to take measures to prevent injury to employees and others under the Health and Safety at Work (Etc.) Act 1974 and a wide range of statutory instruments. A breach of statutory duty that results from a failure to comply with the requirements of a statutory instrument may give rise to criminal proceedings as well as to a civil claim in damages[6].

A term of a contract, the breach of which may give rise to a claim, may be a written term of a contractual agreement or may be a term implied by law, such as is

---

6   Section 69 of the Enterprise and Regulatory Reform Act 2013 removed the automatic liability for damages for breach of health and safety regulations from October 2013 so that a civil claim will depend on proof of negligence on the part of the employer, not simply a breach of a duty under the various regulations.

the case in an employer/employee relationship or in a doctor/patient relationship when receiving private medical care. In most personal injury claims – typically, car accidents, slip and trips or workplace accidents - the issue of breach of duty is not a matter for expert medical evidence. However, breach of duty is a matter central to the role of medical experts in clinical negligence claims, where patients are owed a duty of care by the clinicians who treat them. Medical expert evidence is essential in helping the court to decide what the standard of care reasonably to be expected of the treating clinicians is in a particular situation and so whether the duty of care owed by the clinical team to the patient has been breached[7].

There are also situations in the area of workplace or industrial disease claims, where medical evidence may contribute to considerations of the relevant standard of care and the foreseeability of injury in exposing employees to potentially hazardous agents. These would include chemicals, vibration, dust or noise, or exposure to unusual or repetitive activities. Psychologists or psychiatrists may be asked to address the 'reasonable foreseeability' of psychiatric illness arising from exposure of the claimant to particular situations or stressors.

2.2.2 Injury, Loss or Damage

The injury (the term to include a medical condition or disease), loss or damage suffered by the claimant must be 'more than minimal' for the claimant to be able to claim damages. However, damage must be extremely trivial before the court will conclude that there has been no damage sufficient to establish a claim. A small cut resulting in a very minor scar or a blow resulting in a black eye is regarded as enough of an injury to enable a claim for damages to be made, although somewhat paradoxically, asymptomatic pleural plaques resulting from exposure to asbestos (and indicative of a risk of developing terminal disease but not visible to another person) are not at this point considered by the court in England and Wales to be sufficient to bring a personal injury claim[8]. Medical evidence may therefore be required to establish whether or not an injury caused by a breach of duty is asymptomatic and therefore should be regarded as minimal.

The quantification of loss arising from an injury, particularly in more serious cases, often requires the work of care and therapeutic professionals to establish the nature and extent of the care package reasonably required by the claimant.

2.2.3 Causation

In every claim, the claimant has to establish that the injury, loss and damage in relation to which damages are claimed were caused by the breach of duty of the defendant and compensation will not be awarded for any such injury or loss that would have occurred in any event. Medical evidence is often crucial in establish-

---

7   We will discuss Clinical Negligence claims in detail in Chapters 8 and 9

8   *Johnston v NEI International Composition* [2007] UKHL 39 although in relation to claims under Scottish law and in Northern Ireland by recent statute law it is now again possible to recover damages for pleural plaques (as was the case prior to 2007).

ing causation – the issue being whether or not the claimed breach of duty by the defendant actually caused the injury to the claimant[9].

2.2.4   Contributory Negligence

Where the claimant proves that there has been a breach of a duty owed by the defendant to the claimant, the defendant may allege that the claimant's damages should be reduced to reflect his/her own contribution of negligence or blame-worthiness for the accident or injury. Such allegations of contributory negligence commonly arise in road traffic accidents (the failure to wear a seat belt may result in such a finding) as well as in workplace accidents. It would be unusual for such an allegation to be made in the context of a clinical negligence claim, although it could be asserted in a case where it is said that the claimant failed for no good reason to follow a recommended course of treatment that would have improved the eventual outcome.

2.3   Adversarial Litigation Process

Legal proceedings are adversarial and not inquisitorial. The judge is not an inquisitor who attempts through his own investigation of the evidence to uncover the truth of the matters before the court, but rather hears the case of each party and makes a decision based on the evidence placed before the court. Each side will seek to put its case in the best light possible with a view to obtaining a favourable decision from the court and will also seek to discredit the evidence of the other side by cross-examination of its witnesses.

Whilst the claimant must prove his/her claim to the satisfaction of the court, the defendant often seeks only to challenge or undermine the evidence brought forward by the claimant rather than attempting to prove its own case on the facts available. After each party has presented its evidence and cross-examination has taken place, the judge is left to conclude what has or has not been proved to a sufficient standard. If the defendant undermines the claimant's case sufficiently, the claimant will be unable to prove his/her case and no damages will be awarded.

Since the introduction of the *Civil Procedure Rules 1998* (CPR), a more co-operative approach to the conduct of litigation has been codified in order to make the litigation process more efficient. Provisions for concurrent evidence by experts (so called "hot tubbing"), introduced in April 2013, create a procedure for the judge to question experts prior to examination in chief and cross-examination by the parties' advocates[10]. However, the litigation process itself remains adversarial.

---

9   See the detailed discussion in Chapter 6

10   This is discussed further in Sections 2.8.12 and 4.7.5

> The testing of evidence in court requires that the expert sets out clearly in the report the reasons (or the reasoning process) that supports each opinion expressed. There is no place for unsupported opinion in an expert report and the courts will criticise an expert if court time is wasted owing to an expert's failure to explain the rationale underlying an opinion.

2.4   Proof

In a civil case, the claimant must prove his/her case to the civil standard of proof, 'on the balance of probabilities'. This means that the claimant must satisfy the judge that it is more likely than not that his/her injuries and the consequential loss for which damages are claimed were caused by the defendant's breach of duty. Similarly, the claimed loss must also be established on the balance of probabilities.

Once a fact is proved to the judge's satisfaction on the balance of probabilities (i.e. as being more likely than not), then this fact is established for all purposes in the case. Similarly, once the judge decides that one expert opinion - for example as to the nature of the injury sustained - is to be preferred on the balance of probabilities, then this will be the expert opinion on which the claim will be resolved[11].

2.5   Damages: Underlying Principle

Once it is established that there has been a breach of duty that has caused injury or damage to the claimant, the legal principle underlying the assessment of an award of damages is known as the '100% Recovery Principle'[12]:

> 'In settling the sum of money to be given for reparation of damages you should as nearly as possible get at that sum of money which will put the party who has been injured, or who has suffered, in the same position as he would have been in if he had not sustained the wrong for which he is now getting his compensation or reparation.'[13]

This principle may be applied without great difficulty to past loss, where for example loss of earnings can be based on the earnings received immediately before the accident or on the earnings of a comparable employee and where expenses reasonably incurred can be proved with receipts. For future loss of earnings, in a straightforward case, the court can assess damages on the basis of the likely level of earnings along a probable career path. However, valuing damages for non-financial loss, such as a physical or psychological injury or the

---

11   Proof is considered in more detail in Chapter 5

12   *Wells v Wells* [1999] 1 AC 345 at 382H, *Thompstone v Tameside & Glossop Acute Services* [2008] EWCA Civ 5

13   Lord Blackburn in *Livingstone v Rawyards Coal Company* (1880) 5 App Cas 25 at 39

loss of ability to enjoy certain aspects of the claimant's pre-injury lifestyle, defies a truly logical approach.

Assessing the compensation necessary to achieve full and fair recovery in relation to losses that have not yet been incurred is often fraught with difficulty and may enter the realm of educated guesswork:

> 'The object of the award of damages for future expenditure is to place the injured party as nearly as possible in the same financial position as he or she would have been in but for the accident. The aim is to award such a sum of money as will amount to no more, and at the same time no less, than the net loss.'[14]

As a result, the parties will need to adduce evidence addressing not only what the consequences of an injury on the claimant's capabilities are and probably will be, but also what would probably have occurred in the claimant's life in the absence of the injury sustained. Both aspects will probably be full of uncertainty, but the court will have to establish the probable scenarios and will almost certainly rely on expert opinion to achieve this.

> The medical expert must assist in identifying the consequences of the injuries sustained by the claimant, by describing his/her physical restrictions and limitations.

In reality, a full recovery of a loss sustained may not in fact be achievable in relation to many aspects of claim. It is not really possible for the court to fully compensate a claimant for loss of an active sex life or for loss of a place in a county tennis team or for the risk of developing post traumatic arthritis. However, subject to the practical difficulties of making assessments based on a degree of speculation and uncertainty, 100% recovery is what the court will expressly aim to achieve.

2.6 Types of Claim for Damages

Damages fall into two basic categories: non-pecuniary (non-financial) and pecuniary (financial) loss. Non-pecuniary damages are often referred to by lawyers as 'general damages' or 'generals' and pecuniary damages are referred to as 'special damages' or 'specials'. General damages are related to the impact of the injury on the claimant, while special damages are specific to the particular circumstances of the claimant and therefore the financial loss he/she has suffered. Special damages are based on a mathematical calculation of the financial cost or loss actually incurred or to be incurred. Sometimes lawyers will use 'specials' as shorthand for past losses only.

There is no limit to the types of claim or 'heads of claim' that can be included in a claim for damages. Heads of claim are the categories or types of loss for which

---

14   Lord Hope in *Wells v Wells* [1999] 1 AC 345 at 390A

compensation is claimed. What can be claimed will depend on the particular circumstances of the claimant and the case, and on the imagination of the claimant's lawyers.

2.6.1 Non-Pecuniary Loss

Damages for non-pecuniary loss consist mainly of pain, suffering and loss of amenity. The terms pain and suffering are self-explanatory - though how these are valued is not without difficulty. The assessment of damages will depend on the type and level of impact upon the particular claimant of the pain and suffering that has been caused by the injury. Loss of amenity covers any impact that reduces the claimant's enjoyment of life or impairs his/her physical senses. Damages may also be awarded for loss of the enjoyment of a congenial occupation as a result of an injury, although generally only for loss of a public service occupation.

2.6.2 Pecuniary Loss

Anything that can be seen as financial loss that is consequential upon the injury sustained can be compensated for in damages. The claimant may have been planning a career as a professional footballer or may have been unemployed and living on produce grown from his own allotment: the provable financial impact on these activities, both in the past and for the future, can form a basis for the assessment of damages.

Examples of potential items of claim for pecuniary loss include:

1. any items damaged in the accident;

2. loss of earnings to date and for the future;

3. a disadvantage in the employment market, which may result in the employed claimant having greater difficulty finding employment in the future;

4. loss of pension resulting from reduced or lost earnings until the age at which without the injury the claimant had planned to retire or loss of employment benefitting from a non-contributory pension scheme;

5. the cost of medical and therapeutic treatment reasonably incurred and reasonably to be incurred in the future;

6. the cost of care and assistance that has reasonably been provided;

7. the cost of care and assistance reasonably to be incurred in the future (which in the case of a serious injury is likely to be by far the largest head of claim);

8. the reasonable cost of employing others to perform tasks which have previously been carried out by the claimant and can no longer reasonably be carried out;

9. the value of the care and assistance or the help with other tasks provided gratuitously by others including family members;

10. any equipment purchased or now reasonably needed as a result of any disability resulting from the accident;

11. any additional transport costs arising from the injury including costs of travelling for treatment and costs of adaptations to vehicles or changes in the means of transportation resulting in additional costs;

12. any additional accommodation costs resulting from any disability – from handrails and raised toilet seats to stair lifts, bungalows or additional rooms for carers;

13. any additional holiday costs resulting from disability; and

14. where life expectancy has been reduced, a proportion of the net income that would have been earned during the period of 'lost years'.[15]

Although this list contains the majority of items that can be claimed, the medical expert should always ask a claimant about how an injury has affected his/her activities of daily living and what limitations the claimant attributes to the injuries sustained. This information will be critical to the experts who will be instructed to deal with the quantum issues in the case.

2.6.3 Death

Where the claimant dies, whether or not as a result of the injury sustained, his/her personal representatives can claim for the benefit of the deceased's estate all the losses that the deceased could have claimed up to the moment of death – such as, damages for the injury itself, care and assistance, loss of earnings, and expenses incurred up to death. Lawyers refer to this type of claim as a 'Law Reform Act claim'.[16]

If the injury that is the subject of the claim caused the death, then in addition to a Law Reform Act claim, the deceased's dependant(s) can make a 'Fatal Accidents Act claim'.[17] Where the dependants are children, the claim will be made on their behalf. The potential heads of claim in a Fatal Accidents Act claim are different to those made by an injured claimant. The dependants can claim for the financial loss

---

15 Although if the claimant dies before the claim is completed, this head of claim does not pass to his/her Estate

16 The claim is made under the Law Reform (Miscellaneous Provisions) Act 1934

17 Under the Fatal Accidents Act 1976

they have suffered, being the loss in a share of the deceased's income from which they would have benefited but for the death or the loss of what the deceased would have done for them for nothing, but which must now either be done by others or purchased as a service. Certain dependants can also recover a statutory sum by way of bereavement damages. Funeral costs are also recoverable.

2.6.4 Possible Future Complications and Provisional Damages

A claimant can recover damages for the possible future complications of his/her injuries. The law states that a claim can be made for a provisional award of damages:

> '[...in] an action for damages for personal injuries in which there is proved or admitted to be a chance that at some definite or indefinite time in the future the injured person will, as a result of the act or omission which gave rise to the cause of action, develop some serious disease or suffer some serious deterioration in his physical or mental condition.'[18]

As a result, the court can reserve the position when awarding damages so as to enable further damages to be awarded in the future for something that has not yet occurred. A provisional award of damages is an assessment of damages made on the basis that a serious disease or a serious deterioration in the claimant's condition will not occur, but allowing the claimant to return to court for a further award of damages should it occur. Such future complications need to be expressly identified and addressed by the medical expert, so that the lawyers can advise whether to make a claim now for damages to cover the possibility that the complication will occur or instead seek a provisional award of damages which does not include compensation for that risk, with the option to make a further claim should the complication actually occur[19].

Some guidance as to what amounts to a serious disease or serious deterioration for the purposes of this provision, and therefore what the expert must have in mind and must address when considering possible future complications, has been given by the Court of Appeal:

> "A disease or deterioration could be serious because of the effect on the activities and capabilities of the injured party; or because of its effect on his or her life expectancy, or because of the effect on his or her financial position ...
> The disease or deterioration must be such that an award of damages which included a sum for the chance [of such disease/deterioration] would be wholly inadequate to compensate the claimant for the position in which he would find himself once the chance had materialised."[20]

---

18   Section 32A Senior Courts Act 1981 (known prior to October 2009 as the Supreme Court Act 1981) and Section 51 County Courts Act 1984

19   We consider the expert's approach to the evidence in such cases further in Section 6.5.4

20   *Curi v Colina* (The Times 14.10.98)

The claimant or the court itself may decide to deal with this risk by an award of immediate damages reflecting the degree of risk that the complication will occur. These are extremely important decisions and any decision as to how appropriately to compensate the claimant for the risk must be made in the light of a clear medical opinion as to the degree of risk that the complication will occur and the implications for the claimant of such a complication occurring.

Examples of conditions where these considerations might apply include:

- epilepsy following a head injury;
- mesothelioma or lung cancer following exposure to asbestos fibres;
- sympathetic ophthalmia;
- recurrence of cancer; or
- traumatic arthritis.

2.7   Valuation of the Claim

The valuation of the claim will be based on the evidence (or in the case of a settlement prior to trial, the anticipated evidence) of the claimant, other lay (non-professional) witnesses and the evidence of experts. The lay witnesses in a case may include the claimant, family members or friends, and employers – past, present or prospective. The valuation may be based on medical expert evidence or on any other expert evidence from such disciplines as the court directs (for example, care experts or accountants).

2.7.1   Non-Pecuniary Loss

Valuing damages for non-pecuniary loss (such as for pain, suffering and loss of amenity) is not in any sense a mathematical exercise relying on calculation. The amount of damages awarded is based on the amounts awarded in previous cases even though the facts of each case will normally be unique. Lawyers develop a feel for what a claim is worth and while there is no "right" or "wrong" answer, normally there is an identifiable range of damages within which the court will make an award[21].

Since 1992, the Judicial Studies Board , and more recently its successor the Judicial College, has attempted to collate the level of damages awarded for different injuries into a small book, *Guidelines for the Assessment of General Damages in Personal Injury Cases*[22] (known now as "the JC Guidelines"). This book has now become the first port of call in assessing general damages, although lawyers will also rely on reported court decisions for further assistance. Medical experts are well advised to take a look at the categories of injuries within their own field, as set out within the JC Guidelines, in order to

---

21   Lawyers commonly make use of publications such as *Kemp & Kemp: The Quantum of Damages* (Thomson, Sweet & Maxwell) and various on-line resources for reports of previously decided cases.

22   *Guidelines for the Assessment of General Damages in Personal Injury Cases* Oxford: Oxford University Press (2013) and now in its 12th edition

appreciate those aspects of the injury or its impact that the court is likely to find most helpful in assessing general damages[23].

From 1st April 2013 (as part of the 'Jackson reforms'[24]) damages for pain and suffering and loss of amenity have been increased by 10% where the claimant's funding arrangement for the litigation is entered into after that date. Rather than a recognition of the generally low level of such damages, this is intended as a kind of 'compensation' to a claimant who will have to pay any success fee to which his/her lawyers are entitled (and which may be up to 25% of damages for non-pecuniary loss and of past losses) out of these damages. Whether or not the additional 10% is awarded will therefore depend on whether the claimant entered into a conditional fee agreement with a lawyer before or after 1st April 2013[25].

2.7.2   Pecuniary Loss

Valuing pecuniary loss is essentially a mathematical exercise. An essential element of the claimant's case is the 'Schedule of Loss', a document in which the detailed valuation of the claim is set out. An example of a schedule of loss is included in Appendix 7. There is no specific format for these schedules, so they vary greatly from case to case and between different lawyers. The schedule of loss should list each of the heads under which damages are claimed and set out for each such head how the claimed damages are calculated.

The lawyers for both claimant and defendant will be looking to see the extent to which the evidence in the case supports the heads of claim and the calculations. This evidence will be both the evidence that the lawyers anticipate that non-expert witnesses will give, which will be contained in witness statements, and also the evidence of experts such as medical, care and therapeutic, and accounting experts instructed in the claim.

For the claimant to be likely to recover damages, most of the heads of claim and the calculations within these will need to be supported directly or indirectly by expert medical evidence. The claimant will not succeed in recovering substantial loss of earnings unless medical evidence confirms that the injury has reasonably resulted in a restriction in the ability to follow paid employment. A claim for the cost of care or for carrying out tasks that the claimant asserts can no longer be carried out will not succeed in the absence of medical evidence that indicates that these restrictions have resulted from the injuries sustained in the accident, and describes the extent and effect of such restrictions, and will generally require a further report from a care expert assessing the amount of care reasonably required.

---

23   Some insurers use a computer model for assessing damages (such as 'Colossus'), although these are reputed by many lawyers consistently to under-assess damages when compared with court awards. Lord Justice Jackson's 'Review of Civil Litigation Costs: Final Report' (December 2009) recommended that a working group be set up to establish a uniform calibration for all software systems used in assessment of damages for smaller claims.

24   See Section 2.8

25   *Simmons v Castle* [2012] EWCA Civ 1288

The defendant responds to the claimant's schedule of loss with a 'Counter Schedule'. The counter schedule sets out the defendant's calculations and those figures that are disputed and those that can be agreed. A trial, in so far as it relates to the value of the claim, will be based around these two documents and an assessment of the evidence, both factual and expert, that each side relies on in support of its own schedule.

> Medical evidence must address the consequences to the claimant of any restriction caused by the injury sustained.

2.7.3   Future Pecuniary Loss

Compensation for future losses can be by way of periodical payments or a lump sum payment, or a combination of both. More commonly, damages will be awarded by way of a one-off lump sum payment. This is tax free when received in the hands of the claimant[26] and the claimant is free to spend it as he/she wishes. The amount will have been carefully calculated as representing compensation for future loss of earnings or the amount necessarily and reasonably to be incurred in dealing with the claimant's future additional needs as a result of the injury sustained, or both. However, once received, the claimant is free to spend the award on a luxury cruise, to gamble it away or to invest it all for the benefit of his/her children.

Periodical payments as a way of providing compensation were first introduced in 1996[27] in circumstances where the parties agreed to this. From 1st April 2005, the court has had the power to impose an order for periodical payments on the parties. Periodical payments are sums paid regularly (for example monthly or more commonly annually) for a determined period normally to compensate for loss of earnings or to provide for the additional costs of care resulting from the injury. For care costs, the payments will usually be payable for life.

A lump sum to compensate for future losses is calculated by making assumptions as to life expectancy. These assumptions will inevitably in time be proved wrong so that the sum awarded will be too much or too little. A periodical payment, subject to defining an appropriate formula for increasing it to allow for increased future costs, should (theoretically at least) be just what is required and no more or less. Periodical payments are increasingly used in large value claims as part of a compensation "package" involving lump sum payments as well. The annual increases can now be related to a suitable index other than the Retail Prices Index.

To calculate a lump sum value for items of future pecuniary loss the court will start with a valuation based on present day costs. Where there is a loss or cost that

---

26   Hence damages for loss of earnings are calculated net of tax and national insurance contributions

27   Section 2 Damages Act 1996 as subsequently amended by section 100 Courts Act 2003

will be incurred continuously or at regular intervals, such as loss of earnings or care costs, the court will value the total annual loss at present day values and then multiply it for the number of years for which it will be lost. The actual number of years will be discounted to reflect the number of years in advance that the money is being paid. The discount is applied because money received now is worth more than money received in the future – for example, money received now can be invested to increase its value over time. [28,29]

Where there is an anticipated one-off cost in the future (for example, an operation in five years' time) the court will discount the current cost to provide adequate money now, which if invested should provide the sum needed at the relevant time in the future [30]. Increases in costs in the future are ignored – the actuarial tables which are used for this exercise allow for future RPI inflation, but not for the higher rates of healthcare and wages inflation.

The limitations of this basis of assessment of loss and of providing full recovery of loss to the claimant is well recognised by the court:

> 'It is the nature of a lump sum payment that it may, in respect of future pecu-
> niary loss, prove to be either too little or too much. So far as the multiplier
> is concerned, the [claimant] may die the next day, or he may live beyond his
> normal expectation of life. So far as the multiplicand is concerned, the cost of
> future care may exceed everyone's best estimate. Or a new cure or less expen-
> sive form of treatment may be discovered. But these uncertainties do not
> affect the basic principle. The purpose of the award is to put the [claimant] in
> the same position, financially, as if he had not been injured.' [31]

2.8 Costs of Litigation and the 'Jackson Reforms'

Fundamental changes to the costs' regime under which civil litigation operates were introduced on 1 April 2013. In large part, these are the product of a report

---

28 Technically, the discount applied to the annual cost is known as the 'multiplier', while the annual cost is known as the 'multiplicand'. The multiplier is applied to the multiplicand to provide a sum now, which if invested in an interest bearing financial instrument, should provide adequate money with which to fund the cost in the future and be used up at the end of that period. The multiplier is found by using actuarial tables, commonly referred to by lawyers as the "Ogden Tables", but more formally entitled, *Actuarial Tables with explanatory notes for use in Personal Injury and Fatal Accident Cases* issued by the Government Actuary's Department (currently in its 7th edition). Lawyers often access these tables and other data relevant to the assessment of damages in *Facts & Figures: Tables for the Calculation of Damages* published by Sweet & Maxwell and the Professional Negligence Bar Association

29 In fact, the Government has continued to decline to vary the discount rate, which was set in July 2001 when the economic climate was very different, so that any financial adviser would regard the current rate as resulting in a substantial undervaluation of damages

30 Using the Ogden Tables to identify the appropriate multiplier

31 Lord Lloyd in *Wells v Wells* [1999] 1 AC 345 at 363H

on the costs of litigation carried out by Lord Justice Jackson[32]. Costs will include the costs of the lawyers, expert witnesses and the court fees, which are paid at various stages in the litigation and which have increased greatly in recent years. Such costs may substantially exceed the damages recovered or sought.

2.8.1 The 'Jackson Reforms'

We will explore, in the next chapter, how the *Civil Procedure Rules 1998* ('CPR'), which contain the rules by which the court manages litigation, were the result of Lord Woolf's report into civil litigation. That report, whilst identifying many other failings with the then existing management of litigation, was critical of the expense involved in litigation.

The resulting reforms of 1998 were intended in part to address that issue. However, it became clear over time that the new rules had not been successful in containing the expense of litigation, so Lord Justice Jackson carried out an investigation to see what should be done.

At the conclusion of his 2009 investigation into the cost of civil litigation, Lord Justice Jackson made a number of wide ranging recommendations. The foreword of his report (in its entirety) explained:

> *'In some areas of civil litigation costs are disproportionate and impede access to justice. I therefore propose a coherent package of interlocking reforms, designed to control costs and promote access to justice.'*

The report contained 109 specific recommendations covering all aspects of civil litigation and many of no relevance to this guide. The recommendations formed the basis of wide-ranging reforms introduced by the Government with effect from 1 April and 31 July 2013, but these reforms neither implemented all of the recommendations nor limited themselves to those recommendations, hence the use of inverted commas when referring to the 'Jackson reforms' in the title to this section and elsewhere in this guide.

In relation to personal injury litigation, the Government consulted (amongst others) with the insurance industry. The resulting reforms were intended to reduce the cost of personal injury litigation to the insurance industry and intended to control what was perceived as 'the compensation culture' and 'the claims industry' which had developed following the introduction of conditional fee agreements ('no win, no fee' agreements) and the development of claims management companies that advertised for clients and sold on the claims to solicitors (by charging referral fees).

As these reforms have taken hold in litigation, so they have radically changed the environment within which personal injury lawyers work. This changed environ-

---

32   Lord Justice Jackson's 'Review of Civil Litigation Costs: Final Report' (December 2009) is available at http://www.judiciary.gov.uk/publications/review-of-civil-litigation-costs-final-report/

ment, as we shall see, has begun to impact on expert witnesses and will continue to effect significant changes in the relationship between experts and those instructing them and the manner in which expert evidence is in future used in litigation.

2.8.2 Costs of Litigation

When we speak of the costs of litigation, we include all of the constituent parts of the bill which traditionally a party to litigation would be liable to pay to his lawyers for running the litigation on his or her behalf – in particular the fees of the solicitors and barristers, the fees charged by the court and the cost of using experts. Generally, the winner in litigation recovers from the other side those costs of bringing or defending the claim. This means that the loser pays all the costs in the action. Such costs may substantially exceed the damages recovered or sought.

This harsh reality means that throughout the claim, the lawyers on both sides – and particularly for the defendant – are concerned about the costs that have been, and are still to be incurred, and who is to pay them.

For the lawyers, costs (i.e. their fees) are the commercial reason for being in this line of business, and the costs that can be recovered will depend on the value of the claim. The introduction of fixed costs regimes in recent years, which impose a limit on the fees lawyers can charge in smaller value claims[33], give the claimant's lawyers an additional interest in maximising the value of the claim and the defendant an additional interest in minimising its value. The principle of proportionality of costs – that the costs recovered by the lawyers should be proportionate to the sum in issue[34] – also gives the lawyers an interest in the value of the claim when seeking to justify to the court the costs claimed at the end of the litigation process.

A series of changes resulting from the 'Jackson reforms' has fundamentally changed the costs' regime and has had very substantial effects on not only the way in which cases are run but also on the profitability for the lawyers of such litigation.

2.8.3 Conditional Fee Agreements

Nearly all personal injury claims and clinical negligence claims are now funded on the claimant's side by way of 'Conditional Fee Agreements' (also known as 'CFAs'). CFAs are commonly but not always accurately called 'no win, no fee' agreements. These were introduced when Legal Aid was removed from virtually all such claims in April 2000, in order to ensure that all litigants had 'access to justice'. The CFA regime was substantially reformed as from 1 April 2013 as part of the 'Jackson reforms'.

---

33 On 1 April 2010, a fixed costs regime was introduced in road traffic claims with a value up to £10,000 and from 31 July 2013 this was extended to most personal injury claims (not clinical negligence) with a value up to £25,000. See Sections 2.8.8 and 3.4.

34 CPR 44.3(2). See also Section 2.8.7.

Under a CFA, the claimant's lawyers are only paid for the work they do and the costs they incur, which often includes the fees of medical experts, if the claim is successful. Success for these purposes is generally defined as recovering damages[35]. If the claimant's lawyers are successful, they may recover on top of the normal 'base' costs an additional sum. In CFAs entered into before April 2013, this will be equivalent to a percentage of the 'base' costs - a percentage up to 100%[36]. This additional sum is to compensate the lawyers for the cases they take on, spend time and money on (as for example in obtaining medical reports), but which do not succeed, whether through abandoning the claim as a result of its poor prospects or losing at court.

When a claim funded by a CFA is successful, in relation to a pre-April 2013 CFA, both the costs and the additional sum to be paid under the CFA will be paid by the defendant; if it is not successful, then normally the claimant will have purchased 'After the Event' (or 'ATE') insurance which will pay the costs of the defendant for which otherwise the claimant would be liable. The losing defendant will have to pay the cost of the premium for such insurance in addition to the base costs and the success fee of the claimant's lawyers.

For all CFAs entered into since 1 April 2013 any success fee is paid by the claimant from the damages recovered and its amount is much restricted[37]. This additional sum cannot be more than 25% of the damages recovered for pain and suffering and loss of amenity and for past losses, and will normally be a much smaller sum than under the pre-April 2013 scheme. An ATE insurance premium is no longer recoverable, but in most cases the losing claimant is not expected to pay the defendant's costs because of Qualified One Way Costs Shifting ("QOCS") (see Section 2.8.4). There is a small exception enabling ATE insurance premiums to be recoverable for the cost of a breach of duty or causation medical report in a clinical negligence claim[38].

Some claimants have 'Before the Event' (or 'BTE') insurance, such as may be purchased at very modest cost as an add-on to motor or household insurance. This will provide cover for incurring legal costs in a claim and the costs of the other side should the claim be lost up to a defined limit, which is generally adequate for an average claim.

Whilst within the limit of the cover provided by the BTE insurance, the claimant is not at risk of paying the costs of the claim. Trades Union members may also have access to funding arrangements that enable them to bring claims without

---

35 Although frequently it is necessary also to 'beat' a defendant's Part 36 offer of settlement in order to recover all costs (see Section 2.8.5)

36 In many types of claims these percentage uplifts are fixed by the *Civil Procedure Rules 1998* (Part 45)

37 At the time of writing, mesothelioma claims are the only exception to these changes so that success fees and ATE insurance premiums are still recoverable by a successful claimant from the defendant.

38 The Recovery of Costs Insurance Premiums in Clinical Negligence Proceedings Regulations 2013

any liability for their own costs or any risk of incurring the other side's costs in the event of losing. These arrangements generally involve the lawyers working under a CFA.

Therefore, under the pre-April 2013 regime, except in the exceptional circumstances where the claimant is privately funding the claim without a CFA or has a CFA but is unable to afford insurance to cover the defendant's costs in the event of losing, the claimant's personal interest in costs is limited[39]. From 1 April 2013, the claimant under a CFA is likely to see some of his/her damages taken by the legal team as a success fee if successful and can lose a sum no greater than the total damages recovered if taken in costs by the defendant, for example, for not bettering a defendant's Part 36 offer to settle (see Section 2.8.5). In certain circumstances the claimant can incur liability for the defendant's costs greater than the damages recovered (see Section 2.8.4).

The 'Jackson reforms' also saw the introduction of a new system for funding claims, 'damages based agreements', which are contingency fee agreements in which the lawyer may agree to take a percentage of damages if successful and cannot recover any additional amount in costs from the defendant[40]. This percentage is limited in personal injury claims to no more than 25% of the damages for pain and suffering and loss of amenity and past losses (after deduction of any state benefits which may be deducted from damages). These terms are not regarded by lawyers as being likely to be sufficiently beneficial to wish to make general use of such agreements.

2.8.4 Qualified One-Way Costs Shifting

Introduced as a part of the 'Jackson reforms' in April 2013, Qualified One-Way Costs Shifting ("QOCS") was created to remove the need for claimants to take out insurance premiums to cover the possible liability for paying the defendant's costs, the premiums for which were part of the additional sum paid by a losing defendant to a successful claimant under a pre-April 2013 Conditional Fee Agreement.

From 1 April 2013, an order for costs against a claimant for losing the claim or some aspect of the claim, or losing an application during the claim or because of a failure to beat a Part 36 offer of settlement is limited to the total of damages and interest recovered by the claimant[41]. Therefore, in the case of a claimant who loses a claim completely and recovers no damages, the default position is that the defendant will recover none of the costs of successfully defending the claim. However, in the case of a claimant who recovers damages but fails to beat a Part 36 offer of settlement, all of the damages may well be taken by the defendant in costs.

---

39   There is also a very small number of cases which are still eligible for public funding from the Legal Services Commission where the considerations are slightly different, but we leave further consideration of this to other texts

40   The Damages-Based Agreements Regulations 2013

41   CPR 44.14

This protection for a claimant is lost in certain circumstances, including where the claim is found, on the balance of probabilities, to be 'fundamentally dishonest'[42]. This term is not defined within the CPR and it is to be seen whether a claim which has been dishonestly exaggerated is to be regarded as 'fundamentally dishonest'[43].

2.8.5   Part 36 – Offers to Settle

To increase the pressure on the parties to compromise each side is entitled, at any stage before as well as after proceedings have been commenced, to make a formal offer to the other side to settle the claim on the basis of a particular amount being paid to the claimant together with costs - the offer being open for acceptance on those terms for 21 days. Where the offer is accepted, this is an end to the claim[44]. Where an offer, whether made by the claimant or by the defendant, is not accepted then the following situations arise:

1.   if the claimant fails to obtain a judgment 'more advantageous' than a defendant's Part 36 offer, almost always the claimant will not only fail to recover his/her own costs from the time the offer was made, but will also be liable for the defendant's costs from that time;

2.   if the claimant obtains a judgment 'at least as advantageous' as an offer the claimant has made to the defendant, then the defendant will almost always be penalised in having to pay additional interest and costs at a higher level to the claimant.

'More advantageous' is defined in the rules as meaning better in money terms by any amount[45].

Since 1 April 2013 the 'Jackson reforms' have increased the incentive for defendants to settle claims. An additional penalty is imposed on the defendant where the claimant does better than a defendant's offer. The claimant may recover an additional amount calculated as 10% of the damages recovered up to £500,000 and 5% up to £1,000,000, a possible maximum of £75,000[46].However to keep this in perspective, for the roughly 80% of claims where damages are unlikely to exceed £15,000, the potential additional amount will of course be up to £1,500

These rules are modified in relation to claims running in the Portal under the Pre-Action Protocols for Low Value Personal Injury Claims in Road Traffic Accidents and Employers' Liability and Public Liability Claims[47] and in relation to

---

42   CPR 44.16(1)

43   It was, in a county court case *Gosling v Screwfix* 29.3.14

44   Such offers by a defendant had, until 6 April 2007, to be backed up by paying into court the sum of money offered ("a payment into court"). That is no longer required of the defendant.

45   CPR 36.17(2)

46   CPR 36.17(4)

47   See Section 3.3

offers made in soft tissue only claims[48] made by insurers in the absence of medical reports[49].

The failure by a party to beat at trial a Part 36 offer of settlement can have significant consequences. The claimant may see all of the damages awarded going in discharging his/her own and the other side's costs. The lawyers may recover none of the costs for a large proportion of the claim, including the substantial expenses of a trial (including the attendance fees of experts). The pressure placed on a defendant by a well-positioned claimant's Part 36 offer is significantly less than that on the claimant side, because the nature of the sanction (additional interest, costs at a higher rate and an additional amount calculated with reference to the damages paid) is generally less damaging and less threatening to a defendant such as a large insurance company.

The importance to both sides, in deciding whether and at what amount to settle a claim or to go to trial, of having reliable and well understood expert evidence and expert opinion which will withstand cross-examination can be readily understood.

2.8.6 Referral Fees

In order to obtain new work, solicitors rely on word of mouth, passing trade (if they have a high street location), referrals from other solicitors who do not wish to carry out that particular form of litigation, or advertising. Additionally, in recent years, solicitors have obtained new work by 'buying in' cases from (and paying referral fees to) organisations who obtain 'leads' through advertising or by other means.

Under the 'Jackson reforms' payment of referral fees by solicitors for acquiring claims from claims management companies or from other solicitors has been banned, although currently many schemes are evolving which under the current legislation will effectively permit the payment by lawyers for cases to continue. This, it is said, will reduce the cost of litigation for lawyers and it has been argued that it justifies the reduction in the costs recoverable by them at the end of the litigation. In response, solicitors would point out that if they cannot 'buy in' cases, they will still have to incur additional expenditure in marketing their services, but are now expected to pay that additional expenditure out of the reduced income from costs.

2.8.7 Proportionality of Costs

Further control on the level of legal costs recoverable by a successful claimant at the end of a claim is introduced by three measures. Firstly, the CPR are amended to emphasise that the overriding objective, the standard by which all rules in the CPR are to be interpreted, includes dealing with a case 'at proportionate cost', and

---

48   'soft tissue injury claim' means a claim brought by an occupant of a motor vehicle where the significant physical injury caused is a soft tissue injury and includes claims where there is a minor psychological injury secondary in significance to the physical injury (para 1.1(16A) of the Pre Action Protocol for Low Value Personal Injury Claims etc)

49   CPR 36.14A

costs will only be recovered to the extent that they are shown to be proportionate. Therefore now, even if the costs are incurred reasonably and necessarily for the purposes of conducting the litigation, they will be disallowed (and therefore will not be recovered by the successful claimant) if the court considers them disproportionate. The rules provide no mathematical guide as to what will be regarded as 'proportionate' but provide that costs are proportionate:

'if they bear a reasonable relationship to –

(a) the sums in issue in the proceedings;

(b) the value of any non-monetary relief in issue in the proceedings;

(c) the complexity of the litigation;

(d) any additional work generated by the conduct of the paying party; and

(e) any wider factors involved in the proceedings, such as reputation or public importance.' [50]

The effect, therefore, is that the courts will only now allow a successful party to recover at the conclusion of a case an amount in costs which is considered by the court to be proportionate to the value of the claim and therefore part of the costs incurred may well be disallowed, even if those costs were incurred reasonably and necessarily in order to present a coherent claim. In addressing proportionality, the court will impose its 'feel' for what proportion of the value of damages claimed the costs should reasonably bear given the court's view of the nature of the claim.

2.8.8 Extension of Fixed Costs

Further control on the recoverable amount of legal costs has been imposed on Fast Track claims. The costs recoverable in the Fast Track (currently generally claims where damages up to £25,000 may be recovered) are for most claims fixed by a scale which is related to the damages in fact recovered[51]. Road traffic claims with a value up to £10,000 have been dealt with through an online portal since April 2010 with a scale of fixed costs recoverable by the successful claimant's lawyer, the claim falling out of the portal (and into court) if liability is disputed. For accidents after 31st July 2013, virtually all claims up to £25,000 for road traffic accidents, employers' liability claims and public liability claims now start in the portal, with a scale of fixed costs recoverable by the successful claimant's lawyer, and should they 'fall out' of the portal they will be caught by a further scale of fixed costs.

The level of these fixed fees is such that many lawyers have ceased to take on low value claims, and those that continue to do so have had to find ways of cutting down on the costs of the litigation, such as running such claims from parts of the

---

50   CPR 44.3(5)

51   See Section 3.4

country where business costs are low and by employing lesser qualified staff to run the claims.

2.8.9   Costs Budgeting

An additional measure to control costs in litigation is the introduction of 'costs budgeting' in multi-track claims (generally claims where damages are likely to exceed £25,000). In these claims, the court will make a 'costs management order' at the first procedural hearing, setting a costs budget for the entire claim. Save in exceptional cases, or if the court agrees a revision because of a change in the assumptions on which the order was made, the winning party will not be able to recover at the end of the case more than the costs budget[52]. However, as the court will carry out a more detailed assessment of costs at the conclusion of the case (in those cases where the parties cannot agree the amount of costs to be paid), the amount in fact recovered may be reduced to a level less than that allowed in the costs budget.

Each party produces for the costs management hearing a detailed estimate of the costs for the entire claim set out in a court form, identifying the anticipated costs for each defined process in the claim and, in what is a broad brush approach, the court adjudicates on what it considers to be the 'proportionate' cost for each process and for the case as a whole.

Court of Appeal decisions will no doubt in due course help to define what costs are in fact 'proportionate' and how the courts should approach this exercise, but the process and the outcome is largely at the discretion of the judge dealing with the costs management hearing.

2.8.10 Enforcement of Court Orders and Timetables

Under the 'Jackson reforms' the court has also been given greater power to punish a party for a breach of a rule, practice direction or court order - as for example in failing to comply with a court timetable - by striking out a claim or a defence to a claim, or preventing reliance on evidence provided out of time[53]. We consider this further in Section 3.6.

2.8.11 Control of Expert Evidence

Specifically in relation to the use of expert evidence, a party applying for permission to rely on expert evidence is now required to provide an estimate of the cost of using the expert[54] and the court in granting permission for the expert to give

---

52   See for example *Elvanite Full Circle Ltd v Amec Earth & Environmental (UK) Ltd* [2013] EWHC 1643 in which the experts' fees claimed of £200,000 were allowed only up to the £30,500 in the costs budget approved by the court.

53   CPR 3.9(1) and *Mitchell v News Group Newspapers Ltd* [2013] EWCA Civ 1537 and *Denton, Decadent and Utilise* [2014] EWCA Civ 906

54   CPR 35.4(2) and see Section 4.1.5

evidence may specify the issues that the expert is to address[55]. Therefore, in giving permission to use an expert, the court will take into account the likely cost of so doing and may decline to grant such permission if the cost is considered dispro-portionate. The estimate of the cost of the expert will also have been considered in the cost budgeting process at which the maximum amount of expert costs that may be recovered if the claim is successful will have been decided by the court.

2.8.12 Concurrent Evidence ('hot tubbing')

In relation to the giving of evidence, provision is now made for the court to be able to direct that experts of like discipline should give their evidence at trial by way of concurrent evidence (so called, 'hot tubbing') in which, prior to the tradi-tional questioning of an expert by the advocates for the parties, the judge initiates the questioning[56].

The process of concurrent evidence is intended to enable the judge personally to investigate the area or areas of dispute between the experts and to try to clarify the nature, extent and reasons for the dispute. The process is therefore dependent on the judge having a good understanding of the issues. This understanding will have been obtained, not (as with counsel) by meeting with and having a discussion with one or more of the experts prior to the hearing, but largely (if not entirely) from the written evidence of the experts submitted in their expert reports and joint statement. Given the non-specialist judiciary usually assigned to cases, it cannot be assumed that the judge will have any background or experience prior to the case relevant to the issues involved. Therefore, the importance of the expert addressing effectively the salient issues in an expert report, using language which can be readily understood by a judge with no specialist knowledge of the technical background to the dispute, cannot be overstated[57].

2.8.13 Overall Impact of the 'Jackson Reforms'

These reforms have exerted a severe downward pressure on the costs that can be recovered by the lawyers at the successful conclusion of litigation and an unsuc-cessful claim will generally mean that the claimant's lawyers recover nothing for the work they have done or the expenses they have incurred, including for the fees of the experts in the case while the successful defendant is now unlikely to recover any of its legal costs (including experts' fees).

Inevitably, this means that there will be downward pressure on what lawyers will wish to agree to pay the expert and will increase the numbers of solicitors who want to pay the expert at the conclusion of the case. The estimate of the expert's fees will be part of the total budget, which will be assessed for proportionality at the commencement of the claim in court, and the larger the expert's fees, then generally the more adverse an impact this will have on the proportion of those fees

---

55   CPR 34.4(3)

56   PD35 11.4

57   See also Sections 2.3 and 4.7.5

that the court allows as 'proportionate' costs. The costs that are deemed proportionate will be the total income for the lawyer, which will cover the lawyer's fees and costs and other costs in the litigation including court fees. It also means that additional fees charged by experts, for example in providing further unexpected (and unbudgeted) reports, will almost certainly not be recoverable from the other party if the claim is successful.

For the lawyer, time is money, and the case must be run within a court imposed costs budget. Lawyers therefore also need to be able to absorb the salient points from an expert report as quickly as possible, and to be able to assess the apparent strength of the opinions expressed in the minimum of time. It follows that the expert who can provide concise reports with clear reasoning and opinions will have a considerable practical advantage to the lawyer over one whose report takes many hours to read and to interpret.

The fact that no costs are recoverable in an unsuccessful claim, and that the claimant lawyer's winning cases will now provide a much smaller 'fighting fund' (when compared to the pre-April 2013 level of success fees) to cover the cost of lost or abandoned claims, means that the lawyers have a still greater interest in controlling the level of the expert's fees and a greater need to have confidence in the quality of the expert's advice and opinions.

Lawyers will also increasingly seek to obtain from an expert an advisory report on the prospects of litigation or an aspect of the claim or will seek to be provided with 'informal' guidance short of a full CPR compliant report in order to reduce the potential exposure to expert fees.

Conclusion

The process of assessing the value of a claim is not supported effectively by medical evidence that is simply an investigation of the claimant's medical situation. The lawyers and the court are not interested in the medical aspects of a case for their own sake, but focus inevitably on the financial consequences of the injuries sustained. Medical evidence is often the starting point for experts who need to report on the financial loss likely to be incurred in the future.

The issue is always what can or cannot be proved to have been suffered, or is likely to be suffered in the future, as a consequence of the injuries sustained. The medical expert's role is to assist the lawyers in the efficient progression of a claim through the litigation process, by dealing both with the issues upon which the lawyers seek expert opinion and those issues relevant to the claim that the expert, using his/her expertise when reporting on the claimant, identifies as material to the claim.

The costs of litigation, including the costs of obtaining expert evidence, are an increasingly important consideration in the conduct of litigation. The downward pressure on such costs has increased a great deal since April 2013 and continues.

Key-Point Summary

1. The only instrument of civil justice in a claim for personal injury is the award of money (damages).

2. Damages will only be awarded where the claimant can prove four elements of the claim: that the defendant is in breach of a duty owed to the claimant, that the breach of duty caused damage, that the damage suffered is more than minimal, and the claimant can prove the nature of the injury, loss and damage.

3. Civil litigation is an adversarial process, where the claimant has to prove his/her case.

4. All civil cases are decided to the civil standard of proof – 'on the balance of probabilities'.

5. The principle underlying the award of damages is the '100% Recovery Principle'. The court attempts to put the claimant back into the position he/she would have been in in the absence of the accident and the consequent injury, loss and damage.

6. A claimant cannot recover for a loss he/she would have suffered in any event because the claimant would have failed to prove, on the balance of probabilities, that the claimed breach of duty caused injury, loss and damage.

7. Damages can be awarded as a lump sum or as periodical payments.

8. Costs – a substantial sum in most claims – are paid by the losers of the action although a claimant's liability will normally be limited to the damages (if any) recovered.

9. Both parties will consider making Part 36 offers of settlement during the claim to increase the pressure on the other side to settle in order to avoid the risk of an increased liability in costs.

Next Steps

In the next chapter, we will explore the progression of a claim - from its inception, the pre-action phase, issuing of proceedings and through to trial.

3

Progression of a Claim

Introduction

The entire civil litigation process is controlled and regulated by detailed rules of court. The legal process by which an injured person seeks to claim compensation for an injury sustained is laid down in the *Civil Procedure Rules* 1998 (CPR) with the associated *Practice Directions* and *Pre-Action Protocols*. The CPR came into force in April 1999, introducing new procedural rules that deal with every stage of court proceedings, as well as the conduct of the parties and their lawyers within the proceedings. The CPR also specifically regulate the use of expert witnesses and the duties of experts instructed in a claim. (We will examine the detailed duties of expert witnesses in Chapter 4.)

Chapter Outline

In this chapter, we will examine the fundamental legal principles that underlie the CPR and the specific rules that impose these principles on the parties. We will explain how the parties prepare the claim before proceedings are issued and the role of the court in managing cases. We will also introduce the roles of the legal professionals involved in a case: solicitors, barristers and judges.

3.1   Civil Procedure Rules 1998

In July 1996, Lord Woolf, the then Master of the Rolls (the senior civil judge), presented his final report entitled 'Access to Justice', on his proposals to reform the civil justice system. In the first section of the report, he detailed the problems in the system that his proposed reforms were seeking to address:

> 'The defects I identified in our present system were that it is too expensive in that the costs often exceed the value of the claim; too slow in bringing cases to a conclusion and too unequal: there is a lack of equality between the powerful, wealthy litigant and the under resourced litigant. It is too uncertain: the difficulty of forecasting what litigation will cost and how long it will last induces the fear of the unknown; and it is incomprehensible to many litigants. Above all it is too fragmented in the way it is organised since there is no one with clear overall responsibility for the administration of civil justice; and too adversarial as cases are run by the parties, not by the courts and the rules of court, all too often, are ignored by the parties and not enforced by the court.'[1]

His assessment of the use of experts in litigation was also the subject of much discussion within the legal profession:

> 'There is widespread agreement with the criticisms I made in the interim report of the way in which expert evidence is used at present, especially the point that experts sometimes take on the role of partisan advocates instead of neutral fact finders or opinion givers.'[2]

In essence, Lord Woolf wanted a system of justice that was fair, cost-effective, easy to use, comprehensible to litigants and efficient. To achieve this, he rewrote the procedural rules of the civil courts. His revision of the rules came into force in April 1999 and created a new framework for the conduct of litigation in the civil courts.

3.1.1   Court Managed Litigation

Since April 1999, the court has actively managed cases to ensure the efficient and just disposal of the claim. The parties are required to co-operate with the court and with one another to achieve these aims. This contrasts with the previous

---

1   *Access to Justice - Final Report to the Lord Chancellor on the civil justice system in England and Wales* by The Right Honourable the Lord Woolf, Master of the Rolls (July 1996) (Ch 1 para 2)

2   As Above (Ch 13 para 5)

system in which the court was largely reactive to the parties' requests for intervention, which resulted in much delay and inefficiency.

Each party is required to adopt a "cards on the table" (face up!) approach to litigation. This means that all the evidence in a case on which a party intends to rely at court is disclosed to the other side. The purpose of this approach is to facilitate the early settlement of claims and to limit the number of claims that actually reach court. The extent to which any particular claim is run on a co-operative rather than a tactical basis varies greatly, depending on the issues in the claim, the personalities of the lawyers, the approach of the insurer and the degree of intervention by the court.

Although it is generally recognised amongst those old enough to recall operating under the previous system that the process of civil litigation has been improved by the CPR, there has been considerable concern that the changes introduced by the CPR failed to deal satisfactorily with the issue of legal costs and indeed may have had the effect of increasing such costs. As Lord Justice Jackson stated in his Preliminary Report in his 'Review of Civil Litigation Costs'[3]:

> 'Those reforms have brought huge benefits to civil litigants. Far more cases are settled before issue. Those cases which are contested proceed far more swiftly from issue to trial. We no longer have the repeated tragedy (for such it was) of meritorious claims being 'struck out' for want of prosecution.
>
> The case management function, which the court has assumed following the Woolf reforms, prevents cases from being parked indefinitely whilst the parties or their lawyers attend to other matters. The creation of tracks for cases ensures that each type of case receives an appropriate allocation of resources and degree of attention from the court.
>
> The fast-track ensures that the lower-value cases are brought to trial with expedition and that the trial costs (although not pre-trial costs) of such cases are fixed.'

3.1.2   The 'Jackson Reforms' 2013

We have seen in the previous chapter (Section 2.8) the many changes introduced since 2013, following Lord Justice Jackson's report. Although primarily aimed at reducing the cost of litigation, the reforms to the CPR have also provided the court with very much more power to enforce its orders and timetables.

Readers of the previous edition of this book will be surprised by the number of changes, some subtle and some very much more fundamental, which have been introduced. Many of these changes will impact, either directly or indirectly, on the manner in which expert evidence is instructed and used in civil litigation.

---

3   Lord Justice Jackson's 'Review of Civil Litigation Costs: Final Report' (December 2009)
     www.judiciary.gov.uk/reports/civil-litigation-costs-review-final-report/

Expert witnesses will undoubtedly be affected, now or in the future, by the 'Jackson Reforms' and it is worth spending the time necessary to adjust to the changes to enable the dual imperatives of producing higher quality evidence, yet doing so more cost-effectively.

3.2 Structure of the CPR

The CPR continue to develop, with the introduction of the 80th series of amendments with effect from April 2015[4]. Currently, there are 88 'Parts' dealing with civil proceedings (each Part draws together rules that relate to a particular stage or aspect of the litigation process), from how to start proceedings through to enforcement of the judgments obtained. The rules in each Part are supported by 'Practice Directions', which generally give directions and guidance supportive of the rule to which they refer. Participants in the litigation process must give equal regard to the rules and the practice directions.

The CPR and practice directions are printed with commentaries by several publishers and in a variety of electronic formats as well as being available on the internet. It is unnecessary for expert witnesses to be familiar with the whole of the CPR, though many of the deadlines given to expert witnesses arise directly from the programme for the litigation imposed by the court or the CPR[5]. Part 35 of the CPR and its practice direction relate specifically to expert witnesses and these are considered in detail in Chapter 4.

3.2.1 Overriding Objective

The overriding objective of the CPR is set out in the first rule. It is the standard by which the entire CPR is to be interpreted and applied:

The overriding objective

CPR 1.1   (1)   These Rules are a new procedural code with the over riding objective of enabling the court to deal with cases justly and at proportionate cost.

      (2)   Dealing with a case justly and at proportionate cost includes, so far as is practicable -

          (a)   ensuring that the parties are on an equal footing;

          (b)   saving expense;

          (c)   dealing with the case in ways which are proportionate -

---

4   In the first edition of this book we noted the 55th Amendments came into force in April 2011 and that there were 79 Parts. The CPR, Practice Directions and Pre-Action Protocols can be found at www.justice.gov.uk/courts/procedure-rules/civil

5   It is essential that experts check that they can meet such deadlines before accepting instructions to act in a particular claim.

      (i)   to the amount of money involved;

      (ii)   to the importance of the case;

      (iii)   to the complexity of the issues; and

      (iv)   to the financial position of each party;

(d)   ensuring that it is dealt with expeditiously and fairly;

(e)   allotting to it an appropriate share of the court's resources, while taking into account the need to allot resources to other cases; and

(f)   enforcing compliance with rules, practice directions and orders.

Application by the court of the overriding objective
CPR 1.2   The court must seek to give effect to the overriding objective when it -

(a)   exercises any power given to it by the Rules; or

(b)   interprets any rule.

Duty of the parties
CPR 1.3   The parties are required to help the court to further the overriding objective.

In the first section of the CPR the important principle of 'Proportionality' is introduced. The principle of proportionality means that the expense incurred in bringing a claim should be proportionate to its value, complexity and importance. This principle underlies how the court manages the litigation and the way the parties should conduct themselves. The parties are also required to co-operate with the court as it seeks to deal with cases 'justly' and can be penalised in costs if they do not do so.

3.2.2   Court Management

The court, in pro-actively managing its proceedings, must apply the overriding objective in all of the decisions that it makes:

Court's duty to manage cases
CPR 1.4   (1)   The court must further the overriding objective by actively managing cases.

The court's powers, in seeking to further the overriding objective, include:

1.   requiring a party or his legal representative to attend the court;

2.   holding a hearing by telephone;

3. directing a separate trial of an issue or the hearing of a preliminary issue;

4. excluding an issue from consideration; and

5. taking any other step or making any other order for the purpose of managing the case and furthering the overriding objective[6].

All decisions taken by the court in relation to the progress of a claim will be made to give effect to these objectives. These will include, for example, decisions as to the nature and number of experts to be permitted to provide reports or give evidence, whether one or both parties should be entitled to rely on such evidence, and whether it should be provided by a single joint expert[7]. It will also include decisions as to what, if any, clarification of the expert report needs to be given by the expert.

3.3   Pre-Action Protocols

A third tier of guidance beyond the CPR and practice directions is provided by the 'Pre-Action Protocols' (PAPs). PAPs were initially introduced to detail the steps that should be taken by the parties prior to the commencement of proceedings and are intended to facilitate the early settlement of claims by the parties.

These PAPs were drawn up with substantial input from practitioners involved in the applicable area of litigation and represent good practice in the conduct of litigation. A failure to comply with the relevant PAPs can have a significant impact on the manner in which the claim once commenced in court is dealt with and can have a significant costs impact against the interest of a party failing to comply with the relevant PAP.

PAPs relevant to compensation claims in which medical experts will be instructed are:

• Pre-Action Protocol for the Resolution of Clinical Disputes;
• Pre-Action Protocol for Personal Injury Claims; and
• Pre-Action Protocol for Disease and Illness Claims.

In addition, on 30 April 2010, the Pre-Action Protocol for Low Value Personal Injury Claims in Road Traffic Accidents was introduced. This has been replaced by an amended version of the protocol, which applies to road traffic accident claims notified after 31st July 2013 and is joined (for accidents after that date) by the Pre-Action Protocol for Low Value Personal Injury (Employers' Liability and Public Liability) Claims. These protocols are different in nature from the others, setting out the scheme for an on-line portal for such claims outside the court system, and are dealt with further in Section 3.4.

---

6   See CPR 3.1

7   A detailed consideration of the rules in respect of the appointment of a single joint expert is given in Section 4.5.

A fundamental principle in all PAPs is that the claimant's solicitor should set out in detail the nature of the claim and the damages sought in a 'Letter of Claim' or, in the case of the PAPs covering low value claims in a 'Claim Notification Form' sent to the defendant (or the defendant's insurer). In turn, the defendant should respond in detail within a fixed period and generally provide all documentation relevant to the main issues indicated in the claim.

The aims of PAPs are set out in the Practice Direction – Pre-Action Conduct (most recently updated in October 2014):

1. to enable parties to settle the issues between them without the need to start proceedings; and

2. to support the efficient management by the court and the parties of proceedings that cannot be avoided[8].

In relation to the use of experts, the Practice Direction - Pre-Action Conduct states:

Where the evidence of an expert is necessary, the parties should consider how best to minimise expense[9].

Annex C provides the parties with guidance on instructing experts at this pre-action stage.

1. Parties should be aware that once proceedings have been started –

    (i)   expert evidence may not be used in court without the permission of the court;

    (ii)   a party who instructs an expert will not necessarily be able to recover the cost from another party; and

    (iii)   it is the duty of an expert to help the court on the matters within the expert's scope of expertise and this duty overrides any obligation to the person instructing or paying the expert.

2. Many matters can and should be resolved without the need for advice or evidence from an expert. If an expert is needed, the parties should consider how best to minimise the expense for example by agreeing to instruct –

    (i)   a single joint expert (i.e. engaged and paid jointly by the parties whether instructed jointly or separately); or

    (ii)   an agreed expert (i.e. the parties agree the identity of the expert but only one party instructs the expert and pays the expert's costs).

---

8   See Practice Direction – Pre-Action Conduct para 1.1 and 1.2

9   Practice Direction – Pre-Action Conduct para 9.4

3. If the parties do not agree that the nomination of a single joint expert is appropriate, then the party seeking the expert evidence (the first party) should give the other party (the second party) a list of one or more experts in the relevant field of expertise whom the first party would like to instruct.

4. Within 14 days of receipt of the list of experts, the second party may indicate in writing an objection to one or more of the experts listed. If there remains on the list one or more experts who are acceptable, then the first party should instruct an expert from the list.

5. If the second party objects to all the listed experts, the first party may then instruct an expert of the first party's own choice. Both parties should bear in mind that if proceedings are started the court will consider whether a party has acted reasonably when instructing (or rejecting) an expert.

When subsequently the court gives directions in proceedings, it will take into account whether or not a party has complied with the Practice Direction (Pre-Action Conduct) and any relevant PAP in deciding what order to make[10].

PAPs are important because the court will take into account a party's compliance or non-compliance with them in making court management orders such as:

- orders refusing an extension of time in which to carry out a particular procedural step[11];
- orders for costs – where 'conduct before as well as during the proceedings, and in particular the extent to which the parties followed the Practice Direction – Pre-Action Conduct or any relevant pre-action protocol' are expressly relevant[12];
- orders that money be paid into court where a party has without good reason failed to comply with a rule, practice direction or relevant PAP[13];
- orders to strike out a statement of case for failure to comply with a rule, practice direction or court order[14];
- orders to deny a successful party an award of interest or awarding interest at a lower rate than would normally be applied[15]; and
- orders awarding interest at a higher rate against a losing party[16].

All of these sanctions are designed to encourage the parties in an action to pursue the claim following best practice. PAPs encourage all parties to co-operate in bringing the claim forward in a cost-efficient manner and to avoid overly adversarial behaviour and tactics.

---

10   CPR 3.1(4)

11   CPR 3.1(4)

12   CPR 44.3(5)(a)

13   CPR 3.1(5)

14   CPR 3.4(2)

15   Practice Direction – Pre-Action Conduct para 2.3(3)

16   Practice Direction – Pre-Action Conduct para 2.3(4)

The expert has to meet the solicitor's deadline for producing the expert report. Pre-Action Protocols impose time constraints on the parties, as does the timetable imposed by the court once the claim is issued, and there can be implications for costs, the admissibility of evidence and even the survival of the party's case if a party does not meet these deadlines. If there is any doubt on first being instructed as to whether such deadlines can be met, the expert must refuse the instruction. Once the expert is instructed, the expert is committed to the court's timetable for the case.

3.3.1 Pre-Action Protocol for the Resolution of Clinical Disputes

The PAPs of most relevance to medical experts are those concerning clinical negligence, personal injury, disease and illness claims, and low value claims.

The Pre-Action Protocol for the Resolution of Clinical Disputes, most recently updated to June 2015, sets out a summary of the stages to be followed before court proceedings are commended. A summary of the stages is set out below:

1. Medical records are obtained by the claimant's lawyers applying on standard forms

2. Expert evidence is obtained by the claimant's lawyers

3. The claimant's lawyers send a Letter of Notification to inform the health care provider and the NHSLA/medical defence organisation that a breach of duty and/or causation has been identified and a Letter of Claim is likely to be sent.

4. The defendant acknowledges the Letter of Notification and considers commencing investigations.

5. A Letter of Claim is sent by the claimant's lawyers after analysis of the records and receipt of any further expert advice containing:

(a) a clear summary of facts;

(b) the main allegations of negligence;

(c) a description of the claimant's injuries;

(d) an outline of financial loss incurred;

(e) the discipline of any expert from whom evidence has already been obtained;

(f) reference to relevant documents and sufficient information to enable the defendant to focus investigation and to put an initial valuation on the claim; and it can also include

(g) an offer of settlement (Part 36 offer), in which case there should be a medical report dealing with the injuries, condition and prognosis of the claimant.

6. Within 4 months the health care provider should reply:

(a) with a reasoned response in a Letter of Response;

(b) making clear what issues of breach of duty or causation are admitted, and which denied and why, with specific comments on the allegations of negligence;

(c) making clear whether it is intended that any admissions will be binding[17];

(d) if supportive expert evidence has been obtained, identifying the disciplines of expert evidence which have been relied upon and whether in relation to breach of duty or causation;

(e) stating if copies of any relevant medical records obtained by the claimant are required and providing copies of any additional documents relied upon;

(f) supplying details of any relevant insurer if not indemnified by the NHS;

(g) informing the claimant of any other potential defendants to the claim; and if relevant

(h) responding to any claimant's Part 36 Offer and may also make a counter-offer of settlement.

7. The parties should consider negotiation or some other form of alternative dispute resolution before the claimant considers issuing proceedings.

Expert Reports in Clinical Disputes

The Pre-Action Protocol for the Resolution of Clinical Disputes provides that:

4.1 In clinical negligence disputes separate expert opinions may be needed:—
- on breach of duty
- on causation
- on the patient's condition and prognosis
- to assist in valuing aspects of the claim.

---

17 Therefore, if the proposed defendant admits a breach of duty or causation of injury in the letter it will have to justify to the court subsequently reneging on such an admission when proceedings are commenced.

4.2   It is recognised that in clinical negligence disputes, the parties and their advisers will require flexibility in their approach to expert evidence. The parties should co-operate when making decisions on appropriate medical specialisms, whether experts might be instructed jointly and whether any reports obtained pre-action might be shared.

4.3   Obtaining expert evidence will often be an expensive step and may take time, especially in specialised areas of medicine where there are limited numbers of suitable experts.

4.4   When considering what expert evidence may be required during the Protocol period, parties should be aware that the use of any expert reports obtained pre-action will only be permitted in proceedings with the express permission of the court.

The Pre-Action Protocol for the Resolution of Clinical Disputes therefore seeks to give the parties considerable say in the use of medical experts, in contrast to CPR 32.1, 35.1 and 35.7[18]. This apparent conflict arises because a clinical negligence claim may necessitate the use of a larger number of medical experts than a typical personal injury claim, owing to the difficult issues involved and the additional issue (breach of duty) on which expert evidence is required.

3.3.2   Pre-Action Protocol for Personal Injury Claims

The Pre-Action Protocol for Personal Injury Claims is stated to be 'primarily designed for personal injury claims which are likely to be allocated to the fast track'[19] although the 'spirit' of the protocol should still be followed for claims potentially outside of the fast track limit[20]. The procedure in the Pre-Action Protocol for Personal Injury Claims (most recently updated with effect from 6 April 2015) is similar to (but generally simpler than) the Pre-Action Protocol for the Resolution of Clinical Disputes. It is suggested that the claimant might wish to send a Letter of Notification 'as soon as they know a claim is likely to be made' and should consider as early as possible with the defendant whether the claimant has reasonable needs that could be met by medical treatment or other rehabilitative measures. Otherwise, the first step is the requirement for a detailed 'Letter of Claim' from the claimant, rather than obtaining documents relevant to liability.

The defendant is then required to give a reasoned response within 3 months. The letter of claim should provide sufficient information to enable the defendant (or normally the insurer) to assess liability and make an estimate of the likely size of the claim.

---

18   See Section 3.7 Court 'Control of Expert Evidence' and Section 4.5 'Single Joint Experts', below, which emphasise the court's control over the use of experts.

19   See Section 3.5.1. This is generally claims with a value up to £25,000.

20   Protocol para 1.1.2

No further investigation of liability should then be carried out on behalf of the claimant until the defendant has responded (though the claimant's solicitor will normally suggest documents considered by the solicitor to be relevant to the issue of liability in the letter of claim). If the defendant then denies liability or causation, it should give reasons and disclose in its letter of reply any documents material to those issues.

In relation to experts, the protocol provides as follows:

7.2   Save for cases likely to be allocated to the multi-track, the Protocol encourages joint selection of, and access to, quantum experts, and, on occasion liability experts e.g. engineers. The expert report produced is not a joint report for the purposes of CPR Part 35. The Protocol promotes the practice of the claimant obtaining a medical report, disclosing it to the defendant who then asks questions and/or agrees it and does not obtain their own report. The Protocol provides for nomination of the expert by the claimant in personal injury claims.

7.3   Before any party instructs an expert, they should give the other party a list of the name(s) of one or more experts in the relevant speciality whom they consider are suitable to instruct.

7.4   Some solicitors choose to obtain medical reports through medical agencies, rather than directly from a specific doctor or hospital. The defendant's prior consent to this should be sought and, if the defendant so requests, the agency should be asked to provide in advance the names of the doctor(s) whom they are considering instructing.

7.5   Where a medical expert is to be instructed, the claimant's solicitor will organise access to relevant medical records – see specimen letter of instruction at Annexe D.

7.6   Within 14 days of providing a list of experts the other party may indicate an objection to one or more of the named experts. The first party should then instruct a mutually acceptable expert assuming there is one (this is not the same as a joint expert). It must be emphasised that when the claimant nominates an expert in the original Letter of Claim, the defendant has a further 14 days to object to one or more of the named experts after expiration of the 21 day period within which they have to reply to the Letter of Claim, as set out in paragraph 6.2.

7.7   If the defendant objects to all the listed experts, the parties may then instruct experts of their own choice. It will be for the court to decide, subsequently and if proceedings are issued, whether either party had acted unreasonably.

7.8   If the defendant does not object to an expert nominated by the claimant, they shall not be entitled to rely on their own expert evidence within that expert's area of expertise unless—

    (a)   the claimant agrees;

    (b)   the court so directs; or

    (c)   the claimant's expert report has been amended and the claimant is not prepared to disclose the original report.

7.9   Any party may send to an agreed expert written questions on the report, via the first party's solicitors. Such questions must be put within 28 days of service of the expert's report and must only be for the purpose of clarification of the report. The expert should send answers to the questions simultaneously to each party.

7.10   The cost of a report from an agreed expert will usually be paid by the instructing first party: the costs of the expert replying to questions will usually be borne by the party which asks the questions.

7.11   If necessary, after proceedings have commenced and with the permission of the court, the parties may obtain further expert reports. It would be for the court to decide whether the costs of more than one expert's report should be recoverable.

The Pre-Action Protocol for Personal Injury Claims aims to create a process in which achieving an early settlement in the case is more likely, though litigation remains the ultimate step.

Pre-Action Protocol for Personal Injury Claims – Jointly Selected Experts

As the paragraphs quoted above indicate, the protocol encourages the parties to identify an expert who is acceptable to both sides by a process of 'joint selection' or 'agreed selection' from a list provided by the claimant to the defendant. This can either be by naming an identified expert or naming a medical reporting agency, in which case the defendant can still require to know the identity of the expert the agency intends using.

The claimant will instruct the expert and disclose the report to the defendant, unless the claimant chooses not to rely on the report. The claimant can choose not to disclose the report if it is not considered to be favourable, or for any other reason is not considered to be satisfactory. The decision not to rely on a report has implications for costs and for the tactical development of the case. If the claimant chooses not to rely on an expert report, the cost of the report is not recoverable from the defendant and the defendant will be aware that an expert was instructed by the claimant, and as the report was not disclosed will presume that it gave an unfavourable opinion[21].

---

21   However the court has a discretion under CRP 35.4 to require the unfavourable report obtained under the PAP to be disclosed as a condition of allowing the party to rely on a subsequent report (*Edwards-Tubb v J D Weatherspoon Plc* [2011] EWCA Civ 136)

Therefore a 'Jointly Selected Expert' under the pre-action protocol is an expert instructed by the claimant alone and is contracted only to the claimant. This is in contrast to a 'Single Joint Expert', who is instructed by both parties. We deal with this distinction further in Section 4.5.1.

It should be noted that the cost of instructing the expert will usually be the claimant's cost, but the costs of obtaining answers to questions of the expert will usually be borne by the party asking the questions. This is in contrast to the usual position in multi-track cases[22].

3.3.3 Pre-Action Protocol for Disease and Illness Claims

The Pre-Action Protocol for Disease and Illness Claims (most recently updated in July 2013) combines features from the other two pre-action protocols. It is expressed to cover claims involving 'any illness physical or psychological, any disorder, ailment, affliction, complaint, malady or derangement other than a physical or psychological injury solely caused by an accident or other similar single event'[23] and is not limited to diseases occurring in the workplace.

The practice under the Pre-Action Protocol for Disease and Illness Claims is as follows:

1. The occupational health records and personnel records of the claimant are obtained by the claimant's lawyer from the defendant, and the general practitioner records will also normally be obtained.

2. The claimant's lawyer sends the defendant a letter of claim 'as soon as there is sufficient information available to substantiate a realistic claim':

   (a) containing a clear summary of the facts and the main allegations of fault;

   (b) outlining the financial loss incurred;

   (c) identifying any relevant documents.

3. The letter of claim may, but need not, be accompanied by a medical report[24].

4. The defendant should acknowledge the letter of claim within 21 days and provide a reasoned answer within 90 days of the acknowledgement admitting the claim or explaining why it is not admitted.

The PAP notes that expert opinions in such claims "may be needed on one or more of the following –

---

22   See PD35 6.2 and Section 4.4

23   Para 2.2

24   Para 6.8

- knowledge, fault, causation and apportionment;
- condition and prognosis;
- valuing aspects of the claim[25]."

It also emphasises that a flexible approach should be adopted in obtaining medical expert reports, and that the parties should decide whether to instruct experts jointly, and whether to disclose their reports sequentially or by exchange[26]. Where the claimant sends a medical report with the letter of claim, the defendant will be entitled to obtain its own medical report. Where instructing a single joint expert is considered appropriate, then a procedure is suggested for the expert's nomination and instruction[27].

3.4   Low Value Personal Injury Claims

3.4.1   Low Value Personal Injury Claims in Road Traffic Accidents

New rules, pre-action protocols and practice directions were introduced to simplify the procedure for personal injury claims arising out of road traffic accidents after 20 April 2010. A new on-line claims process was established for claims where the level of general damages for pain, suffering and loss of amenity was at least £1,000 and total damages did not exceed £10,000 (excluding interest and vehicle related damages). From 31 July 2013, the scheme was extended to claims where damages did not exceed £25,000.

For these purposes a 'road traffic accident' is 'an accident resulting in bodily injury to any person caused by, or arising out of, the use of a motor vehicle on a road or other public place'[28].

The Pre-Action Protocol for Low Value Claims in Road Traffic Accidents ("the RTA Protocol") does not apply where either party is the personal representative of a deceased person or lacks capacity under the Mental Capacity Act 2005, or if the claimant is bankrupt.

The process is broken down into three stages and the costs recoverable for each stage are fixed. There is therefore consequent pressure on the claimant's solicitor to keep the time spent on the process to a minimum.

It is a largely electronic (paper-less) process[29]. A claim is notified to defendants and insurers in a standard Claim Notification Form and the insurer must make

---

25   Para 9.1

26   Para 9.2

27   Para 9.5 – 9.10

28   RTA Protocol para 1.1(16)

29   See PD 8B and the Pre-Action Protocol for Low Value Personal Injury Claims in Road Traffic Accidents ('The RTA Protocol')

a decision on liability within 15 business days ('Stage 1'). Only claims where an admission of liability is made by the defendant's insurer and where there is no allegation of contributory negligence - other than failure to wear a seatbelt - will remain in the process (moving into 'Stage 2'). All other claims will be dealt with under the normal court-based procedure.

Once the defendant's insurer has made an admission of liability, the claimant's solicitor prepares and submits a settlement pack, which will include any medical reports. The report may already have been obtained prior to reaching Stage 2, and indeed, it may be that only on receipt of the medical report does it become apparent that the claim has a value that would put it within this process. Once the report has been provided to the claimant's solicitor, there is only one opportunity to request that the expert correct any factual errors before the report is sent to the defendant[30].

The expectation is that in most cases one report will suffice, but where one expert cannot deal with all the elements of the injury, additional medical reports may be obtained from other experts where the injuires require reports from more than one medical discipline[31]. Follow-up reports may be obtained on the recommendation of the medical expert, for example, where more time is required before a prognosis can be determined, where the claimant's treatment is continuing, or where the claimant has not recovered as expected in the original prognosis[32].

In a 'soft tissue injury claim', that is 'a claim brought by an occupant of a motor vehicle where the significant physical injury caused is a soft tissue injury and includes claims where there is a minor psychological injury secondary in significance to the physical injury'[33] it is provided that 'is it expected that only one medical report will be required' and a further medical report will only be justified 'where it is recommended in the first expert's report; and that report has first been disclosed to the defendant'[34].

In contrast to the Pre-Action Protocol for Personal Injury Claims, the claimant's solicitor is not required to nominate a medical expert to the defendant. There is no requirement for a jointly selected expert. Apparently, those representing the interests of the insurers felt that current procedures for the selection of experts were effective without the need for the insurer to be involved. However, a procedure of nomination of experts by computer through an on-line system 'MedCo', further described below[35], is compulsory in all soft tissue injury claims from 6 April 2015 so that the first medical report obtained must be a fixed cost medical report from an accredited medical expert selected for the claim via the

---

30   RTA Protocol para 7.3

31   RTA Protocol para 7.2

32   RTA Protocol para 7.8

33   RTA Protocol para 1.1(16A)

34   RTA Protocol para 7.8A

35   See Section 3.4.3

MedCo Portal[36] and the further (recommended) report, although not from an expert selected through MedCo,must be a fixed cost report where fixed costs as provided for (see Section 3.7.4). In contrast with the normal court based process, there is no provision for the defendant/insurer to put any questions to the medical expert, or even to challenge the quality or expertise of the medical expert selected by the claimant. Not only is there no ability for the defendant/insurer to question the report, but further, the process does not provide for the defendant/insurer to obtain or to rely on its own medical reports.

Where the value of the claim is not agreed between the parties on the basis of the submitted settlement pack, there will be a court determination that will be without an oral hearing, unless the parties request one or the court orders it ('Stage 3'). If the defendant/insurer considers that the medical evidence on which to make an offer is inadequate, then by refusing to make an offer the defendant/insurer will cause the claim to leave the process and so enter the normal court-based procedure in which it can then obtain its own medical evidence or question the claimant's expert.

The RTA Protocol provides a standard form of medical report for the process, 'RTA3'. The form itself does not have to be used and it is provided that the information required in Form RTA3 may be provided in a different format to that set out in the form[37]. In fact, Form RTA3 does not comply with all of the requirements of CPR Part 35 which are addressed below. While ensuring that the information required by the form is included in a medical report, which with the exception of an opinion in relation to the effect of not wearing a seat belt is no more than a competent expert would expect to have to provide, the expert is probably best advised to adopt the expert's usual form of report in order to comply with the expert's obligations under the CPR.

In most claims with a value of no more than £10,000 the RTA Protocol provides that the medical expert will not need to see any medical records[38]. The report should make clear that the opinion is provided, if that be the case, without the opportunity of considering the medical records and is therefore a qualified opinion. The report should identify the medical records that have been reviewed and the medical records considered relevant to the claim, and these will be sent by the claimant's lawyers to the defendant with the medical report. Any photographs of the claimant's injuries on which it is intended to rely should also be disclosed with the medical report[39].

The process and RTA3 anticipate that the medical expert will provide, where relevant to the issues in the case, an opinion as to the impact of any failure to wear a seat belt on the claimant's injuries. Paragraph 7.7 provides that "Where the claimant was not wearing a seat belt the medical report must contain sufficient informa-

---

36   RTA Protocol para 7.8A(1)

37   RTA Protocol para 1.5

38   RTA Protocol para 7.5

39   RTA Protocol para 7.4

tion to enable the defendant to calculate the appropriate reduction of damages in accordance with principles set out in existing case law." In cases where the claimant was not wearing a seatbelt, the medical expert therefore is expected to express an opinion as to the extent to which each of the injuries suffered would have been prevented, less severe or no different. While the expert will no doubt wish to assist those instructing him/her and the court, the opinion is, as always, covered by the expert's duty to express an opinion within his/her area of expertise. The expert should make it clear, if asked to address this issue, if he/she considers that it falls outside his/her expertise or where he/she is not able to reach a definite opinion[40]. We consider the relevant law on failure to wear a seat belt and the medical expert's approach to these issues in Section 7.6.

3.4.2 Low Value Personal Injury (Employers' Liability and Public Liability) Claims

Although the Government's own research into the RTA Protocol considered it premature to consider expanding the scheme[41], from 31 July 2013 the on-line portal was extended, not only 'vertically' to encompass RTA claims up to £25,000, but also 'horizontally' to include almost all personal injury claims by extending it to cover claims covered by employers' liability insurance and public liability insurance and relating to accidents on or after 31 July 2013 with a value of not more than £25,000.

The procedure is set out in the Pre-Action Protocol for Low Value Personal Injury (Employers' Liability and Public Liability) Claims ("the EL/PL Protocol").

As in the case of the RTA Protocol, the EL/PL Protocol does not apply where either party is the personal representative of a deceased person or lacks capacity under the Mental Capacity Act 2005, or if the claimant is bankrupt. There are some additional exclusions, including where in a claim arising out of the development of a disease there is more than one employer defendant, if damages are claimed in relation to harm, abuse or neglect of or by children or vulnerable adults, or for clinical negligence or for mesothelioma[42].

The defendant has longer to respond under the EL/PL Protocol than under the RTA Protocol – 30 days for an employers' liability claim and 40 days for a public liability claim. If the defendant does not admit liability or if the defendant alleges contributory negligence in response to notification of the claim, the claim will come out of the EL/PL Protocol. Otherwise the claim moves to Stage 2 and a settlement pack is prepared by the Claimant's lawyers. This will include any medical reports.

The EL/PL Protocol provides a standard form of medical report for the process, 'EPL3'. The form itself does not have to be used and it is provided that the infor-

---

40   PD35 para 2.2 and 2.4 and Chapter 4

41   www.gov.uk/government/uploads/system/uploads/attachment_data/file/217387/evaluating-traffic-accident-process.pdf (July 2012)

42   EL/PL Protocol para 4.3. Note however that reviews are under way into the future procedure for mesothelioma claims and lower value clinical negligence claims.

mation required in Form EPL3 may be provided in a different format to that set out in the form[43]. The observations in the previous Section as to the desirability of the expert instructed under the RTA Protocol using the expert's usual form of report in order to comply with the expert's obligations under the CPR are equally applicable under the EL/PL Protocol.

As with the RTA Protocol, the expectation is that in most cases one report will suffice, but where one expert cannot deal with all the elements of the injury, additional medical reports may be obtained from other experts where the inquires require reports from more than one medical discipline[44]. Follow-up reports may be obtained on the recommendation of the medical expert, for example, where more time is required before a prognosis can be determined, or where the claimant's treatment is continuing or the claimant has not recovered as expected in the original prognosis[45].

The report should identify the medical records that have been reviewed and the medical records considered relevant to the claim, and these will be sent by the claimant's lawyers to the defendant with the medical report. Any photographs of the claimant's injuries on which it is intended to rely should also be disclosed with the medical report[46].

3.4.3 MedCo and The Selection of Experts in Soft Tissue Injury RTA Claims

The Government is in the process of setting up a process which is intended to ensure the independence and adequacy of experts in medical reporting in soft tissue injury claims under the RTA Protocol and to provide for their accreditation. For this purpose MedCo, an online portal, has been established to which lawyers and litigants in person must now apply to identify a medical expert to instruct in a soft tissue RTA claim. Seven experts or Medical Reporting Organisations registered with MedCo will be provided at random for the lawyer to choose between and to instruct[47]. Experts must register with MedCo if they want to report on soft tissue injury RTA claims.

The experts, or 'randomly generated results', will be required to be accredited under a process which is being developed and all experts on the MedCo register will require accreditation. This process 'to assure independent commissioning of medical evidence'[48] is intended in this field of claims to break the relationships which some experts develop with those regularly instructing them out of concern

---

43   EL/PL Protocol para 1.4

44   EL/PL Protocol para 7.2

45   EL/PL Protocol para 7.6

46   EL/PL Protocol para 7.4

47   In July 2015, the Ministry of Justice launched a review of the impact of MedCo in response to the business strategies adopted by some MROs to increase their selection under the randomized selection process

48   'Whiplash reform programme: Ministry of Justice Response to consultation on independence in medical reporting and expert accreditation' 2.12.14 Conclusion para 13

that that relationship may over time prejudice the independence of the experts in providing their opinions.

This process applies in relation to all Claims Notification Forms issued in the RTA Protocol on or after 6 April 2015 and experts will need to be accredited to be eligible under MedCo by 1 January 2016[49].

3.5   Commencement of Proceedings

Where proceedings have not been compromised as a result of following the relevant pre-action protocol or by negotiation between the parties and do not fall to be dealt with under the RTA Protocol or EL/PL Protocol (see Section 3.4), the claimant commences proceedings by issuing a 'Claim Form' at the court and by paying the appropriate fee (which varies depending on the value of damages expected to be recovered[50] – an estimate of this value is provided by the claimant at this stage).

All personal injury claims can be issued in the County Court but only claims with a financial value of £50,000 or more can be commenced in the High Court (except in relation to clinical negligence where there is no minimum value for

issue in the High Court)[51]. There is, therefore, a substantial overlap of jurisdiction between the County Court and the High Court. In practice, claims for damages of several hundred thousand pounds are commonly issued and heard in the County Court. In addition, the courts can transfer cases between themselves when it is considered appropriate (on application of the parties or by a court's own decision). Money claims in the County Court (which from 22 April 2014 is now one unified court sitting in numerous locations rather than a large number of separate independent courts (a difference without a difference for the expert witness) are now issued centrally and will be transferred to the court that is regarded as most appropriate to the parties. The High Court is to be found only in London and regional centres.

The claim form and the claimant's statement of case - called the 'Particulars of Claim' - must then be served on the defendant. The particulars of claim must have attached to it a report from a medical practitioner 'about the personal injuries which he alleges in his claim'[52]. It must also have attached 'a schedule of details of any past and future expenses and losses which he claims'[53], generally referred to as the 'Schedule of Loss'[54]. The defendant is required either to admit the claim, or to serve a 'Defence',

---

49   Details of the accreditation process have not yet been announced, but early indications from MedCo are that the assessment will be an online multiple choice assessment similar to that introduced by some medico-legal agencies in 2013

50   From April 2015, claims for £10,000 or more pay a court fee of 5% of the value, up to a maximum fee of £10 000

51   High Court and County Courts Jurisdiction Order 1991

52   PD16 para 4.3

53   PD16 para 4.2

54   See 2.7.2 above

which sets out the basis on which the defendant takes issue with the claimant's claim.

The defendant is required to respond to the schedule of loss in a document referred to as the 'Counter Schedule'. The defendant is not required at this stage to produce any medical evidence. A court officer provisionally decides to which 'Track' the case should be assigned. The parties then complete 'Direction Questionnaires' (formerly 'Allocation Questionnaires'), which are sent into the court.

3.5.1 Tracks

All cases will be assigned by the court to one of three tracks. Cases in each track are managed differently by the court to support the principle of proportionality. The three tracks are:

> 1. Small Claims Track
> 2. Fast Track
> 3. Multi-Track.

Small Claims Track

This track is for straightforward personal injury cases with a value of no more than £10,000 and where the damages for pain and suffering and loss of amenity do not exceed £1,000[55]. Expert evidence will be in the form of written reports only and the maximum fee recoverable is limited to £750 for each expert[56]. Court directions will be given without a hearing.

Fast Track

This track is for:

- claims outside the small claims limit and with a value up to £25,000 (for claims issued after 6th April 2009, £15,000 prior to that date – CPR26.6(4));
- where one day (5 hours) of court time only is considered adequate for the trial; and
- where expert evidence will be limited to a maximum of two experts (in different fields) per side[57].

As we have seen in Section 3.4, most injury claims within these limits other than clinical negligence claims will at least commence in the on-line portal under one of the two PAPs for low value claims. For those claims which never enter the on-line portal or which fall out of the portal, on allocation to the fast track the court will give directions for the trial setting a period with a three week window

---

55 CPR 26.6(1)

56 PD27 para 7.3(2)

57 In practice given the time limit, there is little opportunity for disputed medical evidence to be heard in a Fast Track case and any case where there is disputed medical expert evidence will be moved to the Multi-Track.

for the trial date, not more than 30 weeks in the future. Court directions will be given without a hearing.

The on-line portal claims process for personal injury claims (arising out of road traffic accidents after 1 April 2010 with a value between £1,000 and £10,000 and extended to RTA claims up to £25,000 and employers' liability and public liability claims up to £25,000 from 31st July 2013[58]) is not part of the fast track and has a different and simplified procedure. Medical expert evidence will only be in the form of written reports – there will be no oral evidence.

Multi-Track

This track is for all other claims. After allocation to the multi-track the court will normally hold a Case Management Conference (often abbreviated by lawyers to 'CMC') with the parties' representatives. The court will decide what directions for the progression of the case should be given. These directions will normally include a timetable leading to a trial window, perhaps six months in the future. The court will also generally hold a costs case management conference at which costs budgeting will take place.

3.6   Court Directions

The court issues directions to the parties generally reflecting the principles set down in the relevant pre-action protocol. Court directions will require the parties to disclose any relevant documents and to exchange witness statements. The court will also deal with permission to rely on expert evidence in proceedings (including the evidence of medical experts) and will identify whether only the claimant or both parties may rely on expert evidence. The court will direct the specialities of the experts whose reports the parties may rely upon and the date any such reports are to be disclosed or exchanged. If permission is given to both parties to instruct experts, then there will be directions for the experts of similar specialities to meet and discuss the claim, and to provide a joint statement setting out areas of agreement and disagreement (with reasons for disagreement).

Court directions will also be given for the claimant to provide an updated schedule of loss (in the light of the final medical evidence) and for the defendant to respond to this schedule in a counter-schedule.

At the CMC, it will not normally be apparent whether or not there will be conflicting medical opinions or the extent of any medical dispute that will need to be resolved at trial. The defendant may well not have obtained any medical evidence at this stage. The court therefore defers the question of whether or not the parties should have permission to rely on the oral evidence of medical experts at trial (to enable them to be cross-examined) to a future date, nearer to the likely trial date. The issue will then be resolved at a further CMC or 'Pre-Trial Review'. Parties may have to apply to the court subsequently for alterations to court directions if they consider, for example, that experts in further areas are needed or if the defendant

---

58   See Section 3.4

seeks to challenge the expert evidence that the claimant has obtained. The parties may also apply if for any reason it has not proved possible to comply with the directed time limits.

At the CMC, a trial date or a trial window - a period ranging from a few days to several weeks or even months - will be provided for. Where medical experts are likely to give oral evidence, a trial date within the trial window will be found that suits all the parties and the availability of their experts, or at least as many of them as possible, consistent with the effective use of court time.

As noted when considering the 'Jackson reforms' in Section 2.8, the court's powers to enforce its order have been strengthened. If a party fails to comply with an order of the court, or indeed any rule or practice direction, it has to apply for 'relief from any sanction' that might be imposed as a consequence of that breach.

Generally, the sanction is that if a party is late in taking a step, for example, in serving an expert report, then it cannot do so - ever. In considering whether to grant 'relief from sanction' the court is required, in dealing 'justly' with the application, to take into consideration all of the circumstances including the need:

(a) for litigation to be conducted efficiently and at proportionate cost; and

(b) to enforce compliance with rules, practice directions and orders[59].

This change in emphasis has resulted in the court taking punitive action where there has been perceived inefficiency resulting in a failure to comply with an order, rule, practice direction or timetable[60].

3.7   Court Control of Expert Evidence

Expert evidence is only admissible on matters for which such specialist knowledge is required and therefore if such knowledge is not required the expert will normally be prevented from giving any such evidence. The court is also concerned to control the use of experts in order to ensure that the claim is managed proportionally to the issues in the claim and its value.

3.7.1   Purpose of Expert Evidence

Where a court requires specialised knowledge to decide matters, it will admit expert evidence. The evidence of a expert may be necessary in any number of circumstances:

1. to explain or interpret facts that a judge or lawyer would be unable to understand without medical expertise;

---

59   CPR 3.9(1)

60   See *Mitchell v News Group Newspapers Ltd* [2013] EWCA Civ 1537 and *Denton, Decadent and Utilise* [2014] EWCA Civ 906

2. to understand the implications of a particular injury;

3. to understand the relevance of test results or the significance of an entry in the medical records;

4. to obtain a medical opinion that would be beyond the ability of the judge or lawyer to provide;

5. to understand the expected degree of disability resulting from an injury;

6. to assess the likelihood of further recovery or future complications of an injury;

7. to understand the appropriate treatment (or acceptable range of treatments) in the specific circumstances faced by a doctor involved with treating the claimant; and

8. to assess the nature and quantity of the care or therapeutic needs of the injured claimant.

3.7.2   The Court's Powers

Before April 1999, the date when the CPR came into force, it was the parties who managed the litigation and they would frequently instruct a multitude of expert witnesses. In his final report, Lord Woolf concluded that many of these instructions were unnecessary, time-consuming and disproportionate to the value of the claim. The CPR introduced the court's powers to restrict evidence, including expert evidence.

The court now has a general power to control evidence (whether or not it is expert evidence) and can exclude evidence even if it is relevant and in the correct form. It will exercise this controlling power whenever giving directions or hearing a party's application in the course of proceedings:

CPR 32.1   (1)   The court may control the evidence by giving directions as to -

(a)   the issues on which it requires evidence;

(b)   the nature of the evidence which it requires to decide those issues; and

(c)   the way in which the evidence is to be placed before the court.

(2)   The court may use its power under this rule to exclude evidence that would otherwise be admissible.

Part 35 of the CPR begins with a rule that restricts the availability of expert evidence and the number of expert witnesses that can be relied upon in a case. The parties are required to justify to the court why any expert is necessary and the particular disciplines that are necessary. It is for the court to rule if expert evidence in any particular discipline or any at all, is necessary to resolve the proceedings:

CPR 35.1   Expert evidence shall be restricted to that which is reasonably required to resolve the proceedings.

In deciding how to exercise this power, the court will take into account such matters as:

- the overriding objectives under Part 1 of the CPR;
- the potential for the narrowing of issues;
- proportionality and costs;
- whether written reports alone will suffice or whether oral evidence and cross examination is necessary; and
- the use of single joint experts.

Even if a medical report is used in the proceedings, it is open to the court to refuse to permit the party instructing the expert to recover the cost of the report from the losing party if the expenditure is not considered proportionate to the matters at issue in the case[61].

3.7.3   Limiting Experts' Fees

The court has the power to limit 'the amount of a party's expert's fees and expenses that may be recovered from any other party'[62]. This is a limit on the amount of the expert's charges that can be recovered from the other side, but not on the charges the expert can seek from the instructing party. Proportionality may dictate that the recoverable fees are limited in a smaller value case, even though the expert evidence may be reasonably required and obtained at the reasonable market rate. For obvious economic reasons, the lawyers for the party concerned will normally be anxious to limit the expert's fees to the amount they are able to recover from the other side.

In the case of a single joint expert, that is an expert who is instructed by both parties, the court can limit the amount of fees payable to that expert[63].

CPR 35.8   (4)   The court may, before [a single joint] expert is instructed –

(a)   limit the amount that can be paid by way of fees and expenses to the expert; and

---

61   See for example *Murray v Smith* (Lawtel AC0138117) where it was said that '*a solicitor should not blindly set about obtaining a medical report and only then ask himself what medical evidence was appropriate to the case, but should plan in advance what medical evidence should be obtained*'.

62   CPR 35.4 (4)

63   Single joint experts are considered in more detail in Section 4.5.

(b)   direct that some or all of the relevant parties pay that amount into court.

(5)   Unless the court otherwise directs, the relevant parties are jointly and severally liable for the payment of the expert's fees and expenses.

3.7.4   Experts in 'Soft Issue Injury Claims'

Additional provisions have now been made to deal with so-called 'whiplash claims' which the government felt were spiralling out of control. A category of 'soft tissue injury claim' has been defined, as 'a claim brought by an occupant of a motor vehicle where the significant physical injury caused is a soft tissue injury and includes claims where there is a minor psychological injury secondary in significance to the physical injury'[64].

The costs recoverable for such a report and the speciality and circumstances of the expert who can provide such a report are restricted when the claim is one within the RTA Protocol. Permission to rely on a medical expert 'may not be given initially unless the medical report is a fixed cost medical report'[65]. Permission may not then be given to obtain a further medical report if the medical expert is a Consultant Orthopaedic Surgeon, a Consultant in Accident and Emergency Medicine, a General Practitioner registered with the GMC or a Physiotherapist registered with the Health and Care Professions Council unless, once more, the report is a fixed cost medical report[66].

A 'fixed cost medical report' is defined in the RTA Protocol as 'a report in a soft tissue injury claim which is from a medical expert who, save in exceptional circumstances —

(a)   has not provided treatment to the claimant;

(b)   is not associated with any person who has provided treatment; and

(c)   does not propose or recommend that they or an associate provide treatment[67]'.

These are the only reports that a claimant should obtain in an on-line RTA Protocol soft tissue injury claim and on which a claimant is permitted to rely.

The CPR fix the costs which can be recovered for a report for such a claim within the RTA Protocol. This means that only this fixed sum can be recovered by a successful claimant from the losing party, whether the claim remains within the

---

64   RTA Protocol para 1.1(16A)

65   For the process of selection of the expert for the first report through MedCo see Section 3.4.3

66   CPR 35.4(3B)

67   RTA Protocol para 1.1(10A)

on-line portal or falls out of it. The fixed cost is as follows:

(a) obtaining the first report from any expert permitted under para 1.1(12) of the RTA Protocol: £180;

(b) obtaining a further report where justified from one of the following disciplines—

    (i) Consultant Orthopaedic Surgeon (inclusive of a review of medical records where applicable): £420;

    (ii) Consultant in Accident and Emergency Medicine: £360;

    (iii) General Practitioner registered with the General Medical Council: £180; or

    (iv) Physiotherapist registered with the Health and Care Professions Council: £180;

(d) addendum report on medical records (except by Consultant Orthopaedic Surgeon): £50; and

(e) answer to questions under Part 35: £80[68].

These fixed fees do not apply to any claims outside the RTA Protocol and even within the RTA Protocol they do not apply if the claim is other than a soft tissue injury claim. Within the RTA Protocol, the cost of obtaining a further report from an expert outside the categories set out above is not fixed even in such claims, although the use of the expert and the cost will have to be justified to the court[69].

If in a claim under the RTA Protocol the defendant provides an account of the accident which is different to the claimant's, then that account must be provided to the claimant's medical expert as part of the instructions to the medical expert 'for the sole purpose of asking the expert to comment on the impact, if any, on diagnosis and prognosis if—

(a) the claimant's account is found to be true; or

(b) the defendant's account is found to be true[70]:

In order to discourage insurers from making offers to settle soft tissue claims arising in traffic accidents without even seeing a medical report, it is provided that an offer to settle the claim made before a fixed cost medical report has been obtained and disclosed to the defendant will have no adverse costs consequences until after the report is disclosed[71]. Therefore the claimant

---

68   CPR 45.19(2A)

69   CPR 45.19(2C)

70   RTA Protocol para 7.1A

71   CPR 36.21 (4)

can safely decline an offer, so far as any risk on legal costs is concerned, until after obtaining his own medical report.

3.8 Legal Professionals Involved in a Case

There are three types of legal professional involved in the majority of cases that come to trial:

- solicitors
- barristers
- judges.

3.8.1 Role of the Solicitor

In a typical personal injury claim, the claimant who wants professional assistance to manage his claim will instruct a solicitor. This may in fact involve using a free-phone number to speak to a solicitor many miles away in response to an advertisement, rather than walking into a solicitor's office on the high street to speak to a solicitor across a desk. The defendant may well be dealt with initially by an insurance company or claims handler rather than a solicitor, with a firm of solicitors only becoming involved when proceedings are issued by the claimant. Thereafter, the extent to which the insurer continues to run the case varies from insurer to insurer and from case to case.

The development of Alternative Business Structures permitted since October 2011 means that persons other than solicitors may now be involved in the management and control of businesses carrying out the traditional work of solicitors and that outsiders may invest in such businesses. For example, an insurance company can now acquire an interest in a law firm, although the structures have to be approved by the Solicitors Regulation Authority.

In practice, the person handling the claim in the solicitor's office may not be a qualified solicitor. Members of the Institute of Legal Executives or unqualified 'para-legal' staff do much of the day-to-day case work. A solicitor, however, remains responsible for their work on the case and has the day-to-day control of the litigation on behalf of the party on whose behalf he/she is instructed.

The solicitor will maintain a file and manage the litigation (usually with the assistance of case management software), deal with correspondence and communicate with the solicitor for the other party to the litigation. The solicitor for the claimant will be responsible for ensuring that appropriate funding is in place to cover the cost of making the claim and potentially also of losing it (whether such funding be insurance based, Trades Union based or private funds), as well as obtaining the claimant's detailed instructions, collating the necessary documentation, finding witnesses and preparing witness statements.

The extent to which a barrister is used in a claim depends on the solicitor, who in consultation with the claimant will decide whether a barrister needs to be instructed. Practice amongst solicitors varies. Many solicitors are content to draft statements of case and schedules and to assess the value of the claim. Many solicitors will also attend procedural court hearings, such as a CMC, while others will instruct a barrister to do all of this on their behalf. Even when it comes to a trial, some solicitors will appear on behalf of their clients and argue the case, while others will instruct a barrister. The extension of the on-line portal under the RTA Protocol and the EL/PL Protocol and fixed costs in fast track claims have made it less likely that a solicitor will use a barrister in the course of the claim.

3.8.2 Role of the Barrister

A barrister[72] is a self-employed lawyer[73]. Although barristers are commonly involved in relatively small claims, the larger a claim becomes the more likely it is that the solicitor will instruct a barrister. Barristers work within 'Chambers' with a number of other self-employed barristers. Being in a chambers is essentially a way for a barrister to share administrative and marketing costs with other barristers. In recent years, chambers increasingly market themselves collectively and many chambers now specialise in particular areas of law.

The training and experience of a barrister is more focused upon litigation and presenting a claim before a court than that of a solicitor. Although courts require or expect a greater quantity of written submissions than used to be the case, the barrister is still primarily an advocate, skilled in presenting a case to a judge and cross-examining witnesses. As such, a barrister is often better placed to assess the likely outcome of a court hearing and so to advise on the merits of a claim and on its value. The barrister does not maintain a file for each case, but is briefed (sent instructions and relevant papers) only when his/her assistance is required.

In the field of personal injury, clinical negligence and industrial disease claims, once instructed the barrister will usually perform the following functions:

- draft the statement of case;
- prepare the schedule or counter schedule;
- advise on the merits of the claim and its value;
- advise on the evidence required for the case;
- advise in conference (a meeting) with the solicitor, the party and with experts;
- appear for the party at procedural hearings;
- represent the party at negotiation meetings; and
- appear at trial.

The barrister may also advise the solicitor on the identity of an appropriate expert for the case and draft questions for clarification of the expert reports.

---

72   A barrister is also known as 'counsel'

73   From January 2014, barristers have been able to form businesses with others in order to provide their services, although such entities will need the approval of the Bar Standards Board

Until recently, barristers could only be instructed through a solicitor. There are now specified circumstances in which barristers may take instructions directly from a lay client and many will now do so. Barristers can also now be authorised to conduct litigation, that is to carry out certain steps in litigation which work was previously only the province of solicitors, such as issuing proceedings on behalf of a client and dealing with correspondence. The distinction between the roles of barristers and solicitors in litigation is increasingly being eroded.

3.8.3   Role of the Judge

The Procedural Judge will normally be a District Judge in the County Court or regional High Court, or a Master (which term covers male and female judges) in the High Court in London. The Procedural Judge will determine the procedural issues in the case, including the use to be made of experts. This determination is performed with reference to the CPR and the facts of the particular case. There may be other procedural issues relating to the disclosure of documents or payment of interim damages that will also be determined at this level. These hearings are often now heard on the telephone, but if in court will normally be heard in a private room (although legally in fact open to the public).

The expert evidence is prepared for the trial judge who will assess the evidence in the very small minority of cases that reach trial. Depending on the value of the claim, or how complicated it is, the trial judge may be a High Court Judge, a Circuit Judge (in the County Court) or a District Judge (also in the County Court). Masters (in the High Court) also hear some disputed matters.

In addition, cases are heard by barristers and solicitors sitting as part-time judges in the High Court (Deputy High Court Judge) or County Court (Recorder or Deputy District Judge). There is no presumption that the judge hearing the case has any experience of personal injury, clinical negligence or industrial disease litigation, or even of cases involving medical expert evidence. The expertise of a judge is as a judge, not as an expert in any particular area of law or type of dispute. It is the judge's role to decide the facts, on the balance of probabilities. It is also for the judge to decide what weight to attach to an expert's evidence.

The court is not bound to accept such evidence simply because it comes from someone designated as being an expert. Where there is a conflict between the evidence of experts, a judge exercises his/her judgement in deciding which opinion to prefer, although the judge is required to give a coherent and reasoned opinion for rejecting expert evidence. The judge can even make his own assessment and come to a conclusion unsupported by either side's expert's evidence, although the judge must give good reason for doing so and must not take on the role of expert[74].

> 'In resolving conflicts of expert evidence, the judge remains the judge; he is not obliged to accept evidence simply because it comes from an illustrious source; he can take account of demonstrated partisanship and lack of objec-

---

74   *Huntley v Simmons* [2010] EWCA Civ 54

tivity. But, save where an expert is guilty of a deliberate attempt to mislead (as happens only vary rarely), a coherent reasoned opinion expressed by a

suitably qualified expert should be the subject of a coherent reasoned rebuttal, unless it can be discounted for other good reason.[75]

So, for example, when faced with different opinions from two experts on the period of acceleration of symptoms from a pre-existing condition as a result of an accident, the judge may decide on a period between those given by the experts if there is no reason to disregard the opinion of either. It is also for the judge to decide whether the proffered expert has sufficient expertise to be treated as an expert and whether the expert is assisting the court from matters within his/her expertise.

3.9 Judge's Approach to Conflicting Expert Evidence

It comes as a surprise to many medical experts the manner in which a judge makes a decision as to which expert's evidence is to be preferred and which rejected. In the absence of any medical expertise of his/her own and faced with differing opinions from two honest and respectable medical experts, the judge has to assess which expert's opinion is more likely to be correct. The judge does this in much the same way as when deciding any conflict in the evidence in a case.

The classic explanation of this assessment process is in the much quoted passage of Lord Justice Stuart-Smith[76]:

'The court has to evaluate the witness and the soundness of his opinion. …this involves an examination of the reasons given for his opinions and the extent to which they are supported by the evidence. The judge also has to decide what weight to attach to a witness's opinion by examining the internal consistency and logic of his evidence; the care with which he has considered the subject and presented his evidence; his precision and accuracy of thought as demonstrated by his answers; how he responds to searching and informed cross-examination and in particular the extent to which a witness faces up to and accepts the logic of a proposition put in cross-examination or is prepared to concede points that are seen to be correct; the extent to which a witness has conceived an opinion and is reluctant to re-examine it in the light of later evidence, or demonstrates a flexibility of mind which may involve changing or modifying opinions previously held; whether or not a witness is biased or lacks independence

[…] There is one further aspect of a witness's evidence that is often important; that is his demeanour in the witness box. As in most cases where the court is evaluating expert evidence, I have placed less weight on this factor in reaching my assessment. But it is not wholly unimportant; and particularly in those

---

75   *Eckersley v Binnie* (1998) quoted in *Penney v East Kent HA* [2000] Lloyds Rep Med 41

76   *Loveday v Renton* [1990] 1 Med LR 117 at 125

instances where criticisms have been made of a witness on the grounds of bias or lack of independence… the witness's demeanour has been a factor that I have taken into account.'

It is important for all professionals involved in a claim to understand the approach of a judge to conflicting expert evidence, even though most cases are settled before they reach court. In making decisions about settling the claim, the parties' lawyers are mentally projecting the evidence into a courtroom situation and making assessments of how the judge would be likely to respond to the evidence. The quality and content of the expert reports will form an essential part of this assessment prior to a settlement being negotiated by the parties.

Consistency of opinion is also important if an expert's evidence is to be accepted by the court, as illustrated by the following excerpt from a judgment:

'I found [the expert's] evidence surprising (and I doubt that I was alone in this respect). On going into the witness box, he sought to resile from the joint statement in a number of respects and chose to attack the Claimant on grounds that he had not even touched upon in his written material. It was noteworthy that he had not offered a prognosis in his earlier report – presumably because he felt unable to do so. Yet he now offered the view that the resolution of the litigation would have a "profound" effect on the Claimant and might well mean that no further anti-depressant treatment would be required. His original view was that it would be needed indefinitely, and at least for several years. He was at a loss to explain why none of this had been mentioned before. Furthermore, he expressed himself surprised that the Claimant had made no effort to retrain for fresh employment. Yet again, this had been wholly unexplained or in any way heralded in his written evidence. He even said that his observation of the Claimant in the witness box had led him to conclude that he was not suffering from any significant depressive disorder – despite his earlier prediction that he would need to continue with anti-depressants for some time to come. Up to that point, no one had suggested that the Claimant was other than highly motivated to improve his quality of life, for the sake of himself and his family, or that he was in any way less than genuine in his presentation of symptoms.' [77]

However in contrast to that, the same judge took a different view with another expert:

'It is not for me to speculate on how [he] came to change his mind, at the eleventh hour, and to take an altogether more cautious and pessimistic view on prognosis, but I am quite satisfied that it is more rational, rigorous and evidence based than the earlier rather vague comments…'

The Criminal Practice Directions[78], although strictly applicable only to crimi-

---

[77] *Downing v Peterborough & Stamford Hospitals NHS Foundation Trust* [2014] EWHC 4216

[78] https://www.judiciary.gov.uk/publications/criminal-practice-directions/

nal cases, provides useful guidance as to the approach a judge is likely to take in assessing the reliability of the more technical (scientifically based) expert opinion. Expert opinion must be strong enough, and the reasoning process shown to be strong enough, to withstand an analysis of this kind as to its reliability:

33A.5 ... factors which the court may take into account in determining the reliability of expert opinion, and especially of expert scientific opinion, include:

    (a) the extent and quality of the data on which the expert's opinion is based, and the validity of the methods by which they were obtained;

    (b) if the expert's opinion relies on an inference from any findings, whether the opinion properly explains how safe or unsafe the inference is (whether by reference to statistical significance or in other appropriate terms);

    (c) if the expert's opinion relies on the results of the use of any method (for instance, a test, measurement or survey), whether the opinion takes proper account of matters, such as the degree of precision or margin of uncertainty, affecting the accuracy or reliability of those results;

    (d) the extent to which any material upon which the expert's opinion is based has been reviewed by others with relevant expertise (for instance, in peer-reviewed publications), and the views of those others on that material;

    (e) the extent to which the expert's opinion is based on material falling outside the expert's own field of expertise;

    (f) the completeness of the information which was available to the expert, and whether the expert took account of all relevant information in arriving at the opinion (including information as to the context of any facts to which the opinion relates);

    (g) if there is a range of expert opinion on the matter in question, where in the range the expert's own opinion lies and whether the expert's preference has been properly explained; and

    (h) whether the expert's methods followed established practice in the field and, if they did not, whether the reason for the divergence has been properly explained.

33A.6 In addition, in considering reliability, and especially the reliability of expert scientific opinion, the court should be astute to identify potential flaws in such opinion which detract from its reliability, such as:

(a) being based on a hypothesis which has not been subjected to sufficient scrutiny (including, where appropriate, experimental or other testing), or which has failed to stand up to scrutiny;

(b) being based on an unjustifiable assumption;

(c) being based on flawed data;

(d) relying on an examination, technique, method or process which was not properly carried out or applied, or was not appropriate for use in the particular case; or

(e) relying on an inference or conclusion which has not been properly reached

3.10 Conclusion of the Case

One of the complaints of expert witnesses is that, having provided a report, they do not find out when the claim is concluded and what the final outcome of the case is. In reality, expert witnesses are unlikely to receive any feedback about their involvement in the claim and the usefulness or otherwise of their report and any contribution it may have made to the outcome. The Guidance for the Instruction of Experts in Civil Claims (see Chapter 4) does now provide:

Guidance 87   When a case has been concluded either by way of a settlement or trial the solicitor should inform the experts they have instructed.

This provision does not require the lawyer to provide any information to the expert as to the outcome of the case, but does mean that the expert at least knows when his potential further involvement in the case is over. If the terms of appointment provide for deferred payment, then the expert is entitled to be paid. The expert can, of course, enquire as a response to this information what the outcome was and whether or not his/her report contributed to that outcome, but this may not result in any useful feedback from the instructing solicitor.

Conclusion

The entire progression of a claim, from its intimation through to trial, is controlled by court rules (including here practice directions and pre-action protocols). Compliance with court rules ensures that the parties will minimise the cost of running the claim, while enhancing the chances of an early settlement. Once proceedings are commenced, it is the court rather than the parties that manages the litigation. In particular, the court will set down the programme (ending in a trial) and issue directions to the parties that have to be followed, failing which the court may well impose sanctions or financial penalties in costs. The court also controls the use of experts in the claim and in all multi-track claims it sets a cost budget for the entire claim at the first procedural hearing.

Key-Point Summary

1. The *Civil Procedure Rules 1998* and associated practice directions and pre-action protocols are the framework within which all claims are brought before the court.

2. The overriding objective of the CPR is to deal with cases justly, while introducing the principle of proportionality into the administration of justice.

3. The court actively manages cases, giving directions to the parties on how the case should progress.

4. Pre-action protocols are important guidance, representing best practice for the lawyers in preparing claims, with penalties in costs for any party that does not follow them.

5. The use of experts is controlled by the court and the numbers of experts may be limited by the Rules, Practice Directions and Pre-Action Protocols.

6. The Pre-Action Protocol for Personal Injury Claims encourages the joint selection of a mutually acceptable medical expert (who is then instructed by the claimant's solicitors), enabling the parties to settle the claim without having to obtain a second expert report.

7. The court has the power to impose on the parties a single joint expert (who is instructed by both parties), although there is no presumption in favour of instructing a single joint expert and in clinical negligence cases the parties have considerable say in the use of medical experts.

8. Experts must ensure that they do not confuse their position as a jointly selected or mutually acceptable medical expert instructed by one party, with that of a single joint expert instructed by both parties.

9. In managing cases, the court places cases into one of three tracks depending on the value and importance of the case – the small claims track, the fast track, and the multi-track. Larger cases (with a value above £50,000) can be heard in the County Court or the High Court and cases can be moved from one court to another as appropriate to achieve the overriding objective.

10. The likely decision of the judge at trial is a critical concern for all parties in a claim, and the assessment by the parties of how the judge will approach the evidence will be an important factor in their approach to settlement negotiations and in making decisions on offers to settle from the opposing party.

11. The judge's role is to decide facts and to assess expert opinion evidence in order to reach a decision. Judges look for accuracy and consistency in expert evidence and a clear rationale to support the opinions reached by the expert.

Next Steps

In the next chapter, we will explore the roles and duties of an expert witness instructed to give evidence in a civil claim.

4

Role and Duties of the Expert Witness

Introduction

All expert witnesses preparing evidence for civil litigation must comply with the rules in Part 35 (CPR 35) and the practice direction to Part 35 (PD35)[1]. There is also extremely useful guidance for experts in interpreting and complying with these rules in the *Guidance for the Instruction of Experts in Civil Claims* ("The

---

1   Experts should remain alert to the possibility that in specialist courts, additional guidance may supplement the CPR. If unsure, ask your instructing solicitor, who should know if there are any additional requirements.

Guidance"), published by the Civil Justice Council and referred to in PD35[2]. Paragraph 52b of the Guidance and PD35 3.2(9) require an expert to state in the report that he/she is aware of and has complied with the requirements of CPR 35, PD35 and the Guidance.

Chapter Outline

In this chapter, we will outline the key themes relating to expert evidence in the CPR. We will comment on those rules that relate directly to the form and content of expert reports and illustrate the importance of these rules both in the writing of the report and in understanding the decision-making process that the court has to undertake should an action come to trial.

4.1   Duties of Experts

Many of the rules that are contained within Part 35 existed before 1998 and Lord Woolf's drafting of the CPR. However, Part 35 does contain for the first time a clear and authoritative statement of the law, so far as it relates to the duties of expert witnesses.

Adherence to the framework of rules within Part 35 is mandatory. Reports that do not comply with these rules may be excluded from litigation, leaving the party seeking to rely upon the evidence in severe difficulties. Reports that do not comply with the CPR also reflect extremely badly on the competence of the expert. It is fundamental to the duties of an expert witness to produce evidence that complies with all of the requirements of CPR 35, PD35 and the Guidance.

4.1.1   GMC Guidance

Acting as an expert witness also carries responsibilities in respect of an expert's professional standards. The GMC Guidance *Acting as a witness in legal proceedings*[3] provides important and helpful guidance:

> 5. You must understand your role as a witness throughout the court process. You must cooperate with case management, making sure you meet the timescales for producing reports and going to conferences, meetings or court hearings.

> [...]

> 18. You must understand and follow the law and codes of practice that affect your role as an expert witness. You should consider undertaking training for the role, where available ... In particular, you should make sure you understand:

---

2   It is a requirement in CPR that experts are aware of this guidance and comply with it.

3   March 2013, available at www.gmc-uk.org and replacing the previous guidance *Acting as an expert witness*

(a) how to write a report that follows the procedures set out by the courts

(b) how to give oral evidence.

More specifically the GMC Guidance provides:

6. You must make sure that any report that you write, or evidence you give, is accurate and not misleading. This means you must take reasonable steps to check the accuracy of any information you give, and to make sure that you include all relevant information.

7. People who do not have a medical background may rely on your advice and evidence to help them make decisions. Where it is possible to do so without misleading anyone, you should use language and terminology that people who are not medically qualified will understand. You should explain any abbreviations and medical or other technical terminology you use. Diagrams with explanatory labels can be useful.

17. You must make full and accurate notes of meetings or interviews with the people involved in the case at the time an event happens or as soon as possible afterwards. Any notes or reports you make must be written fairly and impartially.

It should be noted that the giving of evidence in court by an expert witness or the preparation and content of a report for use in court might be of such a nature or degree of incompetence or negligence that it amounts to professional misconduct without the need to prove any bad faith or recklessness on the part of the expert[4].

> There is no excuse for an expert witness not to be familiar with the requirements of the CPR (Part 35, PD 35 and the Guidance). These rules are fundamental to producing expert reports and giving oral evidence and familiarity with these rules will help the expert to perform the role of expert witness appropriately.

4.1.2 Underlying Principles of CPR Part 35

Many of the principles underlying Part 35 are drawn directly from the judgment of Mr Justice Cresswell in an Admiralty case called *The Ikarian Reefer*[5]. The judge, having been forced to sit through a relatively straightforward case for the best part of six months, is reported to have been extremely annoyed by the conduct of the expert witnesses in court.

---

4   *Kumar v GMC* [2012] EWHC 2688

5   [1993] 2 Lloyd's Rep 68. Cases involving ships are called 'Admiralty cases' and are known by the name of the ship at issue in the litigation. This particular case involves a fire in the engine room of the *Ikarian Reefer* that led to the ship running aground.

In his judgment, he took the unusual step of setting out the duties and responsibilities of expert witnesses in civil cases:

> '...because I consider that a misunderstanding on the part of certain expert witnesses... as to their duties and responsibilities contributed to the length of the trial...

> The duties and responsibilities of expert witnesses in civil cases include the following:

> 1. Expert evidence presented to the Court should be and should be seen to be the independent product of the expert uninfluenced as to form or content by the exigencies of litigation...

> 2. An expert witness should provide independent assistance to the Court by way of objective unbiased opinion in relation to matters within his expertise... An expert witness in the High Court should never assume the role of the advocate.

> 3. An expert witness should state the facts or assumptions on which his opinion is based. He should not omit to consider material facts which detract from his concluded opinion...

> 4. An expert witness should make it clear when a particular question or issue falls outside his expertise.

> 5. If an expert's opinion is not properly researched because he considers that insufficient data is available then this must be stated with an indication that the opinion is no more than a provisional one...

> 6. If after exchange of reports, an expert witness changes his view on a material matter... such a change of view should be communicated... to the other side without delay and when appropriate to the court.

> 7. Where expert evidence refers to photographs, plans, calculations... survey reports or other similar documents these must be provided to the opposite party at the same time as the exchange of reports...'[6]

Cresswell J's *Ikarian Reefer* principles first appear in rule 35.3:

CPR 35.3 (1) It is the duty of experts to help the court on the matters within their expertise.

(2) This duty overrides any obligation to the person from whom experts have received instructions or by whom they are paid.

---

6   [1993] 2 Lloyd's Rep 68

4.1.3 Independence

Expert witnesses owe a duty to the court as well as a duty to exercise reasonable skill and care in providing their services to the party instructing them[7]. This simple and straightforward concept seems to cause many experts far more problems than it ought. That one party is paying the expert's fee does not mean that the expert needs to give a favourable opinion to that party or even to temper an unfavourable one. The requirement is simply that the expert demonstrates the independence of mind and the strength of character to give an unbiased opinion.

> 'There is no conflict between the duty owed by an expert to his client and his overriding duty to the court. His duty to the client is to perform his function as an expert with the reasonable skill and care of an expert drawn from the relevant discipline. This includes a duty to perform the overriding duty of assisting the court. Thus the discharge of the duty to the court cannot be a breach of duty to the client. If the expert gives an independent and unbiased opinion which is within the range of reasonable expert opinions, he will have discharged his duty both to the court and his client. If, however, he gives an independent and unbiased opinion which is outside the range of reasonable expert opinions, he will not be in breach of his duty to the court, because he will have provided independent and unbiased assistance to the court. But he will be in breach of the duty owed to his client.'[8]

As the Guidance states:

> Guidance 11 Experts must provide opinions that are independent, regardless of the pressures of litigation. A useful test of 'independence' is that the expert would express the same opinion if given the same instructions by another party...

Sometimes there may already be an existing relationship between the expert and the party or the lawyers in that the expert has had an advisory role outside the litigation or contemplated litigation. The Guidance includes the advice that:

> Guidance 23 (d) ...Where an expert advisor is approached to act as an expert witness they [sic] will need to consider carefully whether they can accept a role as expert witness. The potential difficulties for an expert in maintaining this independence have been recognised by the courts

The importance of avoiding pressures that might threaten such independence is reflected in the statement in the Guidance indicating the inadvisability of entering into terms of engagement where payment is contingent on the outcome of the case:

---

7   This duty to the court does not apply where experts are instructed in an advisory capacity, such as to help a solicitor to identify the key medical issues in a case or to advise or comment on the work of a single joint expert, rather than to prepare evidence for the purpose of proceedings. See Guidance para 6.

8   Lord Dyson in *Jones v Kaney* [2011] UKSC 13 at para 99

Guidance   88   Payment of experts' fees contingent upon the nature of the expert evidence or upon the outcome of the case is strongly discouraged. In *ex parte Factortame* the court said 'we consider that it will be a rare case indeed that the court will be prepared to consent to an expert being instructed under a contingency fee agreement'.

An expert should regard any form of payment dependent on results as compromising (actually or potentially) the required independence of the expert, and therefore it should be avoided[9]. An expert who is required to act on such a basis should take legal and professional advice before accepting instructions.

The potential difficulties for an expert in maintaining this independence have been recognised by the courts:

> 'The area of expertise in any case may be likened to a broad street with the [claimant] walking on one pavement and the defendant walking on the opposite one. Somehow the expert must be ever mindful of the need to walk straight down the middle of the road and to resist the temptation to join the party from whom the instructions come on the pavement. It seems to me that the expert's difficulty ... is much increased if he attends the trial for days on end as a member of the litigation team. Some sort of seduction into shared attitudes, assumptions and goals seems to me almost inevitable.' [10]

Even without being present in the courtroom for days, the feeling of being part of a team can develop during conferences with the instructing side, especially where discussions of the case and the evidence of the 'opposing' experts take place.

The potential impact on the independence of expert evidence as a result of a financial connection or even a substantial business relationship between a lawyer and a medical reporting agency has been raised by the Government in the consultation on reforms in whiplash claims, and addressed by the introduction of MedCo and the random selection of experts in such claims[11]. By implication and by extension it could be suggested that an expert receiving repeated instructions from the same source might be at risk of compromising independence, the suggestion being

---

9   Although the previous Protocol (which the Guidance replaces) was written in clear terms stating that contingency fees "must not be offered or accepted", the legal position is less clear cut and this is reflected in the Guidance – see *Factortame Ltd (No 2/ No 8) (ex parte)* [2002] EWCA Civ 932 at para 73 – 'To give evidence on a contingency fee basis gives an expert, who would otherwise be independent, a significant financial interest in the outcome of the case. As a general proposition, such an interest is highly undesirable. In many cases the expert will be giving an authoritative opinion on issues that are critical to the outcome of the case. In such a situation the threat to his objectivity posed by a contingency fee agreement may carry greater dangers to the administration of justice than would the interest of an advocate or solicitor acting under a similar agreement. Accordingly, we consider that it will be in a very rare case indeed that the court will be prepared to consent to an expert being instructed under a contingency fee agreement.'

10   Thorpe LJ in *Vernon v Bosley* (No1) [1997] 1 All ER 577 at 612

11   See Section 3.4

that the commercial pressures (or benefits) of such a relationship might influence expert opinion. The authors would suggest that much of that fear can be overcome if the expert clearly provides properly reasoned and justified opinion in the report.

An independent and unbiased opinion is far more helpful to the lawyers in negotiating a settlement than an exaggerated opinion that is only exposed as such once substantial costs have been incurred on the back of it. Worse still is the situation where an exaggerated opinion collapses under the pressure of cross-examination in court. Any competent solicitor will say that an opinion that is not supported by the evidence is extremely costly, misleading and ultimately damaging to a client's case. It is therefore important that when assisting a party as part of a team of experts involved in a case, the sense of being a 'team player' is not allowed to come into conflict with the duty to assist the court and express an independent and unbiased opinion.

The expert owes his/her duty to the court, and failure to comply with that duty can have serious implications for the party instructing the expert as well as for the expert him/herself. The Guidance sets out the position as follows:

> Guidance 15 Experts should be aware that any failure to comply with the rules or court orders, or any excessive delay for which they are responsible, may result in the parties who instructed them being penalised in costs, or debarred from relying upon the expert evidence.

Therefore, in a case where the conduct of the medical experts was found to have fallen well below what could properly be expected from expert witnesses in that they had not addressed their responsibilities or conducted themselves properly as expert witnesses, the party instructing them was ordered to pay the opposing party's costs attributable to dealing with their evidence on the higher – 'indemnity' – basis[12]. What subsequent arrangement the experts and their client or their solicitors subsequently came to as to who would pay this bill is not revealed.

There is also a duty of care owed by experts to the party instructing them, as there is in any contract to provide services. However, the duty of care owed to that party is subject to the obligations imposed on the expert by the CPR. Until 30 March 2011, the expert had the benefit of immunity from being sued for anything said in the course of giving evidence and in preparation for giving evidence, which included his/her conduct in a joint discussion and in the preparation of a joint statement. That immunity has now ceased to exist as a result of the decision of the Supreme Court in *Jones v Kaney*[13]. The position now is that the expert witness can be sued for damages by his/her client for negligence in relation to the expert's participation in any legal proceedings. It has been suggested that:

---

12   *Williams v Jervis* (Costs) [2009] EWHC 1837

13   *Jones v Kaney* [2011] UKSC 13

'The most likely broad consequence of denying expert witnesses the immunity accorded to them [hitherto] will be a sharpened awareness of the risks of pitching their initial views of the merits of their client's case too high or too inflexibly lest these views come to expose and embarrass them at a later date. I for one would welcome this as a healthy development in the approach of expert witnesses to their ultimate task (their sole rationale) of assisting the court to a fair outcome of the dispute (or, indeed, assisting the parties to a reasonable pre-trial settlement).

The other signal advantage of denying immunity to expert witnesses is, of course, that in the no doubt rare case where the witness behaves in an egregious manner such as is alleged in the instant case or, indeed, otherwise causes his client loss by adopting or adhering to an opinion outside the permissible range of reasonable expert opinions, the wronged client will enjoy, rather than have denied to him by rule of law, his proper remedy.' [14]

This potential liability of the expert witness to be sued by his/her client for negligence in performing the services of an expert witness will extend to reports prepared for the purposes of litigation, any out of court statements, such as in a conference with the client and instructing lawyers and in a joint statement prepared following a discussion between experts, and the giving of evidence itself.

In addition to this liability for any negligence, at all times experts remain subject to their professional codes of ethics and may in appropriate instances of bad conduct or apparent incompetence be referred by the judge to their professional body for consideration of disciplinary proceedings[15]. The Guidance states:

Guidance   4.1   Experts always owe a duty to exercise reasonable skill and care to those instructing them, and to comply with any relevant professional code. However when they are instructed to give or prepare evidence for the purpose of civil proceedings they have an overriding duty to help the court on matters within their expertise (CPR 35.3). This duty overrides any obligation to the person instructing or paying them. Experts must not serve the exclusive interest of those who retain them.

An expert must always ensure that there is no possible conflict of interest when producing a report and that there is no possible appearance of bias. For example, when advising in a clinical negligence claim, it is important to draw attention to any possible connection that the medical expert may have with any party being made the subject of possible criticism.

---

14   Lord Brown in *Jones v Kaney* at para 67 and 68

15   See for example *Kumar v GMC* [2012] EWHC 2688 and Section 4.1.2

The standard court direction in clinical negligence claims in the High Court includes the direction that:

> 13 Experts shall, at the time of producing their reports, produce a CV giving details of any employment or activity which raises a possible conflict of interest.

Objectivity is an important aspect of independence. A judge is entitled to expect an expert to maintain objectivity as part of the duty to be independent. A generous degree of understanding was shown by the judge in the following example, but such lack of objectivity might normally be expected to be harmful to the expert's credibility:

> '[In relation to the evidence of one expert] I formed the view that there was a tendency to hear, interpret and report things in a manner that tended to be adverse to the Claimant. I do not think that she did it consciously but, in my view, it led to regular over-interpretation of, for example, the extent to which [the Claimant] had recovered true independence in everyday life or the extent to which he had a real social life or a meaningful circle of friends. However, I remind myself that over-interpretation in this way may be an occupational hazard for all experts; and in preparing this judgment I have attempted to scrutinise the evidence of all the expert witnesses for similar signs before reaching my own conclusions on the facts.'[16]

The court was very much less than impressed in a case where the defendant's expert had failed to reveal that he had worked with the defendant doctor for many years and that the defendant doctor had 'guided and inspired his practice', particularly when it transpired that it was the defendant doctor who had recommended the expert to his legal team[17]. It is essential for the expert to avoid not only such a conflict of interest but also any appearance of possible bias, and expressly to set out at the earliest opportunity any facts which might potentially create such a conflict or such an appearance.

Similarly, the court was quick to reject in its totality the evidence of an expert who was considered to be 'overly keen to find arguments to support the claimant's case' and to seek unfairly 'to nit-pick' at aspects of the evidence[18] and an expert who 'appeared to forget his duty to the court and seemed illegitimately to stray into creative advocacy for the claimant's cause' and 'sought to side-step the evidence'[19].

---

16   *Ali v Caton and MIB* [2013] EWHC 1730

17   *EXP v Barker* [2015] EWHC 1289

18   *Sardar v NHS Commissioning Board* [2014] EWHC 38

19   *Sardar v NHS Commissioning Board* [2014] EWHC 38

4.1.4 Duty to Co-Operate with the Court Process

The expert's duty to the court also includes a requirement to co-operate with the court process.

Guidance 22 Experts should confirm without delay whether or not they accept their instructions.

23 They should also inform those instructing them (whether on initial instructions or at any later stage) without delay if:

(a) instructions are not acceptable because, for example, they require work that falls outside their expertise, impose unrealistic deadlines, or are insufficiently clear;

(b) they consider that instructions are or have become insufficient to complete the work;

(c) they become aware that they may not be able to fulfil any of the terms of appointment;

(d) the instructions and/or work have, for any reason, placed them in conflict with their duties as an expert...; or

(e) they are not satisfied that they can comply with any orders that have been made.

Therefore by taking on medico-legal work, it must be recognised by the busy medical practitioner that the medico-legal practice must be given proper priority. This can become even more difficult when it comes to the possibility of being required to attend at court:

Guidance 85 Experts have an obligation to attend court and should ensure that those instructing them are aware of their dates to avoid and that they take all reasonable steps to be available.

The solicitor has a corresponding obligation to ascertain the expert's availability before the trial date is fixed, keep experts updated with court timetables, give consideration to whether experts could give evidence by a video-link, and inform experts immediately if trial dates are vacated[20].

---

20 Guidance para 84

The attendance of a witness at court can be enforced by the issue and service of a witness summons. Normally, an expert should attend without the need for service of a witness summons, but on occasions an expert may be served in order to require attendance. Whether or not a witness summons is served, the expert has an obligation to attend and the instructing party has an obligation to pay the expert's fee[21].

4.1.5 Estimating Costs

We have seen how the reforms of civil procedure in April 2013 included the strengthening of the provisions as to the 'proportionality' of costs which can be recovered by a successful party and the introduction of 'costs budgeting' in multi-track claims[22]. A party is unlikely to recover from the losing side more than the amount that is approved by the court as the appropriate and proportionate budget for the claim.

In addition CPR 35.4(2) has been amended to provide:

> When parties apply for permission [to call an expert or put in evidence an expert's report] they must provide an estimate of the costs of the proposed expert evidence …

In order to provide the court with the necessary information for costs budgeting and in order to apply for permission to rely on expert evidence, the solicitor will require from the expert an estimate of all of the likely fees to be charged by the expert in bringing the claim to a conclusion. Although it is highly probable that the claim will not proceed to a contested trial, and although it is not necessarily apparent precisely what involvement the expert will have, estimates must be provided.

The estimate should include provision for:

1. providing an initial report, allowing for preparatory reading, reviewing medical records and a consultation;

2. re-examining the client and preparing a supplemental report;

3. reviewing reports prepared by other experts;

4. reviewing further documentation;

5. reviewing surveillance evidence;

6. replying to Part 35 questions from the opposing side;

7. attending case conference(s);

8. attending joint discussions and preparing a joint statement; and

9. attending trial to give evidence (including travel expenses).

---

21 Guidance para 86

22 See Section 2.8

The nature of the claim may indicate to the expert other possible complications and possible additional input which might be required. Costs budgeting is provided on the basis of 'assumptions' as to the litigation, and in a complicated or high value claim the expert should indicate the assumptions upon which the costs estimate is provided, for example the volume of medical records that will have to be read, the hours of surveillance material to be reviewed and the number of days the expert is likely to be required at court for the trial (giving evidence and hearing the evidence of others).

4.1.6   Narrowing the Area of Dispute

To help the court (i.e. the judge trying the case) experts must seek to limit the areas of contention between the parties, and so simplify the dispute and the judge's eventual task:

> 'There are generally many "irreducible and stubborn facts" upon which agreement between experts should be possible and in my judgment the expert advisers of the parties, whether legal or scientific, are under a special duty to the court in the preparation of such a case to limit in every possible way the contentious matters of fact to be dealt with at the hearing. That is a duty which exists notwithstanding that it may not always be easy to discharge.'[23]

4.1.7   The Expert as Fact Finder

In a personal injury claim, the role of the medical expert is to establish, as accurately as possible, what the injuries, symptoms, effects and consequences[24] of the accident have actually been. Since much of the detail in the factual basis of a personal injury report will come directly from the claimant who is seeking compensation, the quality of the presentation of this evidence and the expert's evaluation of it is of the utmost importance[25].

Two points arise:

1.   good note-taking of discussions with the claimant is essential[26]; and where relevant

2.   information from the claimant should be reported in the claimant's own words, rather than being glossed into technical medical language by the expert.

---

23   *Graigola Merthyr Co Ltd v Swansea Corporation* [1928] 1 Ch 31 at p38

24   See Section 6.1 for an explanation of the medico-legal use of these terms

25   In this regard, effective questioning and careful observation of the claimant during the examination are essential skills for experts to develop, though these are beyond the scope of this book.

26   See Section 4.1.1 and the GMC Guidance

These two disciplines enable the lawyers and the court to address any dispute between the claimant and the expert about what took place at the interview and examination[27].

Any notes relating to the interview or examination, whether held on paper or electronically, must be retained until the conclusion of the litigation - i.e. until settlement of the claim or court judgment and the conclusion of any appeal process.

In fact, the expert will be unlikely to know when any of these stages has been reached in the absence of communication from the instructing lawyer. The notes should also be retained following the conclusion of the injury litigation in case of any claim by a party against any of the professionals in the action. Such a claim may not come to the attention of the expert until as much as seven years after the conclusion of the injury claim (there is a 6 year limitation period in claims alleging such professional negligence) or even longer in the case of a child claimant and therefore, as a rule of thumb, the expert is well advised to keep the notes in relation to an adult claimant appropriately filed for at least 10 years.

4.1.8   Investigating Claims

The medical expert's role is to identify the relevant facts, to carry out such examination as is appropriate and to express an opinion. It is not for the medical expert to become involved in the exercise of gathering evidence in the case. His/her role is not routinely that of a sleuth although there may be cases in which, for clinical or related reasons, the medical expert is driven to advance an opinion as to whether or not the claimant's account of how injury occurred, or of the injury received, is to be believed. In *Charnock v Rowan*[28] the Court of Appeal noted that there was implicit in the trial judge's observations:

> 'a suggestion that it is an examining doctor's job to make out the case, if there is a case, for disbelieving a claimant's account of how he or she came to suffer injury, or of the injury he or she has suffered. There are of course cases in which, for clinical or related reasons, the doctor is driven to advance such an opinion; but if it was intended here to suggest that the doctor's role is routinely that of a sleuth, I must record my respectful disagreement. Forensic medical practice has been disfigured in the past by practitioners who took on such a role; but it was to Mr Shah's credit that he confined his report to those divergences which emerged from his own interviews and from the records supplied to him and did not take on himself the task of deciding who was to be believed.'

An example of an unfortunate over-involvement of a medical expert in obtaining evidence in a claim is the case of *Williams v Jervis*[29]. The defendant's expert, having produced his report, came into possession of an earlier report that had

---

27   We consider this aspect of the expert's role further in Sections 4.2.5 and 4.2.6

28   *Charnock v Rowan* [2012] EWCA Civ 2

29   [2008] EWHC 2346

been obtained in the same case by the claimant's lawyers. The claimant's lawyers, as they were entitled so to do, had not disclosed the report to the defendant. This undisclosed report was not favourable to the claimant's case and the defendant's expert in his own opinion evidence agreed with it.

The defendant's expert then sent the report anonymously to his instructing solicitors, who in turn disclosed it to the claimant's lawyers. On investigation at trial, it transpired that the defendant's expert had heard of the existence of the other unfavourable report when he happened to discuss the case with a colleague who was the author of the report. The expert had asked for a copy of it and so created the difficulty for the parties.

In his judgment, the judge stated:

> 'In putting himself in the position of being in possession of [the undisclosed report], [the defendant's expert] displayed very poor judgement. Moreover, the way he dealt with the report and part of the evidence he gave about it in court were not straightforward. He misled his instructing solicitors and I reject the evidence he gave that he had any doubt about the source of the report even if it did arrive in a brown envelope with no covering letter. Accepting, as of course I do, that [the defendant's expert] has no legal training, his claim that he thought his conduct consistent with the discharge of his duties to the court as an expert witness is, in the light of the vast number of medico-legal cases he undertakes, untenable...'

An expert is instructed to report on the evidence in the case and should limit any investigations strictly to those relevant to his/her instructions and should not become involved in the more general investigation of the claim.

On the other hand, it is important that an expert has access to all relevant information and documentation which might be in the possession of the parties. The expert might well be able to identify documents which should exist or which are missing from the copy medical records provided. If they are in the possession of the other party to the proceedings, then the lawyers can apply to have copies of them made available. This could include the details of tests or experiments carried out on the claimant or details of tests or other investigations carried out by the other side's expert. The expert should make a request for such missing documentation in a letter to his/her instructing lawyer, explaining why the information is necessary and its significance in relation to the expert issues in the case. The lawyers can use this letter in seeking the documents from the other party[30].

Not only should the expert seek to ensure that he/she sees such documents, but also, should it appear that the other side's expert in the same discipline has not had access to the information or documentation which the expert has seen, then the expert should notify the instructing lawyer of that fact[31].

---

30   PD35 4 and Guidance para 30-33

31   Guidance para 30

4.1.9 Form of Expert Evidence

Rule 35.5 requires that expert evidence is put before the court in the form of a written report:

CPR 35.5 (1) Expert evidence is to be given in a written report unless the court directs otherwise.

(2) If a claim is on the small claims track or the fast track, the court will not direct an expert to attend a hearing unless it is necessary to do so in the interests of justice.

This rule places great weight on the written report. In smaller cases, there will be no oral evidence should the matter come to court. In larger cases, the report will be taken as read and will stand as the expert's evidence-in-chief[32], so that the expert will not expand upon or explain his/her report in oral evidence and cross-examination of the witness on the contents of the expert's written evidence will proceed without delay.

A high-quality report is essential. All of the evidence that the expert witness wants to bring to the attention of the court needs to be set out in writing and will be read before the expert witness arrives at court. In practice, the written report is important at a far earlier stage of proceedings because approximately 98% of cases will be abandoned or will settle by negotiation based substantially upon the written reports of the experts in the case.

4.2 Content of Expert Reports

The required content of expert reports is first addressed in CPR 35.10, with greater detail set out in PD35 paras 3.1-3.9. Further guidance is provided in paras 48 - 60 of the Guidance. The purpose of these requirements is to make sure that all of the information relevant to the decision-making process of the court is contained in the report:

CPR 35.10 (1) An expert's report must comply with the requirements set out in practice direction 35.

(2) At the end of an expert's report there must be a statement that the expert understands and has complied with their duty to the court.

(3) The expert's report must state the substance of all material instructions, whether written or oral, on the basis of which the report was written.

---

32   The evidence adduced in court by a party from its own witnesses.

PD35 3.2   An expert's report must:

(1)   give details of the expert's qualifications;

(2)   give details of any literature or other material which the expert has relied on in making the report;

(3)   contain a statement setting out the substance of all facts and instructions which are material to the opinions expressed in the report or upon which those opinions are based;

(4)   make clear which of the facts stated in the report are within the expert's own knowledge;

(5)   say who carried out any examination, measurement, test or experiment which the expert has used for the report, give the qualifications of that person, and say whether or not the test or experiment has been carried out under the expert's supervision;

(6)   where there is a range of opinion on the matters dealt with in the report –

(a)   summarise the range of opinion, and

(b)   give reasons for the expert's own opinion;

(7)   contain a summary of the conclusions reached;[33]

(8)   if the expert is not able to give an opinion without qualification, state the qualification; and

(9)   contain a statement that the expert –

(a)   understands their duty to the court, and has complied with that duty; and

(b)   is aware of the requirements of Part 35, this practice direction and the Guidance for the Instruction of Experts in Civil Claims 2014.

PD35 3.3   An expert's report must be verified by a statement of truth in the following form:

---

33   Note that there is no requirement for a 'summary report', only a straightforward 'summary of conclusions'

'I confirm that I have made clear which facts and matters referred to in this report are within my own knowledge and which are not. Those that are within my own knowledge I confirm to be true. The opinions I have expressed represent my true and complete professional opinions on the matters to which they refer.'[34]

The expert's written evidence in a case will be comprised of the expert's report, the expert's answers to questions of clarification, and the joint statement produced by the experts prior to trial. All of these may be subject to cross-examination should a case reach court. The requirements in the CPR and the Guidance will, if properly followed, help to ensure that the expert's evidence is adequate. If the rules are followed, the expert report will demonstrate that the expert has the appropriate qualifications and relevant experience to give opinions in the case. It should also show the basis of the expert's opinions. The report will also confirm – and it will generally be taken at face value – that the expert has understood and complied with his/her duty to the court in the proceedings.

PD35 3.1   An expert's report should be addressed to the court and not to the party from whom the expert has received instructions.

By requiring the expert to expressly refer to the duty to the court and to address the report to the court and not to the instructing party, the role of the expert as an independent and objective professional is emphasised. In practice, this outlaws the practice of producing a report addressed directly to one party, but does not mandate that the report is headed 'To the Court'. A statement that the expert has been 'instructed to produce a Part 35 report for the court' is an elegant way of informing everyone involved that the expert has read and is conscious of the requirements of the CPR.

4.2.1   Instructions

It is by no means the universal practice for solicitors, when instructing experts, to provide any or any adequate guidance as to what is required either generally of an expert report or specifically in relation to a particular case. As Lord Woolf noted:

'From the comments I have received on this point it appears that solicitors' instructions vary from detailed to perfunctory. 'Please provide your usual report' is an example that has been mentioned to me, and it may well be that this is adequate for an experienced expert who is frequently instructed by the same solicitor. Many experts have, however, indicated that they would welcome more detailed and explicit instructions, and I have no doubt that solicitors would benefit from guidance in this area.' [35]

---

34   The Expert's Declaration and Statement of Truth are mandatory statements in an expert report. There are many, often lengthy, statements and declarations generated by various professional bodies that do not comply with the far easier and simpler requirement laid down by the court. See Section 4.2.15-16

35   *Access to Justice – Final Report* (see above) Chapter 13 para 56

The situation persists with perfunctory or inadequate solicitors' instructions still being provided to experts. The expert is therefore frequently on his/her own as to what is required when writing the report. The Guidance provides guidance for lawyers as to what is required as a minimum and encourages experts to respond positively should they feel the need for clarification of what is required of them.

Guidance 20 Those instructing experts should ensure that they give clear instructions (and attach relevant documents), including the following:

> (a) basic information, such as names, addresses, telephone numbers, dates of birth and dates of incidents and any relevant claim reference numbers;

> (b) the nature of the expertise required;

> (c) the purpose of the advice or report, a description of the matter(s) to be investigated, the issues to be addressed and the identity of all parties;

> (d) the statement(s) of case (if any), those documents which form part of disclosure and witness statements and expert reports that are relevant to the advice or report, making clear which have been served and which are drafts and when the latter are likely to be served;

> (e) where proceedings have not been started, whether they are contemplated and, if so, whether the expert is asked only for advice;

> (f) an outline programme, consistent with good case management and the expert's availability, for the completion and delivery of each stage of the expert's work; and

> (e) where proceedings have been started, the dates of any hearings (including any case/costs management conferences and/or pre-trial reviews), the dates fixed by the court or agreed between the parties for the exchange of experts; reports and any other relevant deadlines to be adhered to, the name of the court, the claim number, the track to which the claim has been allocated and whether there is a specific budget for the experts' fees.

21 Those instructing experts should seek to agree, where practicable, the instructions for the experts, and that they receive the same factual material.

There are obligations on the expert, on receipt of instructions and in accepting them, which are spelt out in the Guidance:

Guidance 22 Experts should confirm without delay whether they accept their instructions.

23 They should also inform those instructing them (whether on initial instructions or at any later stage) without delay if:

(a) instructions are not acceptable because, for example, they require work that falls outside their expertise, impose unrealistic deadlines, or are insufficiently clear. Experts who do not receive clear instructions should request clarification and may indicate that they are not prepared to act unless and until such clear instructions are received;

(b) they consider that instructions are insufficient to complete the work;

(c) they become aware that they may not be able to fulfil any of the terms of appointment;

(d) the instructions and/or work have, for any reason, placed them in conflict with their duties as an expert. Where an expert advisor is approached to act as an expert witness they will need to consider carefully whether they can accept a role as expert witness;

(e) they are not satisfied that they can comply with any orders that have been made.

There is an element of proportionality in what is provided by way of detailed instructions and the time spent by the lawyers in providing such instructions. A whiplash type injury with four weeks of symptoms does not require or merit the same length of instructions as would be expected of a claim in clinical negligence for an adverse event following brain surgery. However, the principle remains the same – the medical expert should understand the purpose of the report and what he/she is being asked to report on, and any applicable timetable or time limits for providing the report. If in any doubt, the expert must ask the instructing solicitor for clarification of the instructions.

The substance of all material instructions that the expert has received, whether in writing or orally, is to be included in the report[36]. The expert should summarise the instructions to enable the judge to understand what issues the expert is reporting upon. It is intended that by disclosing the substance of the instructions, the objectivity and impartiality of the expert will be emphasised and encouraged. Any

---

36   PD35 3.2(3)

instruction, for example, not to mention an unfavourable aspect of the case, even if given on the telephone as a supplemental instruction to a letter of instruction, would have to be included in the report. The Guidance states:

Guidance 55 The mandatory statement of the substance of all material instructions should not be incomplete or otherwise tend to mislead. The imperative is transparency. The term "instructions" includes all material that solicitors send to experts. These should be listed, with dates, in the report or an appendix. The omission from the statement of 'off-the-record' oral instructions is not permitted. Courts may allow cross-examination about the instructions if there are reasonable grounds to consider that the statement may be inaccurate or incomplete.

The expert's report must state the 'substance of all facts and instructions which are material to the opinions expressed in the report or upon which those opinions are based'[37]:

I have been asked specifically to express opinion as to:

1.   the likelihood the claimant would have developed symptoms of anxiety or depression in the absence of the accident; and

2.   the date at which it would have been reasonable for the claimant to have returned to full time employment following the accident.

Many experts with established relationships with solicitors understand what the solicitor requires and therefore the expert need simply state his/her own understanding of the instructions. Setting out at the beginning of the report what the expert understands his/her instructions to be can also avoid the risk of the expert's opinions being ruled inadmissible because the expert has, in providing opinion, gone outside the terms of his/her appointment. This is a particular risk for a single joint expert whose terms of appointment may have been set out in a court order[38].

Before agreeing to provide an expert report, the expert must make sure that the instructions received from the solicitor are clear. Clarifying instructions before commencing the work will usually save time and money, and sometimes even the professional relationship between the expert and the solicitor.

---

37   PD35 3.2(3)

38   See for example *Annison v Nolan* [2012] EWCA Civ 54 (a jointly appointed architect who reported on matters outside his appointment)

Documents included in instructions

It has been held that information given to an expert with the instructions was included within the phrase 'material instructions'[39] and this would appear to be the basis for the third sentence in paragraph 55 of the Guidance, that "instructions" includes all material that solicitors send to experts.

The instructing lawyer may be concerned that by referring to the documents provided as part of the information with instructions, privilege in those documents is lost and the other side is therefore permitted to see them. It has however also been held that mere reference to a witness statement in an expert report did not waive such privilege[40] — for that, it was necessary for the witness statement to be relied upon by the expert. This view was also taken by the Court of Appeal in *Bourns Inc v Raychem Corp (No 3)*[41] in which it was said that 'mere reference to a document does not waive privilege; there must be at least reference to the contents and reliance'. Further CPR35.10(4) protects the documents referred to in a letter of instruction from disclosure unless there are reasonable grounds to consider the expert's statement of instructions to be inaccurate or incomplete.

An expert should refer to those documents included in instructions which the expert considers in giving an opinion. A witness statement or expert report which contains information which is considered material to the expert's opinion — and therefore is material 'on the basis of which the report was written'[42] — should be identified.

It may be that the witness statement or other expert report provided to the expert and which is material to the expert's report is subsequently amended prior to the disclosure of the expert's report. In this case, the expert should be given the opportunity to see this further material, and to amend the report as appropriate. It would then be the amended document, and not the earlier version, that is material to the expert's opinion in the finalised report and which should be referred to in the finalised report. If the amended statement or report is not material to the expert's opinion, then it need not be referred to.

The expert may wish to list all of the documents seen, whether or not they are considered material to the 'basis of the report', as a point of reference and to be able to show that they have been seen and considered to be immaterial to the report. If it is clear from the report that they were not considered material, then any privilege in them should not be lost by this reference.

There may sometimes be a conflict between the expert's wish to be as open as possible and, if in doubt, to refer to documents seen (and to identify precisely which documents they were by date etc), even if their relevance to the opinion may be

---

39   *Lucas v Barking, Havering and Redbridge Hospitals NHS Trust* [2003] EWCA Civ 1102

40   *AB v John Wyeth* [1992] 3 Med LR 190

41   [1999] 3 All ER 154

42   CPR 35.10(3)

questionable, and the lawyer's concern not to open up potential areas of dispute with the other side about which documents they are entitled to see, and not to see, and the right of a party to maintain privilege in documents prepared for the purposes of litigation until they are formally disclosed to the other side.

4.2.2 Details of Qualifications

An expert has to show that he/she has the appropriate expertise to express an opinion on the issues addressed in the report. Normally, this can be stated briefly within the report – two or three paragraphs at the start of the expert report summarising the expert's qualifications is usually sufficient, with the option of a CV appended to the report if further detail is likely to be required.

The expert's CV should show the expert's expertise and experience of dealing with the technical issues relevant to the claim. It is also a good discipline to check that the CV, whether included within or appended to the report, is sufficient to establish the expert's credibility in dealing with the issues in dispute in that particular claim.

If the issues to be addressed are particularly specialised or esoteric or if a clear difference of opinion develops between experts, then it may be advisable to provide or make available a more detailed CV with reference to all posts held, research undertaken and papers published.

The Guidance states:

> Guidance   54   The details of experts' qualifications in reports should be commensurate with the nature and complexity of the case. It may be sufficient to state any academic and professional qualifications. However, where highly specialised expertise is called for, experts should include the detail of particular training and/or experience that qualifies them to provide that specialised evidence.

The contents of the standard court directions in clinical negligence claims in the High Court referred to in Section 4.1.3 above should also be noted[43].

The expert's relevant experience of the issues in a case is a significant factor in the court's analysis of the need for a party to instruct a particular expert in the first instance. It is also important in the analysis of the opinion by the lawyers during negotiations between the parties and by the judge should the matter come to court.

So, for example, in a fitness to practise hearing the panel decided that the psychiatrist called as an expert was not qualified to be an expert as he was not on the relevant specialist register, had not completed relevant professional training and was not an expert by reason of his day to day experience as that involved assessing patients in a different setting and in a different context to that on which he was

---

43   "13 Experts shall, at the time of producing their reports, produce a CV giving details of any employment or activity which raises a possible conflict of interest."

offering his expert opinion[44]. The panel also observed that to put oneself forward as an expert witness requires more than clinical experience and knowledge. It also requires the ability to produce an adequate report and to give oral evidence in an authoritative and convincing manner. In that case the panel found that the written report fell short of what was required and that the clinician's evidence at the hearing regarding his experience and expert status was confusing and unclear. Further in his evidence to the panel, the clinician "was also very unclear and often gave long rambling, answers that did not address the question you had been asked." For the purposes of that hearing the panel concluded that "you cannot be considered to be an expert".

An expert whose CV clearly indicates particular expertise in the matters before the court is more likely to be given instructions to produce a report and the report itself is likely subsequently to carry much greater evidential weight.

> It is important that the expert's CV makes clear the expert's expertise and experience of dealing with the issues in the case. This information may influence the court in allowing a party to call the expert and in deciding how much weight to give the evidence. Experts must make sure that the CV set out in the report is relevant to the issues in dispute – a generalised CV that does not address these issues is not helpful.

The expert must be accurate in providing details of expertise and relevant experience. Inaccuracies, even if not dishonestly provided, can be fatal to the expert's credibility:

> 'When asked about his curriculum vitae he gave oral evidence about his experience as a consultant and said he had performed about 2,000 terminations. However, the defendant had done its homework and had obtained figures for the terminations performed over the years at... Hospital. They disclosed that in fact a very low number of terminations had been performed – probably one of the lowest rates in the whole country, and Mr X is not the only surgeon at the hospital performing these operations. Eventually Mr X did admit that he must have been wrong about his figures. Asked how he felt about that he said he did not think it was important.
>
> Another matter is that Mr X told me he had given evidence before in court and, asked whether that was mainly on behalf of [claimants] or defendants, he replied that the split was 80% [claimant] to 20% defendant. However again after further questioning, some of it by me, Mr X admitted he had never given evidence on behalf of any defendant in court.'[45]

Not surprisingly, the judge considered these important matters in assessing the reliability of the expert's evidence.

---

44   *Pool v General Medical Council* [2014] EWHC 3791

45   *Rhodes v West Surrey and North East Hampshire* HA [1998] Lloyds Law Reports: Medical 246

If in the course of the report an expert strays outside his/her area of expertise, the opposing party may apply to the court to have the offending parts of the report redacted on the grounds that they are inadmissible in evidence.

4.2.3   Literature

It is extremely important that experts ensure that they give details of literature and papers they have relied upon in reaching an opinion[46]. This becomes only too clear to the expert who under cross-examination seeks to justify his opinion by reference to literature not previously and expressly disclosed to the other party in good time prior to trial.

The other side is entitled to have the opportunity to consider such literature in order to challenge the expert's reliance upon it, interpretation of it, or its application to the facts of the present case. Not only the other side's expert, but also its lawyers are entitled to this opportunity. If the case has to be adjourned, then there will be issues as to who should pay the substantial costs – the costs of the lawyers and of the experts - resulting from such an adjournment. If the court declines an adjournment, then the expert may not be permitted to rely on the undisclosed literature, with potentially very damaging consequences on the court's approach to the reliability or reasonableness of the expert's opinion.

> The purpose of providing references to medical literature is to support the opinions expressed by the expert. All references provided in the report should be directly relevant to the evidence and generalised lists of references, which the expert habitually adds to each report, should not be used.

An unnecessary proliferation of references must be avoided. The expert should be selective in identifying only the most relevant and appropriate literature and should normally list only the key papers published in reputable journals. When relying on a text book, it is important to ensure that the text book is appropriate to the matter in issue and that it is the appropriate edition (generally the most recent edition, although in the case of clinical negligence, the edition current at the time of the alleged negligence is likely to be relevant on issues of standard of care):

> 'Mr X relied on page 7 of the 1972 edition... The matter which caused me considerable concern was that since 1972 there have been further editions of this, albeit basic, textbook, and in particular a third edition was published six years before the [claimant's] operation and a fourth edition was published two years after. The importance of these later editions is that the word "clumsiness" has been removed.'[47]

---

46   PD35 3.2(2)

47   See *Rhodes v West Surrey and North East Hampshire* HA (as above)

It is also essential to ensure that any paper put forward as supporting the expert's opinion has not been the subject of substantial criticism, even more so (unsurprisingly) if that is a matter of which the expert must have been aware[48]. It should be appreciated by the expert that while the legal team might well not automatically carry out research to ascertain whether the literature relied upon has been subject to criticism, the expert is expected to do so. Of course, if the expert considers, for good reason, that the criticism is unfounded, then it may still be appropriate to rely on the paper.

In many cases, it will suffice to provide relevant footnotes within the report or a short list of references to relevant texts at the end of the report. However, if it becomes apparent that there is a significant difference of opinion between the experts, then the expert should be given the opportunity by the instructing solicitor to consider whether it is necessary to expand the list of relevant and material texts. Once it becomes clear that there is a dispute between the experts, copies of the texts material to the dispute should be provided to their respective instructing lawyers by each expert, as it is unlikely that the lawyers on either side will have these texts or easy access to them. The court's directions, which the expert should (but may well not) have seen, may order that any literature relied upon by an expert is to be disclosed to all parties within some specific period prior to the trial.

The court directions used in clinical negligence claims in the High Court normally provide:

> *12. Any unpublished literature upon which any expert witness proposes to rely shall be served at the same time as service of his report together with a list of published literature. Any supplementary literature upon which any expert witness proposes to rely shall be notified to all other parties at least one month before trial. No expert witness shall rely upon any publications that have not been disclosed in accordance with this direction without the permission of the trial judge on such terms as to costs as he deems fit.*

4.2.4 Factual Basis of the Evidence

Experts need to establish a reliable factual basis for the opinions that they wish to express later in the report. This requires of the expert both the ability to identify all facts that are relevant to the claim and the ability to differentiate between discrete categories of factual evidence in the report. The court's assessment of the expert report will initially be focussed upon the expert's apprehension of the factual basis.

As far as the lawyers are concerned, an essential element of presenting the case is establishing facts to the required standard of proof. Facts that are accepted as true by all parties are known as 'agreed facts', while facts that are disputed between the parties are known as 'asserted facts' or 'alleged facts'. All witnesses will give evidence as to what they perceive the facts to be. Witnesses of fact can only give evidence of what they perceived of the events at the time, while expert witnesses will usually give both evidence of fact and evidence of opinion.

---

48   *EXP v Barker* [2015] EWHC 1289

In expert witness workshops, when we ask groups of doctors for a definition of a 'fact', the suggestion usually arises that a fact is something that can be demonstrated to be true, such as the result of a measurement or a test. A dictionary definition of 'fact' introduces the concept of a fact being something that is indisputably shown to be the case. In court, a fact is something that is perceived through one or more of the five senses of a witness. That a perceived fact may be hotly disputed does not exclude it from the evidence, as it is the judge's role to assess competing facts (perceptions) to decide what the 'true' facts are for the purposes of the case.

> Where facts are in dispute, the judge will decide the facts on the balance of probabilities having considered all the relevant evidence presented to the court.

Expert witnesses are able to increase their range of perception beyond the limits of the five senses through the use of scientific tests and experiments, which allows greater factual accuracy to be established. The use of such experiments and tests will often clarify factual disputes between the parties. However, lawyers are entitled to challenge tests and experiments carried out by experts, by challenging the methodology adopted, the calibration of the equipment used to carry out the test or the relevance of the test results to the issues to be decided in the case. For this reason the Guidance provides:

Guidance 56 Where tests of a scientific or technical nature have been carried out, experts should state:

    (a) the methodology used; and

    (b) by whom the tests were undertaken and under whose supervision, summarising their respective qualifications and experience.

Facts may be provided to the expert in different ways:

- the history or other information provided by the claimant;
- the witness statements provided to the expert by the instructing solicitor;
- information gleaned from medical records;
- the results of examinations or tests carried out by others; or
- the results of observations, examinations or tests carried out by the expert him/herself.

We have seen in Section 4.2 that PD35 3.1-3 introduce specific requirements for the presentation of factual evidence. In summary, the expert is required to differentiate three categories of fact:

1. given facts (relevant to the opinions expressed); [PD35 3.2(3)]

2. facts within the expert's own knowledge; [PD35 3.2(4)] and

3. facts (and possibly opinions) taken from the work of other experts. [PD35 3.2(5)]

The purpose of this requirement is to allow the court to consider the quality and integrity of the factual basis of the report. For each issue in dispute, the court will seek to understand those facts that the expert has taken into account in reaching his/her opinion and, crucially, the basis of those facts and the weight given to each by the expert.

The Statement of Truth addresses this distinction between different types of fact when it requires the expert to confirm his/her belief that 'the facts … within my own knowledge' are true. The expert cannot confirm the truth of facts where such facts have been provided by another (for example, facts from the claimant or the medical practitioner whose medical records have been provided to the expert), although the fact that those facts were provided by the claimant or recorded by other medical practitioners can be confirmed by the expert.

In addition to reporting on the facts provided by the claimant and providing factual evidence from the expert's own medical examination, the expert may also give relevant factual evidence based on observations not specific to an observer with medical expertise. For example, the expert may observe the claimant arriving or leaving for the appointment – on the stairs or in the car park – and find those observations relevant to an opinion as to the degree of actual disability[49].

All of these types of facts can be provided by the expert and may be material to the expert's opinion. Therefore, an expert report will fall short of the required standard if the factual basis for an opinion is not set out clearly in the report.

4.2.5   Incident/Accident Details and Subsequent Events

When describing the history of an accident, the expert should give those factual details that are relevant to the medico-legal issues to be addressed in the report. For example, in a report on injuries sustained in a car accident, an orthopaedic surgeon may be concerned to address issues such as:

1. where the claimant was sitting in the car;

2. the angle of collision;

3. the severity of the collision;

4. whether the claimant was wearing a seat belt;

---

49   See further at Sections 7.4.4 and 7.4.5

5. whether the car was fitted with headrests;

6. whether the claimant was able to brace before impact;

7. whether the claimant was able to get out of the car unaided; and

8. whether the claimant was taken to hospital.

For a psychiatrist, other issues may also be relevant, such as:

1. whether the claimant saw the oncoming vehicle before the collision;

2. what the claimant saw, heard and felt during and immediately after the accident; and

3. who else was in the car and how the claimant reacted to his/her own injuries and the injuries of these others in the car.

Details, such as the colour of the car, are factual issues that are irrelevant to the medical expert's opinion and should be omitted.

Sometimes, the precise circumstances of an accident are an issue in dispute between the parties. The expert must appreciate that if the report includes a detailed description of the circumstances of the accident, this must be an accurate record of what the claimant has said. If the version in the report differs materially from that given in the proceedings by the claimant (for example in the statement of case or in a witness statement), then the claimant's credibility in relation to those and other facts may be attacked on the basis of such inconsistencies. To resolve the issue the expert could become a witness of fact at the trial as to what the claimant said during the interview about the circumstances of the accident – a situation that experts should seek to avoid[50].

The description of the accident as given by the claimant may be lengthy, so if the expert seeks only to summarise this description there is a greater risk of the version recorded in the report being an inaccurate record of what was said. While describing a road traffic accident may generally be straightforward, descriptions of other accidents and particularly accidents at work can often be difficult to understand clearly without photographs of equipment, plans of the workplace or knowledge of the process involved.

If providing a detailed description of the accident in the report is relevant, then the expert must make sure that he/she understands all relevant matters and that the claimant is in agreement with the details that the expert has recorded. It is generally best practice, therefore, for an expert to give only a brief summary of the accident in the report save where the detail is material to the opinions expressed, and when providing details, to ensure that the claimant has had the opportunity to confirm the correctness of the description.

---

50   The importance of accurate note-taking is also discussed in Section 4.1.1 and 4.1.7

A detailed account of the claimant's symptoms since the accident may well be taken from the claimant. This account is likely subsequently to be compared with any other account given by the claimant, to others or in court. Inconsistencies found, for example as to the timing of onset of symptoms or extent of symptoms, will be relevant to the assessment of the reliability of the claimant's evidence. The expert must therefore ensure that the account recorded in the report is accurate. It is good practice to read back to the claimant, for his agreement or amendment, the account as it is understood by the expert.

If the claimant describes or denies variability of symptoms, for example from day to day, then this should be carefully recorded. If surveillance evidence is subsequently produced, such details can prove to be crucial evidence when assessing the relevance and significance of the observations on the video, which may pre-date the examination, or be contemporaneous with it or subsequent to it.

Disputes can also arise as to the amount of time spent by the expert with the claimant, the suggestion sometimes being made that the examination or history taking was cursory or that time pressures made it difficult for the claimant to give a fuller account. A record of time spent with the claimant can easily be made at the time to avoid this potential dispute.

4.2.6 Examination Findings

The examination the expert carries out will generally be fundamental to the opinions that will follow later in the report. The expert will report his/her direct evidence as to the claimant's condition on the day of the interview and examination.

The expert should briefly describe the type of examination that he/she has carried out, so that the lawyers understand what methodology the expert has adopted. It is unnecessary to give a full explanation of the technical terms in the Examination or Mental State Examination section, as any relevant findings will be explained in the Opinion and Prognosis section that follows. However, short explanatory notes can be very helpful in increasing the lawyers' comprehension of the report.

It is important that the expert should take the time to set out clearly all of the examination findings in the report, even where no abnormality or adverse finding is detected. There are two reasons for this:

1. the results of a detailed examination set out in the report reassures the lawyers and the court that the expert has carried out the examination to the required professional standard[51]; and

2. should the case come to court, a challenge may arise as to whether a particular aspect of the examination was carried out at all, as there may be no reference to it in the report.

---

51 Guidance Para 9: '...to exercise reasonable skill and care...and to comply with any relevant professional code of ethics.'

Therefore, recording the examination to an appropriate level of detail provides the basis for opinions that will be expressed in the Opinion and Prognosis section.

However, where there is a lengthy examination from which no or very few findings are material to the opinion subsequently expressed, the expert should consider setting out the examination findings in an appendix to the report. In the main body of the report, the findings need only to be summarised briefly with an appropriate cross-reference. This helps non-medically qualified readers in following the report and not becoming lost in irrelevant detail.

4.2.7 Factual Disputes[52]

It may happen that the parties have different versions of events that are material to the expert's opinion. It may also be that the opinion of the expert would change depending on which version of events the expert uses as the basis for his/her opinion. The expert is therefore faced with a difficulty that cannot be resolved without the court's decision on the facts at issue.

If in relation to a claim arising from a soft tissue injury in a road traffic accident which comes within the RTA Protocol (see Section 3.4) the defendant provides an account of the accident which is different to the claimant's, then that account must be provided to the claimant's medical expert as part of the instructions to the medical expert 'for the sole purpose of asking the expert to comment on the impact, if any, on diagnosis and prognosis if—

(a) the claimant's account is found to be true; or

(b) the defendant's account is found to be true.' [53]

The answer as to how to generally address different assertions of fact which impact on the expert's opinion is straightforward and is dealt with clearly in the Guidance:

> Guidance   58   Where there are material facts in dispute experts should express separate opinions on each hypothesis put forward…

Therefore, where there are factual disputes in the evidence, the expert should express separate opinions on each of the factual bases. How this is set out in the report will depend on the extent of the factual disagreements. Where there are limited conflicts in the evidence, the expert may choose to deal with both sets of facts in the same section within the factual basis of the evidence. As the conflicts in the evidence multiply, it may be necessary to have two separate sections dealing with the factual evidence brought forward by each party.

If in the example of a road traffic accident the two different accounts provided to the expert indicate two very different accidents with very different forces likely

---

52   See also Section 7.3

53   RTA Protocol para 7.8A

to be exerted on the claimant depending on the version which is accepted, the expert's opinion as to the nature of the injury sustained or the causation of continuing symptoms may depend on which version is correct. The expert should therefore provide separate opinions based on each of the two sets of facts and leave it to others to resolve which of the two sets of facts is more likely to be correct.

Experts have the authority only in limited circumstances to express an opinion in favour of one or other of the disputed versions:

> Guidance 58 They should not express a view in favour of one or other disputed version of the facts unless, as a result of particular expertise and experience, they consider one set of facts as being improbable or less probable, in which case they may express that view, and should give reasons for holding it.

It may be, for example, that an expert's specialist knowledge of a particular medical condition enables him/her to conclude that the claimant's version of events cannot be correct – for example, such symptoms cannot be caused by or are not consistent with this condition or such complaints cannot persist for such a period or in such a manner given the nature of the condition. However, there are probably only limited situations in which the expert can confidently dismiss one set of facts entirely. In most cases, the expert will need to express a separate qualified opinion on each of the factual bases.

The importance of expressing separate opinions is perhaps best illustrated by conflicts between medical records and lay witnesses present at the material time[54]. If an expert forms an opinion, for example, that the GP records should be relied upon, because these appear to be contemporaneous and there is no apparent reason for them to be mistaken, and so chooses to discount the evidence of the claimant or the claimant's family, then the expert has created a vulnerability in his/her opinion evidence. Should the court take the view that, on the balance of probabilities, the evidence of the claimant is to be preferred, then the expert would be left without a valid opinion and would provide no assistance to the court or to the parties on that matter.

The expert should therefore be careful before proceeding only on the factual basis as provided by the instructing solicitor. In expressing opinion on the basis of facts set out in a letter of instruction or in witness statements from only one side of the claim, the expert will often be providing a one-sided report and may be ignoring 'facts in dispute' that are material to the provision of expert opinion.

4.2.8　Disputes between Medical Records and the Claimant's Account

Some medical experts adopt the practice of only reading the claimant's medical records after having carried out the interview and examination, the claimant by then having left the consulting room. The motivation for this practice is laudable,

---

54 We consider such conflicts in the evidence in the next Section

namely that the expert can avoid preconceptions about the claimant and have a clear perception of the injuries. However, a practical difficulty with this method arises when the information from the claimant about his/her previous medical history conflicts with the medical records.

Conflicts commonly arise in the claimant's account of his/her previous medical history when this is compared to the clinical records. Possible reasons for these conflicts are:

1. some claimants are trying to manipulate the situation to their advantage;

2. some claimants can be very nervous about seeing a medical expert and do not give a clear account;

3. people are often poor at giving a clear history, whether out of embarrassment or because of a poor or selective memory;

4. medical records may be incomplete, inaccurate or the records may even belong to another person;

5. miscommunication commonly occurs between doctors and lay-people;

6. some claimants overstate their injuries to try to convince the medical expert there is actually something wrong with them; and

7. some claimants understate their injuries so as not to be seen to 'make a fuss'.

Claimant solicitors complain that at interview medical experts expect too much accuracy from claimants regarding their previous medical history and then leap to the conclusion that the claimant is in some way dishonest. We have some sympathy with this view, as for many claimants the environment of a medical interview and examination is nerve-wracking and can even generate anxiety and fear.

Sometimes, a claimant will arrive at the examination with written or printed notes. The expert may appreciate this preparation and the aide memoire may contribute to an effective interview. The claimant may have produced the notes on the advice of lawyers aware of the difficulty the claimant has in giving an accurate or complete history without such help. Alternatively, the claimant may be trying to make a prepared statement for reasons good or bad. The expert must not jump to conclusions as to the validity of these prepared notes.

Some claimants may see the expert as 'working for the other side', even if this should not be the case when the expert is acting in accordance with the CPR, and adopt a defensive or aggressive stance. Whatever the reason, experts should be aware that giving an accurate previous medical history under the conditions of a medical interview and examination can be difficult for some claimants.

It is useful to bear in mind, when there is an apparent conflict between an entry in the medical records and the claimant's account of matters, the legal approach to medical records and their status in proving a fact. Frequently a very casual approach is taken, accepting the accuracy of the records on the basis that they were made at the time by someone with no particular axe to grind and therefore asserting that they should be taken at face value. But where there is a conflict, the court will be concerned about the weight properly to be attached to such evidence. The position is somewhat technical:

> 'It is therefore necessary to remind ourselves of the evidential status of such material. What the doctor writes down as having been told him by the patient, as opposed to the opinion that he expresses on the basis of those statements, is not at that stage evidence of the making of the statement that he records. Rather where, as here, the record is said to contradict the evidence as to fact given by the patient, the record is of a previous inconsistent statement allegedly made by the patient. As such, the record itself is hearsay. It may however be proved as evidence that the patient did indeed speak as alleged in two ways. First, if the statement is put to the witness, she may admit to having made it. Alternatively, if she does not "distinctly" so admit the statement may be proved under section 4 of Lord Denman's Act 1865. Second, by section 6(5) of the Civil Evidence Act 1995 those provisions do not prevent the statement being proved as hearsay evidence under section 1 of that Act. If the court concludes that such inconsistent statement has been made, that goes only to the credibility of the witness; the statement itself cannot be treated itself as evidence of its contents.'[55]

The practical solution, so far as the medical expert is concerned, is straightforward:

> 'To ensure that factual issues in medical cases are economically and efficiently tried, the following procedure should be adopted. First, a party who seeks to contradict a factually pleaded case on the basis of medical records or reports should indicate that intention in advance .... Then, the opposite party must indicate the extent to which they take objection to the accuracy of the records. When the area of dispute is identified, a decision will have to be taken as to whether the records need to be formally proved by either of the means referred to above. Thereby, not only will the ambit of the dispute be clarified in advance, but also it will be clear what interpretation is sought to be put on what [maybe] somewhat Delphic records.'[56]

Therefore, the expert should bring to the attention of the instructing lawyer any significant conflicts between the medical records and the claimant's or a witness's account and explain the importance of these conflicts and the importance of establishing one or other set of facts. The expert should not simply assume that the contemporaneous record (as interpreted) is more likely to be correct and to be accepted by the court.

---

55   *Denton Hall v Fifield* [2006] EWCA Civ 169

56   As above

4.2.9 Interpreting Medical Records

A related issue may arise where the medical expert is asked to interpret what the contemporaneous medical records indicate was likely to have been the state of the knowledge of the medical practitioners or of the claimant at some particular historical date. This arises for example in disease claims where there is an issue as to when the claimant first had knowledge that he/she had suffered a significant injury.

The medical expert is likely to be in a better position than a lawyer to interpret what the records indicate was at that time likely to have been (1) the state of knowledge of the medical practitioners (2) the diagnosis or differential diagnosis (3) the advice or information given to the claimant. The medical expert might also be able to identify, where the records are very old, or where the treating doctors are of a speciality less appropriate for the actual condition as seen now with the benefit of hindsight, relevant different uses of terminology by the treating doctors.

For example, in a claim made for damages for disease arising from exposure to asbestos several decades ago, an issue might arise as to when the claimant first had a symptomatic asbestos-related condition, or was first aware that he had such a condition. The expert will have regard to any references in the notes to 'asbestosis' or 'pleural thickening', any x-rays or scans, and the nature of any co-morbidities. The expert may then be able to express an opinion as to (1) whether the terms were used in the same sense then as a respiratory physician would now use them or understand them (2) whether the observations and findings recorded throw any light on the situation as it was then seen by the clinician and in the context of any co-morbidities and (3) whether there is any indication from the notes or treatment or advice recorded as to what the claimant was probably told.

Whilst it is not for the medical expert to speculate, the contents of the records may provide sufficient information for the medical expert to form an opinion, demonstrating the reasoning process, on the balance of probabilities.

4.2.10 Opinion Evidence

All witnesses are entitled to give relevant evidence of facts of which they have direct experience. Witnesses are not normally entitled or permitted to give evidence of opinion. A witness attempting to do so in court would be stopped by the judge.

In contrast to witnesses of fact, an expert witness has an elevated status in court proceedings and is entitled to express an opinion, so long as it is within his/her area of expertise. Therefore, unless and until the witness proves appropriate expertise, he/she will not be treated as an expert and will be prevented from expressing any opinion. Once the expert has established his/her credentials before the court, careful attention will be given to the factual basis for any opinion expressed and the reasoning process that the expert has followed in reaching a conclusion. As Jacob J said in *Pearce v Ove Arup Partnership Ltd*[57], while it is admissible for an expert to express an

---

57   Ch Div 2 November 2001 quoting from his own earlier judgment in *Routestone Ltd v Minories Finance Ltd* and another [1997] 21 EG 148, [1997] BCC 180

opinion on the question the court has to decide ('the ultimate question'):

> *"what really matters in most cases are the reasons given for the opinion. As a practical matter a well-constructed expert's report containing opinion evidence sets out the opinion and the reasons for it. If the reasons stand up, the opinion does, if not, not."*

An opinion, without reasons for it, is not really worth having (from the lawyer's perspective) or giving (from the expert's perspective). And it follows that "a coherent reasoned opinion expressed by a suitable qualified expert should be the subject of a coherent reasoned rebuttal, unless it can be discounted for other good reasons"[58].

4.2.11 Fact and Opinion

Fact and opinion must be clearly distinguished. For the lawyers and the court when approaching the expert report, this division within the report structure is essential to achieving an accurate interpretation of the text. As the Guidance states:

Guidance   57   When addressing questions of fact and opinion, experts should keep the two separate. Experts must state those facts (whether assumed or otherwise) upon which their opinions are based; experts should have primary regard to their instructions. Experts must distinguish clearly between those facts that they know to be true and those facts which they assume.

Once the expert begins to mix fact and opinion, it becomes difficult for the lawyers and the court of the report to clearly identify what the expert's opinion is and the basis for it.

4.2.12 Qualified Opinion

We have already addressed the issue of qualified opinion:

PD35 3.2   (8)   If the expert is not able to give his opinion without qualification, state the qualification;

It is also important to explain the reason why an opinion may need to be qualified, or even not be addressed in the report.

PD35 2.4   Experts should make it clear -

(a)   when a question or issue falls outside their expertise; and

(b)   when they are not able to reach a definite opinion, for example because they have insufficient information.

---

58   *Eckersley v Binnie* (1998) quoted in *Penney v East Kent* HA [2000] Lloyds Rep Med 41

It should be clear to an expert when a matter lies outside his/her area of expertise, and the temptation to try to assist the instructing solicitor or the court by trespassing onto an area outside the expert's expertise should be avoided. At the point where an expert steps beyond the boundary of his/her expertise, not only does the expert cease to be an expert, but the expert's credibility within his/her area of expertise and credibility as an independent witness may suffer significant damage.

For example, where a claimant is demonstrating non-organic signs on examination, the orthopaedic expert should be wary about expressing an opinion as to the psychological causation of these signs, unless comfortable that this is an area in which he/she has appropriate expertise and experience. A statement in the report advising an assessment by an appropriate expert is the best way to deal with such a situation.

It may happen that an expert is unable to provide a concluded opinion, for example in relation to prognosis, because the recovery is incomplete or further imaging or test results are required. It may be that the opinion is dependent on the reliability of a particular fact, such as when the claimant first developed symptoms, and there is a difference between what appears in the GP notes and what the claimant states to the expert. In both these categories of case, the opinion must expressly be qualified so that the reader of the report can understand the nature and strength of the opinion expressed. The further steps needed to clarify the opinion should also be set out.

4.2.13 Range of Opinion

There are specific provisions in the CPR is made to make clear how an expert should deal with a situation where there is a range of professional opinion on a particular matter:

PD35 3.2   (6)   where there is a range of opinion on the matters dealt with in the report -

      (a)   summarise the range of opinion, and

      (b)   give reasons for the expert's own opinion.

Medical experts often comment that the possible range of opinion in many cases is so vast that a discussion of it would be more difficult than expressing the opinion itself. These experts point out that not only is the likelihood of recovery for a claimant within a given time frame difficult to predict, but also the complex nature of many injuries means that there are no scientific studies in the literature that can provide guidance. The expert has to look at the medical facts and form an opinion without the luxury of reference to a body of medical opinion.

The Guidance attempts to clarify how establishing a range of opinion needs to be carried out:

Guidance 59 If the mandatory summary of the range of opinion is based on published sources, experts should explain those sources and, where appropriate, state the qualifications of the originator(s) of the opinions from which they differ, particularly if such opinions represent a well-established school of thought.

60 Where there is no available source for the range of opinion, experts may need to express opinions on what they believe to be the range that other experts would arrive at if asked. In those circumstances, experts should make it clear that the range that they summarise is based on their own judgement and explain the basis of that judgement.

It is paragraph 60 that probably represents the most common situation that experts have to address. The expert is required not only to express an opinion him/herself, but having done so, to address the opinions of colleagues with whom the expert would probably disagree. The experienced medical expert will tend to be more familiar with the range of opinions that opposing experts might come up with in such cases.

However, in reaching an opinion on a subject where there is no published basis for the opinion (for example, the period of recovery, the period during which symptoms might in any event have developed to a similar level, the timing of future degeneration or the need for future medical intervention), the expert would probably have considered a wider range of periods before settling on a particular period in the light of the facts of the case. The expert can describe the basis of his/her assessment, making it clear that the opinion is based on the expert's own experience of dealing with such injuries in his/her medical practice. An expert who does not set out this process in the report is unlikely at trial to be able to justify convincingly the opinion he/she has expressed. In any event, an opinion expressed without explanation of the basis for it will only carry limited weight.

For example, take the question of how long it is likely to be before the claimant, who suffered injury affecting her hip, would probably require a hip replacement operation. The expert would probably take into account factors such as:

- the nature of the injury;
- the degree of progression that has been observed on x-ray since the accident;
- the age of the claimant and the likely level of activity in the coming years; and
- his/her own experience of similar cases in clinical practice.

The expert will then, based on his/her own assessment of these factors, be able to express a maximum range and to identify within it, with reasons, the range that the expert considers to be appropriate in this particular case. A paragraph in the report will suffice to make clear the basis of the assessment to the lawyers and the court.

4.2.14 Sequential Exchange of Reports

Only the Pre-Action Protocol for Disease and Illness Claims expressly invites the use of sequentially exchanged reports in appropriate circumstances[59]. However, the use of sequential reports is more often agreed by the parties or ordered by the court in a wide variety of personal injury claims. Where an expert is instructed to provide a report sequentially to the other side's expert, it will in effect be responding to that first report. This means that it may be possible to shorten the second report by identifying the areas of agreement with the first report, whether in the background, addressing the facts of the case, findings on examination or assessment, or expressing opinion generally or as to the quantification or valuation of the claim. The second report can concentrate on the areas of difference or disagreement. This commonly occurs, for example, with care reports.

The Guidance provides:

Guidance 63 Where there is to be sequential exchange of reports then the defendant's expert's report usually will be produced in response to the claimant's. The defendant's report should then:

(a) confirm whether the background set out in the claimant's expert report is agreed, or identify those parts that in the defendant's expert's view require revision, setting out the necessary revisions. The defendant's expert need not repeat information that is adequately dealt with in the claimant's expert report.

(b) focus only on those material areas of difference with the claimant's expert's opinion. The defendant's report should identify those assumptions of the claimant's expert that they consider reasonable (and agree with) and those that they do not; and

(c) in particular where the experts are addressing the financial value of heads of claim (for example, the costs of a care regime or loss of profits), the defendant's report should contain a reconciliation between the claimant's expert's loss assessment and the defendant's, identifying for each assumption any different conclusion to the claimant's expert.

If in the second report the examination/assessment of the claimant is entirely agreed, then there is no need (and no benefit to the reader of the report) in setting out details of the examination/assessment in the body of the report. It is sufficient that the body of the report contains just the basic details of the examination/assessment (i.e. the date and circumstances and method used), a summary of the conclusions taken from the examination/assessment and an indication that there

---

59 See Section 3.3.3

are, in the opinion of the second expert, no material points of difference in the assessment.

If the expert wishes to include details of the second examination/assessment then this can be provided in an appendix to the report. The body of the report will then be directed at any differences that there are between the experts in their opinions despite the agreed examination/assessments and the reasons for them. For example, in the case of a medical report differences in identifying restrictions or giving prognosis, or in a care or therapeutic needs report differences in the process of quantifying and valuing needs as a consequence of the agreed assessment.

In contrast, where the examination/assessment is not agreed, then it will be necessary in the second report to focus on the differences between the examinations/assessments and the findings resulting from them, and the reasons for the differences (if these can be explained). In which case, it will be necessary to set out in the report details of the assessment, or parts of the assessment, and how it was carried out, highlighting the differences from the first expert's assessment, and so far as is possible, explaining the apparent reasons for the differences.

It is important that the second (defendant's) report identifies whether the first (claimant's) expert's opinions and conclusions are agreed or the extent to which they are agreed, and where there is disagreement, the nature and extent of disagreement and the reasons for it, if it is possible to do so.

To explain to both sides how the agreement or non-agreement is reached, the second expert needs to give details about the examination/assessment he/she has carried out and the method used. The party instructing the second expert is entitled to understand the expert's approach, even if the first expert's findings are agreed, and this explanation becomes be especially important where there is disagreement between the experts.

This approach with the second report should then comply with the Guidance, so that "the defendant's expert need not repeat information that is adequately dealt with in the claimant's expert report" but does "focus only on those material areas of difference with the claimant's expert's opinion". The report writer should keep in mind the reader of the report (the lawyers or the judge) and try to make clear in simple terms the areas of agreement and include in the report only that detailed reasoning and information which will assist the reader to understand the dispute and the reasons for it. As we have emphasised above, what is important is for the report to comment where possible on the reasons for any difference of opinion.

4.2.15 Summary of Conclusions

A summary of conclusions is mandatory. The Guidance states:

> Guidance   62   A summary of conclusions is mandatory. Generally, the summary
> should be at the end of the report after the reasoning...

Particularly in complex or complicated cases – more often found in clinical negligence or industrial disease claims - the summary placed at the beginning of the report, combined with a brief summary of the factual background and an introduction to the medical issues, can provide a very useful aid to a proper understanding of the body of the report on a first reading.

All of the users of the expert report - client, solicitor, another expert, barrister and judge – will be expected to have read the entire report and to have considered it carefully. An extensive 'summary report' (an executive summary) designed for readers who do not have the time or need to read the detailed report is unnecessary.

A summary of conclusions is a useful discipline to impose on the report writer, as it brings together in one place all the conclusions in the report and allows these to be compared with the instructions upon which the report is predicated. It can also act as a useful starting point for a reader to establish the context of the report he/she is about to read. It can also be a point of reference from which to compare the conclusions of opposing experts.

The summary of conclusions should normally consist of a summary of the expert's concluded opinion in response to each of the issues that the report has addressed. This summary should be short, to the point and be placed at the end of the report.

The Guidance provides further guidance:

> Guidance   62   ...There may be cases, however, where the court would find it helpful to have a short summary at the beginning, with the full conclusions at the end. For example, in cases involving highly complex matters which fall outside the general knowledge of the court the judge may be assisted in the comprehension of the facts and analysis if the report explains at the outset the basis of the reasoning.

4.2.16 Expert's Declaration

There are many, often lengthy, statements and declarations generated by experts themselves or suggested by various professional bodies that do not fully comply with the far easier and simpler requirement laid down in PD35:

> PD35 3.2 (9) [The expert report must:] contain a statement that the expert –
>
> (a)   understands their duty to the court, and has complied with that duty; and
>
> (b)   is aware of the requirements of Part 35, this practice direction and the Guidance for the Instruction of Experts in Civil Claims 2014.

The Expert's Declaration placed at the end of every report must comply with the requirements of the rules, practice direction and the Guidance, by setting out the declaration and the statement of truth as detailed in PD35. However, we also suggest that experts include a further statement (which we set out below in italics), which will provide additional comfort to the parties and the court that the expert has understood fully his/her duties:

> **Declaration**
>
> I confirm that I understand my duty to the court and have complied with that duty.
>
> *Where I am not able to give my opinion without qualification, I have stated the qualification.*
>
> I am aware of the requirements of CPR Part 35, the Practice Direction to Part 35 and the Guidance for the Instruction of Experts in Civil Claims 2014.

4.2.17 Statement of Truth

The form of words for the Statement of Truth is mandatory[60]:

> I confirm that I have made clear which facts and matters referred to in this report are within my own knowledge and which are not. Those that are within my own knowledge I confirm to be true. The opinions I have expressed represent my true and complete professional opinions on the matters to which they refer.

In an expert report, all the opinions expressed are verified as being the 'true and complete professional opinion' of the expert. This requirement should have put an end to the pre-CPR practice of experts who would write a "side-letter" to the solicitor that qualified the opinion expressed in the report.

Prior to the introduction of the CPR, many experts used to act as if they owed their primary duty to the side that instructed them. A favourable medical expert report on a claimant, produced by a so called "claimant-friendly" expert, might be accompanied by a side-letter that pointed out that the claimant's account was in fact inconsistent and implausible. It was not only claimant-friendly experts who behaved in this manner, "defendant-friendly" experts would also produce exculpatory medical reports while, in a side-letter, advising early settlement of the claim. Nor was this practice limited to personal injury claims. Such experts behaved in a similar manner in clinical negligence and industrial disease claims as well.

---

60   PD35 3.3

Since the introduction of the CPR, it would be impossible for any independent expert to honestly sign a Statement of Truth if he/she were to have any reservation about the written conclusions or where the written conclusions were not to represent the complete opinion of the expert.

4.2.18 Date of Signature and Date of Report

The report should be signed and the signature dated. In an expert report in a civil claim, it is unnecessary to sign and date every page. In addition, the report itself should have a date on the front page for ease of reference (and to distinguish the report from any earlier or later reports). Often both the examination date and the date of signing off the report will be provided. If the signing date and the examination date (where there is an examination) are within a day or two of each other, the examination date will suffice. Where there is an extended period between the examination date and the signing date, the expert would be wise to expect to face questioning on this point should the matter come to court, as the delay may be thought indicative of the report having gone through a number of amendments or re-drafts during that period.

4.3   Amendments to Reports

An expert may be asked by a party's lawyers to amend his/her report. Such a request can cause anxiety on the part of the expert who fears that his/her independence may thereby be compromised. In fact, there are circumstances in which it is entirely appropriate for the expert to consider and make amendments to a report. The Guidance recognises three such situations:

Guidance   64   It may become necessary for experts to amend their reports:

(a)   as a result of an exchange of questions and answers;

(b)   following agreements reached at meetings between experts; or

(c)   where further evidence or documentation is disclosed.

The Guidance deals with this issue of amendments as follows:

Guidance   65   Experts should not be asked to amend, expand or alter any parts of reports in a manner which distorts their true opinion, but may be invited to do so to ensure accuracy, clarity, internal consistency, completeness and relevance to the issues. Although experts should generally follow the recommendations of solicitors with regard to the form of reports, they should form their own independent views on the opinions and contents of their reports and not include any suggestions that do not accord with their views.

Amendments necessary to achieve accuracy, clarity, internal consistency, completeness and relevance to the issues are all appropriate for the expert to make. In many instances, the amendments requested are not material to the opinions expressed and the expert can make changes without undue concern.

However, requests to alter or vary facts set out in the report do require very careful scrutiny. Issues do sometimes arise regarding what was or was not said by a claimant during an interview and examination. It is essential that experts keep good notes of these interviews. A claimant who says he is a smoker at interview may seek to deny that information later, on hearing from the solicitor that he has just diminished the damages he may receive. If the expert has a note that the claimant said he was a smoker, then clearly the report should not be amended.

> Reports may be amended to ensure accuracy, clarity, internal consistency, completeness and relevance to the issues. An amendment that distorts an expert's true opinion is contrary to the Guidance.

A request to alter or vary an opinion will require even more careful consideration and the expert must be satisfied that any resulting changes do not put the expert in conflict with his/her duty to the court and with the contents of the Statement of Truth.

4.3.1 Change of Opinion

An expert may wish to revise or change an opinion so that it is no longer consistent with the opinion expressed in the report.

> 'If at any time the expert can no longer support the case of the person who instructed him, it is his duty to say so. Indeed, if the expert forms that view it is far better that he says so sooner rather than later before the litigation costs escalate.'[61]

Such a change of opinion may be as a result of further information coming to light, a subsequent examination of the claimant or even because of the expert's consideration of matters raised in the report of another expert in the case or because flaws in the initial report are pointed out by the opposing expert or lawyers. The expert may simply, on reflection, have changed his/her mind. In such circumstances, two actions are required:

1. the change of opinion must be communicated to the lawyers and the parties without delay; and

2. the change of opinion must be explained to the instructing lawyers and party, as they are entitled to understand the process that has resulted in the change of opinion, particularly if the change is to the detriment of that side's case.

---

61 *Guntripp v Cheney Coaches Ltd* [2012] EWCA Civ 392

If a change of opinion were to result in an opinion that is more favourable to the instructing party and so is to the detriment of the other side's case, then it is important to set out the reasoning in order to explain fully why the change of opinion is justified. Otherwise, the apparent inconsistency could cause the expert to lose credibility before the court and the revised opinion may not be given due weight.

The procedure to follow in such circumstances is set out in the Guidance:

> Guidance 66   ... Where experts significantly alter their opinion, as a result of new evidence or for any other reason, they must inform those who instruct them and amend their reports explaining the reasons. Those instructing experts should inform other parties as soon as possible of any change of opinion.

We must emphasise that a change of opinion, and this includes a change of opinion within a report where the expert continues to support the case of the party by which he/she is instructed, must be communicated to the instructing lawyer without delay[62] (the lawyer being under a duty to pass on that change of opinion to the other party in the case). The client is entitled to know, as soon as is practicable, the basis for a change that may have disastrous and expensive consequences. In failing to communicate the reasons clearly and immediately, the expert is likely to complicate what is almost certainly in any event a difficult situation.

Where a change of opinion occurs at a discussion between experts, the Guidance suggests a slightly different approach:

> Guidance 66   Where experts change their opinion following a meeting of experts, a simple signed and dated note to that effect is generally sufficient.

However, there may be circumstances after a meeting of experts where the change of opinion is such that it is more appropriate to amend the report to reflect the changes of opinion, and the reasons for the changes.

In our opinion, experts should not simply sign a document recording their change of opinion after a meeting of experts, but as more generally with any change of opinion (and for the same reasons) should give reasons for the change. If it is necessary to give a detailed explanation for the change of opinion, then it will be best to follow the suggested alternative of an amended report offering full reasons for the change of opinion. Particularly at this late stage in the litigation, the instructing party is entitled to know why the expert has had a change of mind and is no longer willing to be supportive of the client's case.

---

62   Guidance para 14

4.4   Written Questions to Experts

To facilitate the comprehension by the parties of expert reports, and to assist the parties in having the experts address those aspects of the case that the lawyers regard as most important, any party may now send written questions to an expert witness on his/her report:

CPR 35.6   (1)   A party may put written questions about an expert's report (which must be proportionate) to –

(a)   an expert instructed by another party; or

(b)   a single joint expert appointed under rule 35.7.

(2)   Written questions under paragraph (1) –

(a)   may be put only once;

(b)   must be put within 28 days of service of the expert's report; and

(c)   must be for the purpose only of clarification of the report,

unless in any case –

(i)   the court gives permission; or

(ii)   the other party agrees.

(3)   An expert's answers to questions put in accordance with paragraph (1) shall be treated as part of the expert's report.

(4)   Where –

(a)   a party has put a written question to an expert instructed by another party; and

(b)   the expert does not answer that question,

the court may make one or both of the following orders in relation to the party who instructed the expert –

(i)   that the party may not rely on the evidence of that expert; or

(ii)   that the party may not recover the fees and expenses of that expert from any other party.

The usual position is that the expert is entitled to be paid for answering the questions by the party instructing him/her[63]. However in cases coming within the Pre-Action Protocol for Personal Injury Claims the costs of the mutually agreed expert replying to questions will usually be borne by the party asking the questions[64]. Although the starting point in the CPR is for one set of questions only from each party, the parties may agree to more than one set of questions being asked of the experts – often without telling the experts instructed in the case. The CPR also refer to questions being asked within 28 days of service of the report by one party on the other, but in practice the expert will have no knowledge of this date and the serving of the report could well be many months after the report has been sent off by the expert to the instructing solicitor[65].

When questions duly arrive, the case is unlikely to be fresh in the expert's mind. Answering even a few questions may require the expert to spend a significant amount of time in familiarising him/herself with the details of the case. This is in itself a powerful reason for ensuring that all the likely relevant issues are addressed in the original report.

Questions may be asked 'for the purpose only of clarification of the report'[66]. They must be 'proportionate' and therefore objection can be taken to providing answers if the questions are excessively long[67]. Sometimes a party will use the right to send questions to the expert as a tactic to elicit more information than might appear at first sight to be mere 'clarification' of the report. The term clarification is not defined or explained in the CPR. Whilst it has been said by the court that the questions should not normally amount to cross-examination by post or require the expert significantly to expand on the existing report, it has also been said that questions that 'assist the just disposal of the dispute' are appropriate[68]. In practice, the lawyers are often left with inadequate medical expert reports and have little alternative but to raise questions in order to get the experts to deal with the issues that have not been addressed.

Common examples of the need to address questions to medical experts relate to issues in respect of causation of injury, loss and damage and to seeking the expert's opinion on the various heads of claim being made. Hence questions may seek to clarify the difference between the condition of the claimant as a result of the accident and the condition as it probably would have been in any event, and to clarify the nature of the restrictions resulting from the accident in terms of ability to pursue employment or to carry out particular tasks. For quantum reports, the

---

63   PD35 6.2

64   Para 7.10 Pre-Action Protocol for Personal Injury Claims

65   The Protocol (replaced by the Guidance from 1 December 2014) contained at para 14.1 the sensible advice to instructing solicitors that they should tell experts when their reports are disclosed to the other party. The advice was not repeated in the Guidance although much is to be said for the practice.

66   CPR 35.6(2)(c)

67   CPR 35.6(1)

68   See for example *Mutch v Allen* [2001] All ER D 121

basis of assessment and the justification for aspects of the care package included in the report are often inadequately dealt with in the report and become the subject of questions from the lawyers.

As the answers that the expert will give will form part of the expert's evidence and as the expert report will include both the Expert's Declaration and a signed Statement of Truth, there is no need to include these elements a second time when responding to questions. The Guidance confirms this:

> Guidance 68   Experts' answers to questions become part of their reports. They are covered by the statement of truth and form part of the expert evidence.

Where the expert does not consider that the questions are appropriate as clarification, the Guidance indicates that the parties and their experts should attempt to sort out disputes as to the appropriateness of questions for themselves:

> Guidance 69   Where experts believe that questions put are not properly directed to the clarification of the report, or have been asked out of time, they should discuss the questions with those instructing them and, if appropriate, those asking the questions. Attempts should be made to resolve such problems without the need for an application to the court for directions, but in the absence of agreement or application for directions by the party or parties, experts may themselves file a written request to court for directions (see paragraphs 28-29).

This Guidance would be equally appropriate if the questions were considered to be disproportionate in length.

If therefore the parties are unable to resolve the issue by agreement, then they will apply to have the matter resolved by a hearing at court (to which the expert will not be a party and will not be present), failing which the expert can apply to the court for directions.

A failure by an expert to provide answers to questions is likely to be disastrous for the party on whose behalf the defaulting expert is instructed. The whole of the expert's evidence in the case may be excluded or the instructing party may be unable to recover any of the costs of that expert from the other party[69]. In the latter case, the costs of the expert will fall on the party or the lawyer, or more probably, the instructing lawyer will refuse to pay the expert or will seek to recover any costs already paid. In either case, the expert's reputation, at least with the instructing solicitor, will be irrecoverably damaged. However irritating or apparently irrelevant the questions an expert receives appear to be, and however inconvenient the timing, the expert must provide written answers, unless the court on application orders otherwise.

---

69   CPR 35.6(4)

4.4.1   Format for the Response

There is no prescribed format for the provision of answers to questions. These may be provided in a letter addressed to the lawyer asking them or in a document headed 'Response to Questions from...'

The document containing the answers, whether in the form of a letter or an addendum report or some other document, should set out each question in full, followed by the answer. The importance of this cannot be over-emphasised, even though the CPR and the Guidance do not set out any such requirement. Not only does this make the document stand alone as a comprehensible whole, to the advantage of anyone referring to it subsequently, including for example the expert while giving evidence in court, but it is a good discipline for ensuring that each question, and each part of each question, is fully considered and answered in a manner which is fully consistent with the questions. For quantum reports, the basis of assessment and the justification for aspects of the care package included in the report are often inadequately dealt with in the report and become the subject of questions from the lawyers.

The expert must proceed on the basis that there is a reason for each question asked and that the lawyers have expressed them in the form that they have for a particular purpose. If the expert considers that some further explanation is necessary or other matters need to be addressed in order properly to reflect the expert's opinion, that can be done, but in addition to, and not in substitution for, providing answers to the questions asked.

4.5   Single Joint Experts

In Lord Woolf's report[70], which resulted in the CPR, were the following recommendations:

1. As a general principle, single experts should be used wherever the case (or the issue) is concerned with a substantially established area of knowledge and where it is not necessary for the court directly to sample a range of opinions.

2. Parties and procedural judges should always consider whether a single expert could be appointed in a particular case (or to deal with a particular issue); and, if this is not considered appropriate, indicate why not.

Rule 35.7 gives the court power to direct that both parties share one expert witness – a single joint expert.

CPR 35.7   (1)   Where two or more parties wish to submit expert evidence on a particular issue, the court may direct that the evidence on that issue is to be given by a single joint expert.

---

70   *Access to Justice* (July 1996) – see above

However, both the Pre-Action Protocol for the Resolution of Clinical Disputes and the Pre-Action Protocol for Disease and Illness Claims[71] suggest that this should be a matter for the parties themselves. This is recognised to some extent in PD35 7(e).

PD35   7   When considering whether to give permission for the parties to rely on expert evidence and whether that evidence should be from a single joint expert the court will take into account all the circumstances in particular whether:

(a) it is proportionate to have separate experts for each party on a particular issue with reference to –

    (i) the amount in dispute;

    (ii) the importance to the parties; and

    (iii) the complexity of the issue;

(b) the instruction of a single joint expert is likely to assist the parties and the court to resolve the issue more speedily and in a more cost-effective way than separately instructed experts;

(c) expert evidence is to be given on the issue of liability, causation or quantum;

(d) the expert evidence falls within a substantially established area of knowledge which is unlikely to be in dispute or there is likely to be a range of expert opinion;

(e) a party has already instructed an expert on the issue in question and whether or not that was done in compliance with any practice direction or relevant pre-action protocol;

(f) questions put in accordance with rule 35.6 are likely to remove the need for the other party to instruct an expert if one party has already instructed an expert;

(g) questions put to a single joint expert may not conclusively deal with all issues that may require testing prior to trial;

(h) a conference may be required with the legal representatives, experts and other witnesses which may make instruction of a single joint expert impractical; and

(i) a claim to privilege makes the instruction of any expert as a single joint expert inappropriate.

---

71   See Sections 3.3.1 and 3.3.3

The Guidance reflects the requirement to use a single joint expert when possible:

Guidance 34   …The CPR encourage the use of joint experts. Wherever possible
a joint report should be obtained. Single joint experts are the
norm in cases allocated to the small claims track and the fast track.

35   In the early stages of a dispute, when investigations, tests, site
inspections, photographs plans or other similar preliminary
expert tasks are necessary, consideration should be given to the
instruction of a single joint expert, especially where such matters
are not expected to be contentious. The objective should be to
agree or to narrow issues.

Paragraph 35 will rarely be relevant in the case of a medical issue in a claim.

On any issue seen by the parties as potentially significant in the dispute or of
significant impact upon the value of the claim, the parties will tend to resist the
appointment of a single joint expert. Each side would generally want its own
expert witness in each area of expertise, as there are clear disadvantages to the parties in having to share a single joint expert with whom they cannot communicate
privately. There is also a more general concern that the imposition of a single joint
expert in technical cases may amount to the abdication of decision-making by the
judge to that of the appointed single joint expert[72].

As well as the court directing that there will be a single joint expert, the parties may also agree between themselves that they will instruct a single joint
expert when the issue to be reported on is considered unlikely to be particularly contentious.

> The single joint expert is at risk of being nobody's friend. One or more
> of the parties may be unhappy with the expert's report and all the par-
> ties may wish to cross-examine the expert should the case come to trial.

Each party may separately instruct the single joint expert, although in most cases
the parties will agree one set of instructions between themselves before these are
sent to the single joint expert. Disputes between the parties can arise over the
issues that the expert should address. This results in the expert receiving instructions from each party and having to set out the substance of both sets of instructions in the report, before addressing all of the matters raised by the parties.

---

72   See for example *Bulic v Harwoods, Santander Consumer (UK) PLC and Jaguar Cars Ltd* [2012]
EWHC 3657 where the court considered the principles applicable to an application to replace
the joint expert with a party's own expert.

The Guidance seeks to overcome these difficulties:

Guidance 38   The parties should try to agree joint instructions to single joint experts, but in default of agreement, each party may give instructions. In particular, all parties should try to agree what documents should be included with instructions and what assumptions single joint experts should make.

39   Where the parties fail to agree joint instructions, they should try to agree where the areas of disagreement lie and their instructions should make this clear. If separate instructions are given, they should be copied to the other instructing parties.

The terms of appointment may also be set out in the court order directing expert evidence to be given by a single joint expert. The expert needs to be aware of the terms of any such court order and must ensure that any opinion provided is within the terms of appointment[73].

If instructions have not been received by a single joint expert as any court deadline for the report is approaching, the expert should give the instructing parties a deadline and if necessary begin work on the report in the absence of instructions (see para 41 of the Guidance for further details on how to proceed in this unusual situation). If the instructions received are conflicting, for example in the facts which they provide to the expert, and those conflicts result in the single joint expert coming to different opinions, then the report should contain both sets of opinions (leaving it to the court to determine the facts)[74].

4.5.1   Comparison of a Single Joint Expert and a Jointly Selected Expert

A single joint expert is instructed by both parties to report to them jointly and is an expert with whom neither party has a right of private access separate from the other side. This means no private communication takes place between a party and the single joint expert to discuss the contents of the report or to seek clarification of it and any written communication, for example for clarification of the report, must be copied to the other party, together with any response. In practice, this means that if the single joint expert does not deal clearly with all relevant aspects of the claim, any clarification or explanation must be obtained by questions in writing with copies sent to all other parties and the responses similarly shared. It is rare that a meeting is arranged between the expert and all the parties.

In contrast, a jointly selected expert is instructed by the claimant alone. The solicitor can discuss the report with the expert confidentially in correspondence, on the telephone and in conference. The expert report need never be disclosed to the

---

73   See for example *Annison v Nolan* [2012] EWCA Civ 54

74   See Guidance para 46

other side[75]. The position is the same in relation to any other expert instructed by just one party.

> Before preparing an expert report, it is essential that the medical expert is clear as to the basis upon which he/she is instructed, and by whom, before preparing an expert report. Unfortunately, the distinction between a jointly selected expert and a single joint expert is not always fully appreciated by instructing solicitors, so the expert may need to check the basis of instruction before preparing the report.

4.5.2   Status of a Single Joint Expert's Report

Where the parties are committed to a single joint expert, whether by an order of the court or by agreement between themselves, the report as it is written will generally stand as the only expert evidence in that discipline in the case.

> *'The assumption should be that [once obtained] the single joint expert's report is the evidence. Any amplification or any cross-examination should be restricted as far as possible.'*[76]

Each party is stuck with that expert even in a situation where, once the report is received, the expert is regarded by either or both sides as having taken an unreasonable position – for example, the expert has "fallen for" everything the claimant has said or has "serious reservations" about the credibility of the claimant or has taken an extreme view on some other aspect of the case. In such circumstances, a party may choose to incur the cost of obtaining further expert evidence and, if materially different to the single joint expert's evidence, seek to persuade the court to permit the previous court order or agreement to be overridden "in the interests of justice". The outcome of such an application to the court is generally uncertain.

Written questions may be asked of the single joint expert, just as with any other expert. In the rare event that the court might require the single joint expert to attend court to give oral evidence, then the expert may be questioned by all parties in the case[77].

A single joint expert's status can be challenging.

1.   The expert has of course an overriding duty to the court, but as an expert appointed by the parties, owes each of them an equal duty too, while being required to maintain independence, impartiality and transparency[78].

---

75   See Section 3.3.2

76   *Peet v Mid-Kent Healthcare Trust* (Practice Note) [2002] 1 WLR 2010

77   See Guidance para 47

78   See Guidance para 43

2. The expert must not attend a meeting or conference unless it is with all of the parties by which the expert is instructed unless any absent parties agree in writing beforehand or the court orders[79].

3. The expert must keep all instructing parties informed of steps he/she takes, and copy them in on all correspondence[80].

4. The expert must serve any report on all instructing parties simultaneously[81].

Even where the court does order a single joint expert to be appointed, it is possible that each party may then appoint "shadow experts" to advise on the evidence of the single joint expert.[82] Although shadow reports are not used to support applications to the court for further experts to be permitted, they may well be used to provide the basis for cross-examination of the single joint expert by each party should the matter reach court. Such shadow experts may even sit in court in order to brief the lawyers during the evidence and cross-examination of the single joint expert.

Owing to the limitations inherent in opposing parties sharing an expert, single joint experts are appointed less frequently than was thought likely when the CPR were first introduced.

4.6   Court Orders

The court manages proceedings by way of directions given to the parties. These are in the form of court orders[83]. A failure to comply with a court order may result in the court imposing sanctions on the party guilty of such failure, whether it is the party, the lawyer or the expert witness who is personally at fault.

4.6.1   Notice of Court Orders

Often the expert is not made aware by the solicitors of the contents of court orders affecting the expert and with which the expert is expected to comply. This difficulty has, at least in theory, been overcome by an amendment to PD35:

PD35   8   Where an order requires an act to be done by an expert, or otherwise affects an expert, the party instructing that expert must serve a copy of the order on the expert. The claimant must serve the order on a single joint expert.

---

79   See Guidance para 44
80   See Guidance para 42
81   See Guidance para 46
82   See Guidance para 37
83   See Sections 3.2.2, 3.6 and 3.7.

The Guidance seeks to ensure that instructing solicitors fully inform an expert at the commencement of instructions about relevant time constraints and court orders:

> Guidance 20   Those instructing experts should ensure that they give clear instructions (and attach relevant documents) including the following:
>
> ...
>
> (f)   an outline programme, consistent with good case management and the expert's availability, for the completion and delivery of each stage of the expert's work, and
>
> (g)   where proceedings have been started, the dates of any hearings (including any case/costs management conferences and/or pre-trial reviews), the dates fixed by the court or agreed between the parties for the exchange of experts' reports and any other relevant deadlines to be adhered to ...

Therefore, when required to provide an expert report once proceedings are under way or to arrange a joint discussion and joint statement, the expert should be provided with a copy of the court order setting out that requirement and the court's timetable with which the expert has to comply.

Where an instructing solicitor imposes a tight deadline on an expert because of an order of the court, the expert may wish to request a copy of the order to ascertain on what date it was made. The tight deadline may in fact be caused by the solicitor forgetting until the last moment to notify the expert of the order. Once the date of the order is known then frank discussions between the solicitor and the expert about meeting the order can ensue. In an extreme case, the expert may wish to make his/her own application to the court for directions to resolve difficulties.

4.6.2   Seeking Directions from the Court

In CPR 35.14, an expert is given the power, without any involvement from the instructing lawyer, to ask the court for directions.

> CPR 35.14 (1)   Experts may file written requests for directions for the purpose of assisting them in carrying out their functions.
>
> (2)   Experts must, unless the court orders otherwise, provide copies of the proposed request for directions under paragraph (1) –

  (a) to the party instructing them, at least 7 days before they file the requests; and

  (b) to all other parties, at least 4 days before they file them.

 (3) The court, when it gives directions, may also direct that a party be served with a copy of the directions.

It is unlikely that an expert will ever need to make such an application and this power is rarely exercised. However, this provision is an effective stick that an expert can wave under the nose of a solicitor who is in some way preventing or delaying the expert from carrying out his/her duty. For the most part, solicitors who do not co-operate with expert witnesses do so out of oversight or incompetence rather than malice and the required notification of the expert's intention to seek directions from the court is sufficient to markedly change attitudes. Single joint experts may also resort to threatening solicitors with this power, in order to receive appropriate instructions or necessary information.

The Guidance gives the following guidance regarding applications to the court by expert witnesses:

Guidance 28 Experts may request directions from the court to assist them in carrying out their functions (CPR 35.14), for example, if experts consider that they have not been provided with information they require. Experts should normally discuss this with those who instruct them before making a request. Unless the court otherwise orders, any proposed request for directions should be sent to the party instructing the expert at least seven days before filing any request to the court, and to all other parties at least four days before filing it.

  11.2 Requests to the court for directions should be made by letter, clearly marked "expert's request for directions" containing:

   (a) the title of the claim;

   (b) the claim number;

   (c) the name of the expert;

   (d) why directions are sought; and

   (e) copies of any relevant documentation.

4.7 The Joint Discussion (or Meeting of Experts)

During the progression of a case, it is likely that there will be at least one meeting of experts.

> PD35   9.1   …Parties must consider, with their experts, at an early stage, whether there is likely to be any useful purpose in holding an experts' discussion and if so when.

Under CPR 35.12 the court may direct such a discussion and in practice it will be required now in all cases where permission is given to more than one party to instruct experts of a similar discipline, unless there is no material disagreement between the experts.

The purpose of the discussion is to facilitate the efficient conduct of the litigation. The Practice Direction and the Guidance suggest that the discussion might also identify any actions that may help to resolve the outstanding points of disagreement in the expert evidence[84].

The discussion need not be held face to face and will often be held on the telephone. However, a face to face meeting will normally be necessary in more complicated cases.

4.7.1 Object of the Discussion and the Expert's Role

One of the important objectives of the CPR is to assist the parties by providing a process where the parties have the best opportunity to compromise a claim without the need for a court hearing. A discussion between the experts is part of this process. The object of the discussion is, where possible, to extend areas of agreement and to narrow the issues that remain in dispute.

> CPR 35.12 (1)   The court may, at any stage, direct a discussion between experts for the purpose of requiring the experts to –
>
> (a)   identify and discuss the expert issues in the proceedings; and
>
> (b)   where possible, reach an agreed opinion on those issues.
>
> (2)   The court may specify the issues which the experts must discuss.
>
> (3)   The court may direct that following a discussion between the experts they must prepare a statement for the court setting out those issues on which –
>
> (a)   they agree; and

---

84   PD35 9.2(iii) and Guidance para 71(d)

      (b)   they disagree, with a summary of their reasons for
            disagreeing.

(4)   The content of the discussion between the experts shall not be
       referred to at the trial unless the parties agree.

(5)   Where experts reach agreement on an issue during their
       discussions, the agreement shall not bind the parties unless the
       parties expressly agree to be bound by the agreement.

It should be noted that where issues do remain in dispute, the purpose of the
discussion is to produce a summary of the reasons for the disagreement, and in
appropriate cases, what can be done to resolve these disputes:

PD35   9.2   The purpose of discussions between experts is not for experts to
                   settle cases but to agree and narrow issues and in particular to
                   identify:

         (i)   the extent of the agreement between them;

         (ii)   the points of and short reasons for any disagreement;

         (iii) action, if any, which may be taken to resolve any
              outstanding points of disagreement; and

         (iv) any further material issues not raised and the extent to
              which these issues are agreed.

We must emphasise that the objective is not for the experts to reach a compromise on behalf of the parties. There is an important difference between varying
or adjusting an opinion following discussion, which may result in creating an area
of agreement where previously there was disagreement, and in being prepared to
agree a point outside the range of an opinion held by the expert in order to reach
what may be seen as a sensible compromise of opinions. Narrowing issues is for
experts; compromising an opinion is for the lawyers or the judge. The Statement of
Truth, which applies to the joint statement, makes it clear that the joint statement
must still contain the expert's "true and complete professional opinions on the
matters to which they refer"[85].

But where it is possible and reasonable for the experts to reach an agreed opinion
they should of course do so.

> 'Thus, the express purpose of a discussion between experts is to reach if pos-
> sible an agreed opinion on the expert issues: see CPR 35.12(1)(b). It neces-
> sarily follows that the rule contemplates that as a result of the discussion an
> expert may modify or change the opinion he had previously expressed in his

---

85   PD35 3.3

> report. In the context of trial management that is a most desirable purpose because it will tend to reduce the duration and expense of the trial and encourage a settlement of the case. Thus, the mere fact that an expert has changed or modified his opinion following an experts' meeting cannot by itself be a reason for permitting a party who is disappointed with the change or modification of opinion to adduce evidence from another expert. It would not be possible in such circumstances to suggest that further expert evidence is reasonably required to resolve the proceedings: see CPR Part 35.1[86]

> 'The expert's overriding duty applies not only to the preparation of an initial report, but also to the preparation and agreement of a joint statement with an expert advising an opposing party as well as, of course, to evidence given orally in court. If at any time the expert can no longer support the case of the person who instructed him, it is his duty do say so.'[87]

In stating the points of agreement and disagreement, it is essential that the experts apply the civil standard of proof and the appropriate legal tests, referring expressly to the balance of probabilities and addressing causation of injury and damage as appropriate[88].

The lawyers must not give, and the experts must not accept, instructions not to reach agreement during such discussions on areas within their competence. In complying with his/her duty to the court, the expert must remain independent:

PD35   9.7   Experts must give their own opinions to assist the court and do not require the authority of the parties to sign a joint statement.

The expert's duty remains at all times to help the court on matters within his/her expertise, the duty which overrides any obligation to the person from whom he/she has received instructions[89]. The duty to the court will include the duty of the expert to inform the instructing party, if at any time the expert can no longer support the case[90]. The requirement under the CPR 'where possible, [to] reach an agreed opinion' necessarily contemplates that as a result of the discussion an expert may modify or change the opinion he had previously expressed in his report[91].

---

86   *Stallwood v David* [2006] EWHC 2600

87   *Guntripp v Cheney Coaches Ltd* [2012] EWCA Civ 392

88   We address these issues in detail in the chapters that follow

89   CPR 35.3

90   *Guntrip v Cheney Coaches Ltd* [2012] EWCA Civ 392

91   *Stallwood v David* [2006] EWHC 2600 para 17 approved in *Guntrip v Cheney Coaches Ltd* [2012] EWCA Civ 392

To emphasise these points the Guidance now provides:

Guidance   80   The joint statement should include a brief re-statement that the experts recognise their duties (or a cross-reference to the relevant statements in their respective reports). The joint statement should also include an express statement that the experts have not been instructed to avoid reaching agreement (or otherwise defer from doing so) on any matter within the experts' competence.

4.7.2   The Joint Statement and Sequential Reports

In the case of sequential exchange of expert reports[92], as for example is often the case with quantum only reports, the Guidance provides:

Guidance   73   Where there is sequential exchange of expert reports, with the defendant's expert's report prepared in accordance with the guidance at paragraph 63 above, the joint statement should focus upon the areas of disagreement, save for the need for the claimant's expert to consider and respond to material, information and commentary included within the defendant's expert's report.

4.7.3   Agenda for the Discussion

In a straightforward case, no purpose is likely to be served by a formal agenda and the experts are unlikely to be provided with one. PD35 provides for discussing and agreeing whether an agenda is necessary and what it should contain:

PD35   9.3   Where the experts are to meet, the parties must discuss and if possible agree whether an agenda is necessary, and if so attempt to agree one that helps the experts to focus on the issues which need to be discussed. The agenda must not be in the form of leading questions or hostile in tone.

There are cases where an agenda can be very useful for the experts to guide them in their discussions. An agenda should ensure that the experts do address the issues which the lawyers need to have addressed in order to resolve the dispute.

The Guidance gives further assistance in preparing an agenda:

Guidance   75   In multi-track cases the parties, their lawyers and experts should co-operate to produce an agenda for any discussion between experts, although primary responsibility for preparation of the agenda should normally lie with the parties' solicitors.

76   The agenda should indicate what has been agreed and summarise concisely matters that are in dispute. It is often helpful to include

---

92   See Section 4.2.14

> questions to be answered by the experts. If agreement cannot be reached promptly or a party is unrepresented, the court may give directions for the drawing up of the agenda. The agenda should be circulated to experts and those instructing them to allow sufficient time for the experts to prepare for the discussion.

The Guidance therefore does not anticipate the use of an agenda in smaller value claims that are not in the multi-track.

In clinical negligence claims in the High Court, the standard court directions, which are obligatory only in such cases where they are part of the court order in fact made, reflect this in providing as follows[93]:

14(b) Unless otherwise agreed by all parties' solicitors, after consulting with the experts, a draft Agenda which directs the experts to the remaining issues relevant to the experts' discipline, as identified in the statements of case, shall be prepared jointly by the Claimant's solicitors and experts and sent to the Defendant's solicitors for comment at least 35 days before the agreed date for the experts' discussions.

Claimants' solicitors and counsel should note the obligation to prepare the draft agenda jointly with the relevant expert. Experts should note that it is part of their overriding duty to the court to ensure that the agenda complies with the following direction:

The use of agendas is not mandatory. Solicitors should consult with the experts to ensure that agendas are necessary and, if used, are reasonable in scope. The agenda should assist the experts and should not be in the form of leading questions or hostile in tone. An agenda must include a list of the outstanding issues in the preamble.

[Note: The preamble should state: the standard of proof: the Bolam test: remind the experts not to attempt to determine factual issues: remind them not to stray outside their field of expertise and indicate the form of the joint statement. It may also be helpful to provide a comprehensive list of the materials which each expert has seen, perhaps in the form of an agreed supplementary bundle (it is assumed that the experts will have been provided with the medical notes bundle)]

14(c) The Defendants shall within 21 days of receipt agree the Agenda, or propose amendments;

14(d) Seven days thereafter all solicitors shall use their best endeavours to agree the Agenda. Points of disagreement should be on matters of real substance and not semantics or on matters the experts could resolve of their own accord at the discussion. In default of agreement, both versions shall be considered at the discussions. Agendas, when used, shall be provided to the experts not less than 7 days before the date fixed for discussions.

[Where it has been impossible to agree a single agenda, it is of assistance to the experts if the

---

93   These directions can be found at
       www.justice.gov.uk/downloads/courts/queens-bench/clinical-negligence-model.doc

second agenda is consecutively numbered to the first i.e. if the first agenda has 16 questions in it, the second agenda is numbered from 17 onwards.]

4.7.4   People Present at the Meeting of Experts

PD35 gives clear guidance on who should be present at an experts' meeting and the roles that they should adopt:

PD35   9.4   Unless ordered by the court, or agreed by all parties, and the experts, neither the parties nor their legal representatives may attend experts discussions.

PD35   9.5   If the legal representatives do attend –

(a)   they should not normally intervene in the discussion, except to answer questions put to them by the experts or to advise on the law; and

(b)   the experts may if they so wish hold part of their discussions in the absence of the legal representatives.

Therefore the claimant, defendant, insurer or representative of the healthcare provider clients will not normally be present, and if in a particular case the lawyers are present they will have a very limited role. Even in a case where there is a fear of improper influence from one side, by use of a good draft agenda and if necessary by making a recording of the meeting, the presence of lawyers can usually be avoided[94].

4.7.5 The Joint Statement

It is essential that the conclusions from the discussion are not only put into writing, but that a document containing these conclusions is signed by the experts:

PD35   9.6   A statement must be prepared by the experts dealing with paragraphs 9.2(i) - (iv) above[95]. Individual copies of the statements must be signed by the experts at the conclusion of the discussion, or as soon thereafter as practicable, and in any event within 7 days. Copies of the statements must be provided to the parties no later than 14 days after signing.

A sensible format for the joint statement is to have a section setting out all material matters on which the experts agree, followed by a section identifying each area of disagreement, the opposing opinions and a summary of the reasons for the disagreement. It is unhelpful, but surprisingly common, to have points of disagreement slipped in amongst the section headed "Agreement" and agreed matters listed amongst the section headed "Disagreement". It is also extremely

---

94   *Hubbard v Lambeth, Southwark & Lewisham* HA [2001] EWCA 1455

95   See Section 4.7.1

unhelpful to simply state the disagreement without a brief explanation for it. It must be emphasised that it is on the reasons for disagreement that the trial (or any remaining negotiations) will be focussed, and on which the court and the parties demand clarity.

It is important to emphasise that the section dealing with disagreement should not simply restate each expert's reasoning but should attempt to explain why it is that the experts have reached different conclusions, and if possible the reason why each expert considers his/her approach to be correct or more valid and the opposing approach wrong or less valid. This section should identify for the lawyers and the judge why it is the experts do not and cannot agree, and therefore what it is that will have to be resolved at trial and how it can be resolved.

Where there is an agenda and a series of written questions for the experts to address, the joint statement should set out the questions and provide a clear and precise answer to each question. It may then also be appropriate to expand upon or explain or justify the answer given.

Signing off on a summary of the discussions is essential, whether the discussion is face to face or on the telephone or by e-mail, and should be carried out as soon as practicable after the joint discussion[96]. In a hotly disputed and complex case, the task of the scribe of this document will be a very important one. Lawyers will look to the precise wording of the statement in order to resolve issues in the claim or to assess their prospects of success on those issues should the matter proceed to trial. Whilst there may be an attraction in leaving one's opposite number to carry out the drafting, the draftsperson is likely to have a considerable advantage in ensuring that his/her views are best represented in the joint statement.

Should an expert alter his/her previously expressed opinion in the joint discussion, then it is important to explain why. The party instructing that expert and the legal advisers are entitled to a proper explanation for the change of opinion on which the claim or defence has up to that point been based:

PD35   9.8   If an expert significantly alters an opinion, the joint statement
                must include a note or addendum by that expert explaining the
                change of opinion

The provisions for concurrent evidence (or 'hot tubbing')[97] introduced in April 2013[98] mean that the court is likely to direct that an agenda for concurrent evidence be prepared and this will be based on the areas of disagreement in the joint statement. The agenda is concerned only with the areas of disagreement. In an effective joint statement following a joint discussion, the agenda for the concurrent evidence should already be apparent, with a list of the areas of disagreement and the reasons for such disagreement. Although the 'parties' are ordered to

---

96   See Guidance para 81
97   See Section 3.1.2
98   PD35 11

prepare the agenda, the lawyers will most probably provide the final agenda for concurrent evidence based on the input of the experts, which should have been largely provided in the joint discussion. This agenda, and therefore the joint statement, will be crucial in guiding the process of the concurrent evidence and in assisting the judge to investigate the disagreement with the experts.

4.7.6 Status of the Discussion and Agreement at Trial

The deliberations and discussions at the meeting of experts will not be referred to at the trial unless the parties agree[99]. Where agreement on an issue is reached by the experts, this agreement will not bind the parties unless the parties agree to be bound by the agreement[100]. In the absence of a binding agreement, the statement prepared by the experts at the conclusion of the meeting may still be produced to the court by either party. In practice, an expert giving evidence on oath in court will be in the greatest difficulty if he/she seeks without good reason to renege on concessions made in the discussion and recorded in the statement.

4.8 Terms of Appointment

Before taking any steps to prepare an expert report it is important to agree the terms on which the expert's appointment is made. Not only will this clarify what it is the expert is being instructed to do, but also it should avoid subsequent disputes about what financial terms and timetable will apply.

The Guidance advises both experts and instructing lawyers that:

Guidance 17   Terms of appointment should be agreed at the outset and should normally include:

(a)   the capacity in which the expert is to be appointed (e.g. party appointed expert or single joint expert);

(b)   the services required of the expert (e.g. provision of an expert's report, answering questions in writing, attendance at meetings and attendance at court);

(c)   time for delivery of the report;

(d)   the basis of the expert's charges (e.g. daily or hourly rates and an estimate of the time likely to be required, or a fixed fee for the services). Parties must provide an estimate to the court of the costs of the proposed expert evidence and for each stage of the proceedings (R.35.4(2));

(e)   travelling expenses and disbursements;

---

99   CPR 35.12(4)

100   CPR 35.12(5)

(f)　cancellation charges;

(g)　any fees for attending court;

(h)　time for making the payment;

(i)　whether fees are to be paid by a third party;

(j)　if a party is publicly funded, whether the expert's charges will be subject to assessment; and

(h)　guidance that the expert's fees and expenses may be limited by the court (note expert's recoverable fees in the small claims track cannot exceed £750: see PD 27 paragraph 7).

We have already seen that the expert must be able to provide an estimate of costs for all potential steps in the claim[101], and the terms of appointment can usefully provide the charging basis for all such steps.

It can be agreed that payment of fees will be deferred until the conclusion of the case, but there should not be any agreement that payment will depend on the outcome of the case[102]. Experts should remain alert to the fact that even if fees for expert work that can be recovered from the opposing side is limited, contractually the expert will be entitled to recover from the instructing party the agreed fee. We consider terms of appointment in more detail in Chapter 12.

4.9　Expert's Withdrawal from a Case

In general, once instructed in a case the expert is obliged to see the case through to the end, however inconvenient that may prove. That is a part of the duty owed by an expert to the instructing party and to the court. However, circumstances may arise in which it is no longer appropriate for an expert to continue to act. The Guidance provides:

Guidance　27　Where experts' instructions are incompatible with their duties, through incompleteness, a conflict between their duty to the court and their instructions, or for any other reason, the experts may consider withdrawing from the case. However, experts should not do so without first discussing the position with those who instruct them and considering whether it would be more appropriate to make a written request for directions from the court. If experts do withdraw, they must give formal written notice to those instructing them.

101　See Section 4.1.5

102　See Section 4.1.3

Withdrawal will rarely become necessary, but should the expert find that his/her instructions during the case seek to compromise his/her independence and duty to the court, or seek to alter or influence the opinion the expert expresses in a manner incompatible with that duty, then the expert will have to consider withdrawing unless those instructions are withdrawn. Such a conflict may arise if the expert is refused access by the instructing lawyer to records or documentation that the expert considers important to forming an unqualified opinion.

The expert should first seek to discuss the situation with the instructing lawyer, with an explanation of the expert's position, and it may well be that once the problem is aired and the nature of the instructions are clarified or varied, the perceived conflict is removed. An apparent conflict may be no more than the result of poor communication. However, if that is insufficient, a measured response would be that the expert sets out the position and the basis for the perceived difficulty in writing to the instructing lawyer. In the absence of a satisfactory reply, the expert either seeks directions from the court, if that is considered the appropriate and a practical way forward, or gives formal written notice to the instructing lawyer that the expert withdraws, setting out (again) in full the reasons for doing so.

The consequences of an expert withdrawing may be serious for the party by whom he/she was instructed, and can only be justified by the expert where problems such as those indicated above arise which create a conflict between the expert's duty to the court and the instructions received from the client or his lawyer. Depending on the stage of the proceedings and any court orders that have been made, the party may be in difficulty obtaining permission for a replacement expert.

> It is important that the expert's Terms and Conditions of appointment are clear. The Guidance for the Instruction of Experts in Civil Claims provides useful guidance as to what should be agreed between the expert and the solicitor before accepting instructions. (See Appendix 5 – Para 7)

Conclusion

The role and duties on an expert witness are codified in CPR Part 35 and its associated Practice Direction and the Guidance. By being familiar with the rules and following them, the expert is able to meet the specific requirements of expert evidence and to perform the role to an appropriate professional standard. The expert has at all times to act in accordance with his/her overriding duty to help the court on matters within his/her expertise.

Key-Point Summary

1. Adherence to Part 35 and its associated practice direction and the Guidance is mandatory.

2. The rules relating to expert evidence are written to help the expert perform the role effectively and experts should follow the rules carefully.

3. An expert has an overriding duty to help the court on matters within his/ her expertise.

4. An objective and unbiased opinion is far more helpful to the lawyers involved in the claim than an opinion weighted towards the instructing party.

5. Once proceedings have been commenced, an expert must ensure that he/ she is able to meet the timetable laid down by the court before accepting an instruction to provide evidence.

6. The required form and content of expert evidence is clearly set out in PD35 3.2.

7. An expert must make clear the basis for each opinion expressed, when an opinion is qualified, and where relevant deal with the range of professional opinion on the matter.

8. An expert must not make amendments to a report that distorts his/her true opinion.

9. An expert's written answers to questions of clarification form part of the expert report.

10. The court has the power to order that evidence on a particular topic or in a particular field be given by a single joint expert.

11. An expert should be notified by his/her instructing solicitor of the content of any court order that affects the expert in performing his/her role as an expert.

12. The statement produced at the end of a joint discussion must not only set out the areas of agreement and disagreement, but must also set out the reasons for any disagreement.

13. The expert is bound by the expert's duty to the court and the Statement of Truth in signing off the joint statement.

Next Steps

In the next chapter, we will explore the civil standard of proof and the particular difficulties that applying this standard creates for experts in a variety of disciplines.

5

Proof

Introduction

One of the most challenging aspects of producing opinion evidence is to correctly apply the civil standard of proof. The 'medical mind' has inherent difficulties in grasping the absolute importance of applying this standard in every case, no matter how inconsequential or devastating the facts of the case may have been for the parties involved. As medical evidence is essential for parties who are seeking to prove or defend a claim, medical experts have to be able to apply the civil standard of proof to every opinion they express in their reports. Without this essential clarity in the medical evidence, the quantum experts who subsequently need to rely on the medical evidence have great difficulty producing clear and supported evidence in the claim.

Chapter Outline

In this chapter, we will explore the standard of proof applied by the courts in civil litigation. We will highlight some of the inherent difficulties in applying the standard of proof to the evidence and show its fundamental importance when expressing coherent expert opinion.

5.1 Civil Standard of Proof

In a civil case, the claimant has the burden of proof, which means that the claimant must prove his/her case to the civil standard of proof, namely, 'on the balance of probabilities'[1]. The claimant must therefore satisfy the judge that it is 'more likely than not' that his/her injuries and the consequential claimed losses were caused by the defendant's negligence or other breach of duty.

The outcome of the whole case is decided on this standard of proof. Once a point has been proved to the judge's satisfaction on the balance of probabilities (i.e. that it is more likely than not), the lawyers will treat the decision on the point as an established fact – for the purposes of the litigation certainty on the point has been established.

> 'In our legal system, if a judge finds it more likely than not that something did take place, then it is treated as having taken place. If he finds it more likely than not that it did not take place, then it is treated as not having taken place. He is not allowed to sit on the fence. He has to find for one side or the other. Sometimes the burden of proof will come to his rescue: the party with the burden of showing that something took place will not have satisfied him that it did. But generally speaking a judge is able to make up his mind where the truth lies without needing to rely upon the burden of proof.'[2]

Consider the following illustration of applying the standard of proof to evidence. Let us assume that there is a factual dispute as to whether a road traffic accident occurred in daylight or in darkness. If having heard all the evidence on this point the judge finds as more reliable the evidence of the witnesses who say it was daylight, and so finds that it was more likely than not daylight at the time of the accident, then for all purposes of the case it was daylight and the case will be resolved on that basis. Visibility at the time of the accident will no longer be an issue in the case and the fact that the lights on the vehicle were known to be defective will be no longer relevant in the proceedings.

When medical experts allow themselves to consider the ramifications of the civil standard of proof, their reaction is usually one of disbelief, tinged with deep anxiety. The contrast between the civil standard of proof and the scientific proof

---

1   In criminal cases, the prosecution must prove the case to a standard of proof where the jury is 'sure' of the defendant's guilt before it may convict – the standard of being 'sure' used to be worded as 'beyond a reasonable doubt'.

2   In *re B (Children)(FC)* [2008] UKHL 35 at para 32

that is the basis of medical practice is glaringly obvious: in civil litigation there is little, if any, regard paid to the 95% probability often demanded in scientific proof. Medical experts have to understand that the law is not searching for absolute truth – which would require a very high degree of probability or a superhuman judge – but is rather applying a set of man-made rules in order to resolve disputes.

> ## Science seeks truth, while the law does justice.[3]

Understandably, most medical experts are uncomfortable with being required to apply their hard-earned scientifically-based medical expertise in what is, to their minds, an imperfect and artificial system of rules. Some experts find writing reports in which they apply the civil standard of proof so unnatural and unreal that they will, when they express their opinions, use almost any phrase other than 'on the balance of probabilities'. This lack of comfort in applying the civil standard of proof is often even greater in clinical negligence claims, where the expert is asked to assess, on the balance of probabilities, the quality of medical treatment provided by another practitioner. The expert often recoils from giving an opinion that another practitioner's practice fell below an appropriate standard of care, when to the medical mind the assessment is made to such an inadequate standard of proof.

Judicial recognition of the difficulty that there can be for the medical expert, familiar with applying scientific or medical standards of proof, in providing opinion in a legal context can be found in the following excerpt from a Scottish case, *Dingley v The Chief Constable, Strathclyde Police*[4], The issue in *Dingley* was whether the development of multiple sclerosis had been caused by physical injury sustained in a motor accident. Medical science was not able to demonstrate the connection between the two, and reliance was placed on epidemiological evidence.

> *'In ordinary (non-lawyers') language, to say that one regards something as 'probable' is by no means to say that one regards it as 'established' or 'proved'. Yet in the civil courts, where we say that a pursuer[5] must prove his case on a balance of probabilities, what is held to be probable is treated as 'proved'. I do not suggest that any lawyer will be confused by this rather special meaning of the word 'proved'. But speaking very generally, I think that the civil requirement of a pursuer – that he satisfy the court that upon the evidence his case is probably sound – would in ordinary language be regarded as very different from, and less stringent than, a requirement that his case be established or proved. More importantly in the context of such a case as the present, the fact that the two concepts are distinct in ordinary language, but the same in this legal context, seems to me to give rise to a risk of ambiguity*

---

3   See the discussion of this concept in Jasanoff, S. (1997) *Science at the Bar: law, science and technology in America*. Cambridge, Ma: Harvard University Press

4   (1998) SC 548 at 603 (Lord Prosser)

5   In Scottish law, a 'claimant' is called a 'pursuer'

or misunderstanding in the expressed opinions of expert witnesses. And this risk will be increased if the expert in question would normally, in the exercise of his profession, adopt an approach to such issues starkly different from that incumbent upon a court.

Whether one uses the word 'scientific' or not, no hypothesis or proposition would be seen as 'proved' or 'established' by anyone with any form of medical expertise merely upon the basis that he had come to regard it as probably sound. (Indeed, I think even the word 'probable' would be reserved for situations where the likelihood is thought to be much more than marginal). And even if, in relation to any possible proposition or hypothesis, such an expert even troubled to notice that he had come to the point of regarding it as not merely possible but on balance 'probable' then I think he would regard that point as one from which he must set off on further inquiry, and by no means as being (as it is in the courts) a point of arrival. Mere marginal probability will not much interest him. But it must satisfy a court.'

In a recent case involving the consideration of competing explanations for the occurrence of an event, the court issued a word of warning about the potential for the over use of percentages in addressing the balance of probabilities[6]:

'The civil "balance of probability" test means no less and no more than that the court must be satisfied on rational and objective grounds that the case for believing that the suggested means of causation occurred is stronger than the case for not so believing. In the USA the usual formulation of this standard is a "preponderance of the evidence". In the British Commonwealth the generally favoured term is a "balance of probability". They mean the same. Sometimes the "balance of probability" standard is expressed mathematically as "50 + % probability", but this can carry with it a danger of pseudo-mathematics, as the argument in this case demonstrated. When judging whether a case for believing that an event was caused in a particular way is stronger than the case for not so believing, the process is not scientific (although it may obviously include evaluation of scientific evidence) and to express the probability of some event having happened in percentage terms is illusory.'

> Once a point has been proved to the judge's satisfaction on the balance of probabilities (i.e. that it is more likely than not), the lawyers will treat the decision on the point as an established fact – for the purposes of the litigation, certainty on the point has been established.

5.1.1 Applying the Standard of Proof

In civil litigation, the same standard of proof is applied in every case. It is applied to a claimant's mild symptom of pain as a consequence of a 'slip and trip' accident,

---

6   *Nulty and Wing Bat Security Ltd v Milton Keynes BC* [2013] EWCA Civ 15 at para 35

in the same way that it is applied to catastrophic injuries as a consequence of a motorway pile-up. Whether the case is banal or exceptional, the civil courts apply exactly the same standard of proof.

It is unlikely that any professional in daily practice, other than a lawyer, would be familiar with making important decisions, with profound consequences, on the balance of probabilities. It might, therefore, be assumed that in everyday professional practice only unimportant decisions of little consequence would be made on such a basis. In reality, we in fact make relatively few mundane decisions by applying the standard on the balance of probabilities.

5.1.2 Differential Decisions

We suggest that 'on the balance of probabilities' is a standard that would normally only apply to decision-making in everyday life in two specific circumstances:

1. where the differential in outcome (in terms of the likely consequences) would be inconsequential; or

2. where the differential in outcome (in terms of the likely consequences) resulting from delaying the decision would be so unacceptably large that an immediate decision effectively forces itself upon us.

5.2 Decision-Making in Civil Litigation

In civil litigation, there are very few inconsequential decisions to be made. If no importance rests on the decision, then for all practical purposes the decision is irrelevant and the parties will not waste time and money seeking an opinion upon it. There are also no forced decisions to be made, for everything in compensation claims will have happened months or even years before the claim began. Deadlines set by the court are counted in weeks and months, not minutes and seconds.

The decisions that have to be made in a medical expert's practice are neither inconsequential nor forced and so fall outside the two types of decision that are typically made on the balance of probabilities. Yet, decisions in medico-legal practice are likely to profoundly affect the outcome of the litigation and are made without any pressure of time.

In the context of a personal injury claim, hundreds of thousands or even millions of pounds may rest upon the opinion the medical expert expresses. Such sums may represent the only opportunity for a claimant to re-establish some degree of quality of life after an accident. On the other side of a claim, a defendant may have to live with the knowledge that he/she bears the responsibility for the injuries suffered by the claimant and may suffer heavy financial consequences from the court's decision. Even where the compensation is for a few thousand pounds, this sum may be very significant for the parties involved in the action.

Similarly, the financial consequences to a medical insurer or health care provider of many thousands of small claims being supported (or not) by medical experts also mean that apparently minor decisions are in fact extremely important. In a clinical negligence claim, not only are large sums of money involved but also the professional reputation of one or more medical practitioners may be in the balance. In industrial disease claims, there may be many other potential claimants who have been similarly exposed to the same agent, such that the court's decision could affect thousands of other claims.

So, while experts are told that they 'only' have to express an opinion on the balance of probabilities and that they do not need to be anywhere near 'sure', they are also expected by the lawyers to get the answer right and to present a rationale to justify their opinion. Their opinions need to be firmly based in professional practice and, whenever possible, in the scientific context of their speciality. Indeed, in conference with counsel prior to a court hearing, or during cross-examination in court, an expert can expect to have to justify a difficult opinion, reached on the balance of probabilities by reference to professional experience, published data or scientific reasoning.

This is a paradoxical situation - lawyers seek opinions resting on the balance of probabilities on the one hand, while demanding a scientific rationale on the other. The demand for scientifically supportable opinions from medical experts continues even though the science to support such opinions often does not exist. For example, the law requires that it be told what would have happened to a claimant in the absence of an accident or an adverse event, while demanding a logical, scientifically supported and expert basis for assessing, on the balance of probabilities, that which can never be known to a scientifically validated degree of certainty.

Medical experts are therefore required to assess hypothetical situations, such as 'had the accident or adverse event not occurred, on the balance of probabilities, would the claimant have developed any disease or symptoms and if so when and with what consequences?' and to respond with a logical rationale to satisfy the lawyers and the court. Everyone involved in the process (judges, lawyers and medical experts) agrees that this is a profoundly difficult task, yet it is one that the medical expert must engage with in a manner that is useful to the lawyers in progressing the claim, and that will withstand potentially vigorous cross-examination should such an opinion be challenged in court.

5.3   Applying 'On the Balance of Probabilities'

We have seen that the claimant in civil litigation must prove that the elements of his/her claim are more likely than not to be (or have been) as asserted in the claim. What the claimant cannot prove to this standard of proof, he/she cannot recover. In response, a defendant therefore seeks to establish uncertainty, at least to the point where it cannot be said that something is more likely than not, so as to prevent the claimant from proving the claim.

The civil standard of proof applies to resolving issues of fact, deciding issues of breach of duty (such as negligence), and proving causation of loss and damage in relation to those matters that have occurred by the date of trial. A case that illustrates how the courts apply the civil standard of proof and some of the complexities that arise in its application is *Hotson v East Berkshire Area Health Authority*[7]:

Stephen Hotson fell from a tree, sustaining a fracture of the left femoral epiphysis. He was taken to a hospital where staff negligently failed to diagnose the injury and sent him home. After 5 days he was taken to hospital again and the correct diagnosis was made. He was operated upon, but suffered avascular necrosis of the epiphysis, involving immediate disability. The Health Authority admitted negligence.

The trial judge found that even if the defendants had correctly diagnosed and treated Stephen on his first admission, there was a 75% risk that his injury would have followed the same course as in fact it did. The trial judge awarded Stephen damages for the loss of the 25% chance that, if the injury had been promptly diagnosed and treated, there would have been no avascular necrosis.

The House of Lords reversed this judgment holding that the trial judge's finding of fact showed that it was more likely than not (75:25) that the avascular necrosis itself was an inherent complication of the original injury, and so Stephen had failed to prove causation – i.e. that the Health Authority's admitted negligence had caused the avascular necrosis.

If however Stephen had proved that there was a 51:49 prospect that the avascular necrosis resulted from the negligent delay, as opposed to the fall from the tree, he would have recovered full compensation for the consequences of his disability – i.e. he would have proved that it was more likely than not that the avascular necrosis was caused by the negligent delay in diagnosis[8].

In order to be awarded damages, the claimant has to show that there is a more than 50% chance (i.e. on the balance of probabilities) that the accident or adverse event, or as in Stephen Hotson's case the failure to correctly diagnose, caused the injuries complained of. If this is achieved then there is no 'legal' doubt – as far as the court is concerned, the accident or adverse event (or failure to diagnose or treat appropriately) did cause the injuries, and damages will be awarded on that basis.

Whether the case is banal or exceptional, the civil courts apply exactly the same standard of proof – 'on the balance of probabilities'.

---

7   [1987] AC 750

8   See Section 6.1.1

Life Expectancy

If the life expectancy of the claimant were to become an issue in assessing the damages to be awarded to the claimant, then the judge will hear evidence on what the claimant's life expectancy now is, on the balance of probabilities. This will be expressed as the point in the future at which not more than 50% of the relevant cohort will still be alive and therefore the point at which the claimant will, on the balance of probabilities, be dead. On the basis of the expert evidence, the judge will decide the date of death of the claimant and then this becomes the period for which any lump sum award of damages for future care will be assessed[9]. We discuss life expectancy further at Section 6.5.5.

Factual issues

In a clinical negligence claim, the medical expert evidence will generally have a fundamental role in establishing liability to pay damages. When the factual picture is incomplete, the court often turns to the medical experts involved in the case to give opinions on what the likely factual position would have been at a particular time.

Let us consider a case where resolving the issue as to what would have been an appropriate treatment depends upon what the patient's temperature would have been on a particular occasion when it was not in fact taken. The judge will hear all the factual evidence from the patient, the patient's family, the treating doctor and nursing staff. Then the judge will hear opinion evidence from the medical experts, as to the likely temperature based on various known or presumed factors.

Having heard all of the evidence, and having formed his/her view of the quality and reliability of this evidence, the judge will decide the issue as to what is more likely than not to have been the patient's temperature on that particular occasion – the temperature for which there is at least a more than 50% probability on the available evidence.

5.4 Distinguishing between Proof of Damage and Assessment of Damages

The law treats separately and differently the proof that some damage has been caused in a claim for personal injury and the proof necessary for the assessment of the value of the damage suffered. As we have already seen, damage is an essential element of the claim, one of the ingredients that the claimant has to prove in order to be able to maintain a claim for damages[10]. The claimant must prove on the balance of probabilities that damage has resulted from the breach of duty on the part of the defendant.

---

9   Although it is possible now by awarding periodical payments to avoid the inherent risk of over or under-compensating the claimant on this basis. See Section 2.7.3.

10   See Section 2.2

In assessing the value of the claim, once it is proved on the balance of probabilities that some damage has been suffered, the court must carry out an assessment of the damage suffered and this will require, when dealing with the future, the assessment of the degree of chance that an item of loss will be suffered in the future.

> *'The role of the court in making an assessment of damages which depends upon its view as to what will be and what would have been is to be contrasted with its ordinary function in civil actions of determining what was. In determining what did happen in the past a court decides on the balance of probabilities. Anything that is more probable than not it treats as certain. But in assessing damages which depend upon its view as to what will happen in the future or would have happened in the future if something had not happened in the past, the court must make an estimate as to what are the chances that a particular thing will or would have happened and reflect those chances, whether they are more or less than even, in the amount of damages which it awards.'* [11]

This distinction is not well understood by lawyers, and in the context of issues about 'acceleration of symptoms' as the result of an injury is often ignored. We will consider this issue further in the next chapter when dealing with the proof of the damage caused by an injury[12].

5.5 Establishing Proof

Proof is always established on the available evidence. Such evidence may be the claimant's word, assertion or recollection. It may involve a careful analysis of the claimant's medical records over many years or close scrutiny of x-rays, scans or test results. It may involve many files of documents. It may be informed by the results of learned studies. It may involve contributions from a variety of experts in various fields or the direct evidence of an expert who has carried out an examination or assessment of the claimant.

When an expert is asked to express an opinion as to when, in the absence of the injury sustained, a claimant would have suffered symptoms or a particular level of symptoms from a degenerative condition, the expert will never be able to provide an opinion based on scientific proof. However, based on an analysis of the images of the relevant joints and bones taken on various occasions, information as to the extent of prior symptoms, the age of the claimant, his/her level of activity, and possibly assisted by relevant published papers, the medical expert will usually be able to identify a range of possible periods by which significant symptoms would reasonably be expected to occur. Then, on the balance of probabilities, the expert can usually identify a narrower range based on the particular facts of the case.

Many of the issues that the medical expert is required by the parties to resolve are issues that are simply not addressed in the course of medical practice, and which have no sound basis in medical science:

---

11   *Mallett v McMonagle* [1970] AC 166 at page 176

12   See Section 6.5

By how many years have the symptoms that would have arisen due to the claimant's pre-existing asymptomatic degenerative condition been brought forward by the accident? [13]

When, in the absence of this accident, is it likely that the claimant would have suffered this condition?

How do the consequences of the sensory deficit resulting from the injury compare with those to be expected in any event without the accident?

Had the claimant's condition been correctly diagnosed within 6 hours of his admission to hospital, what would the outcome have been?

The questions that quantum experts have to address are often just as unfamiliar to the experience of ordinary professional practice:

What care and assistance or aids and equipment does the claimant require to put him back, so far as is reasonably possible, in the position he would have been in the absence of the injury?

By applying medical expertise and scientific knowledge, with reference to the expert's professional experience and to the literature, the medical expert can usually provide an answer to the lawyers that is an expression of the expert's medical expertise. It is an answer that can never be tested in any scientific way, yet the expert has to, and should be able to, give a justified rationale for an opinion on the basis of what is more likely than not when dealing with past events and based on the 'degree of likelihood' for future events.

When hearing expert evidence, a judge is not permitted simply to select one professional opinion over another, without having a basis for his/her preference. The role of the judge is to assess every aspect of the evidence and to decide which opinion is more likely to be correct, on the balance of probabilities. For expert evidence, this begins with establishing the relevance of the expert's qualifications and expertise, the methodology adopted by the expert, any assumptions made by the expert, the expert's apprehension of the factual basis, and the rationale for the opinions/conclusions that he/she has reached[14].

It is essential, therefore, that the reasoning process that supports an expert opinion should be no less detailed or nuanced than an opinion an expert would seek to give based on a scientific standard of proof: it simply adopts the civil standard of proof for testing each element of the reasoning process that takes the expert from the factual basis to an opinion. The opinion an expert gives may not be capable of proof in a scientific sense, but in giving an opinion the medical expert should apply a depth of practical expertise and scientific knowledge to justify the opinion.

---

13   In Section 6.4, we will examine how an expert needs to approach giving opinions on symptoms that have been 'brought forward'.

14   See Sections 3.8.3 and 3.9

Tempting though it may be for medical experts to believe that the lawyers seek only an intelligent guess, it is never a guess that is required.

In a difficult case, in which the medical expert is required to address which of several competing matters might be proved on the balance of probabilities, the guidance of Charles J in a civil case concerning children[15] can suggest an effective approach:

> 'It might be more helpful if the medical experts were not asked to express a view on the balance of probabilities but were rather asked to:
>
> 1. identify possible causes setting out in respect of each of the reasons why it might be a cause and thus why it should be considered;
>
> 2. state their views as to the likelihood of each possibility being a cause and the reasons why they include or reject it as a reasonable (rather than a fanciful or merely theoretical) cause;
>
> 3. compare the likelihood of the cause(s) identified as reasonable causes being the actual cause;
>
> 4. state whether they consider that a cause (or causes) was (or were) the most likely cause with reasons why; and
>
> 5. state whether they consider that a cause (or causes) was more likely than not to be the cause, with reasons.'

By applying medical expertise and scientific knowledge, with reference to the expert's professional experience and to the literature, the medical expert can usually provide an answer to the lawyers that is an expression of the expert's medical expertise.

Conclusion

Applying the civil standard of proof to both factual and opinion evidence is fundamental to the role of an expert witness. Every fact has to be considered in the light of this standard as does every expert opinion. The difficulty is that the standard 'on the balance of probabilities' is only ever used in very limited circumstances in everyday life and the conceptual difficulty of the test provides medical experts with a good deal of discomfort. This does not however excuse the expert being unwilling to engage with the civil standard of proof and to use it when producing his/her evidence for the court.

---

15   *A County Council v K, D and L* [2005] 1 FLR 851

Key-Point Summary

1. In civil litigation, the claimant has the burden of proof.

2. In civil litigation, every case is determined to the standard of proof of 'on the balance of probabilities'.

3. On the balance of probabilities is rarely used as a basis for determining professional decisions, except in civil litigation.

4. Large sums of money can rest on the opinion of an expert, so the expert must be comfortable with applying the civil standard of proof to each opinion in his/her evidence.

5. Even though the standard of proof to be applied represents a very low level of certainty from a scientific viewpoint, opinions must be supported by a clear rationale based on the expertise and experience of the expert and, so far as is possible, have a credible scientific or technical basis.

Next Steps

In the next chapter, we will explore the fundamental legal principles that underpin the court's assessment of expert evidence.

6

Opinion Evidence

Introduction

The opinion section of an expert report is of fundamental importance. The opinions expressed by the expert witnesses will ultimately determine whether or not the claimant will be able to pursue a claim for damages for personal injury, industrial disease or clinical negligence and the value of the claim. All opinion evidence must be expressed in terms that are clear, concise and reliable. This demands of the expert the ability to express opinions in a manner that is meaningful to the lawyers and the court.

Chapter Outline

In this chapter, we will explore three fundamental issues in a claim where expert opinion is essential:

1. causation of damage;

2. prognosis and future risk; and

3. consequences of injuries.

The parties in a claim have to rely on medical experts to assess these issues, which are often far from straightforward. Both the legal principles and their practical application to the facts of the case can cause problems for medical experts, for lawyers and for the court.

6.1   Causation of Damage

Judges and lawyers alike want to know what injuries, if any, the claimant has actually suffered as a result of the accident. Usually, there is little difficulty in identifying the injury (or injuries) with which the claimant has presented. However, one of the most important purposes of a medical expert report is to distinguish between those injuries, symptoms and effects that have been caused by the accident (or adverse event) from those that have not. Lawyers use the term 'causation' to describe this issue.

The Court of Appeal has made clear that there is a legal distinction to be made between proof that some damage has been caused by the defendant's breach of duty, the 'legal causation' element of the claim, and the assessment of damages (for the consequential losses arising from the breach of duty), which requires proof of the loss which has been and will be suffered by the claimant, the 'factual causation' element[1]. Expert medical evidence is crucial in addressing both elements of causation, whether the breach of duty caused injury to the claimant and in identifying the nature and extent of those injuries, In dealing with this second issue, the expert needs to go on to report on the consequential loss arising from these injuries from the date of the accident to the date of the examination and for the future.

In this book, we describe this two-stage reporting process of giving opinion on what injuries were sustained and on the nature and extent of those injuries and the consequential loss arising from the injuries as addressing (or dealing with) "causation". The purpose of the medical expert report in personal injury litigation is founded upon these two interrelated issues and crucially how effectively the report gives opinion on these issues.

---

1   *Smithurst v Sealant Construction Services Ltd* [2011] EWCA Civ 1277 and Sections 2.2.2 and 2.2.3

> In a claim arising out of an injury, not only the causation of the injury itself but of all of the subsequent symptoms, effects and consequences have to be proved by the claimant and must be addressed by the medical expert in the expert report.

A claimant can only recover damages for the consequences arising from the accident and not for anything that would probably have occurred or been suffered in any event. A claimant must therefore prove that his/her loss was caused by the relevant accident. To proceed with a claim, the claimant's medical evidence must establish which of the claimant's complaints since the accident and which of the concerns in relation to the claimant's medical health for the future are a consequence of the accident. It must also establish that these complaints and concerns would not have arisen in the absence of the accident.

> Lawyers use the term 'but for' when addressing the issue of causation: 'but for the accident, the claimant would not have suffered...'

The issues of causation and of consequential loss are not generally part of a medical practitioner's assessment of a patient and are not written about in medical reports to colleagues. For the most part, causation is irrelevant to medical practice - a patient is as a patient is and what would have been the situation were circumstances to have been different is of no, or very little, significance. Most medical experts do not recognise or understand the fundamental importance of the issue of causation to lawyers and the need to value the loss arising from the injuries sustained, both of which are an essential part of the litigation process.

Having a clear understanding of causation is one of the fundamental components of the medico-legal mind. When expressing opinions on causation, the expert needs to be accurate and precise in his/her use of language and terminology. It is important that medical experts are aware that some of the technical language in a medical expert report is inter-disciplinary, while other terms have a specific meaning and significance in a medico-legal context. Terms that are used interchangeably in everyday profes- sional practice often have specific meanings in the medico-legal arena.

When addressing causation, one such area of confusion for medical experts (and alas many instructing lawyers) is the distinction in the medico-legal use of the terms: *Injury, Symptoms, Effects and Consequences.* As most experts are unclear precisely how these terms should be used, many substitute one for another, without realising the detrimental effect this has on the quality and clarity of the evidence. However, once the distinction between these terms is understood, experts can use these terms as an agenda to seek out relevant factual information on these aspects of the claim during the interview and examination of the claimant and during the analysis of medical records. Such information is fundamental to addressing the issue of causation.

Let us define these terms and illustrate how to use them in a report:

Injury	the physical/psychological trauma suffered
Symptoms	the physical/psychological manifestations of the injury
Effects	the physical/psychological limitations experienced by the claimant as a result of the injury/symptoms
Consequences	the restrictions on the activities of daily living since the accident, now and for the future, that result from the injury/symptoms/effects

Therefore, to apply these terms in a personal injury report dealing with a claimant injured in a car accident: a soft-tissue *injury* to the claimant's neck caused *symptoms* of severe headaches for two weeks, with the *effect* that the claimant had to rest most afternoons during that period, with the *consequence* that he was unable to work for two weeks after the accident.

In a claim arising out of an injury, not only the causation of the injury itself but of all of the subsequent symptoms, effects and consequences have to be proved by the claimant and must be addressed by the medical expert in the expert report.

The effect of not dealing properly with causation is that the expert evidence prevents the claim being properly assessed or valued, which delays the progress of the claim and initiates the tedious round of correspondence and questions by the lawyers seeking clarification of the expert's opinions.

'Signs' and 'Symptoms'

Doctors make a clear distinction between the terms 'signs' (manifestations of an injury that are objectively ascertainable) and 'symptoms' (manifestations of an injury as reported by the client). Most lawyers do not appreciate this difference, tending to conflate the distinct meanings of these terms. From a legal perspective, signs will either be supportive of (or not supportive of) the injury, symptoms and effects that the claimant claims and so it is important that the expert makes clear what the sign is and what it shows and how it supports or does not support particular aspects of the claimant's claim.

A lawyer would find the following opinions **unhelpful** because in both examples the evidence does not address what consequences actually resulted from the accident:

I am asked to consider whether had the accident not happened Mr J would have been able to continue in his employment until retirement age. It is impossible to say whether in the absence of the accident he would have been able to continue in his employment. That is a hypothetical question and is not capable of a scientific answer.

Based on his account of the circumstances of the accident, his past medical history, scan results and my clinical experience it is my opinion that his pre-existent back problems contribute 10-20% of the present problem while the index event contributes 80-90%.

A lawyer would find the following opinions **helpful** because the evidence provides a clear opinion on causation and gives the rationale that supports the conclusion reached by the expert:

If the accident had not occurred, Mr J would probably have been able to continue in his current employment until age 60, although it is likely that from about that age, in the light of developing and increasing symptoms, he would have had to find lighter work or reduce the number of hours he worked. As a result of the accident and his subsequent medical retirement, those options are no longer available to him.

I consider it is very unlikely that Mr W will return to work before the age of 65. I am of the opinion that given his pre-morbid functioning, the psychosocial/family disruption, his musculo-skeletal problems and his alcohol intake, he would not have worked to the age of 65 in any event. I consider that the culmination of these factors would almost certainly have resulted in his leaving work before his retirement age of 65. Although it is impossible to be precise, I consider it probable that there would have been a reduction of working life of at least 5 years, resulting in his retirement at the age of 60.

6.1.1 Competing Causes of Injury

If there are a number of possible independent explanations for a condition following an accident, then the 'but for' test must be applied to establish whether the condition was, for legal purposes, caused by the accident. In order to recover damages the claimant must prove that in the absence of the accident that is the subject of the claim (i.e. the negligence or other breach of duty) the injury would probably not have occurred.

1. A boy fell from a tree, sustaining a fracture of the femoral epiphysis. The fracture was negligently missed at hospital, and the boy went on to develop avascular necrosis. Damages for the subsequent damage to the leg would not be recoverable if there was at least a 50% risk of avascular necrosis even had the fracture been appropriately diagnosed. The claimant would not be able to prove that it was more likely than not that the avascular necrosis was caused by the negligence – in other words, he is not able to prove that 'but for' the negligence the avascular necrosis would probably not have occurred in any event. The lawyers will look to the medical expert to give opinion on such issues[2].

2. A premature baby developed retrolental fibroplasia after being given excess oxygen by doctors. The hospital trust whose staff had acted negligently and were responsible for the baby receiving excess oxygen would not be found liable in damages for the consequences to the baby unless it were proved that the negligence probably caused the blindness and therefore that in the absence of that negligence the baby would not have sustained damage. If there were a number of other 'innocent' or non-negligent explanations for the development of the condition, then the claim could not succeed unless it were proved that the damage to the baby's vision would not have occurred 'but for' the excess oxygen[3].

The approach suggested in the case of *A County Council v K, D and L* referred to above in Section 5.5 above provides one potential solution to this difficulty of proof where there are multiple competing causes[4].

6.1.2 Material Contribution

In very limited circumstances, the 'but for' test is relaxed and it is sufficient if it can be proved by the claimant that the defendant's breach of duty 'materially contributed' to the injury. This will arise in the limited situation where medical science cannot establish the probability that 'but for' an act of negligence the injury would not have happened, but can establish that the contribution of the negligent cause was more than minimal.

Outside the field of industrial disease claims, it is safe to assume that in the absence of instructions to the contrary, the normal 'but for' test applies. However, the medical expert should remain aware of the possibility of needing to address 'material contribution' in circumstances where there are competing causes of

---

2   See *Hotson v East Berkshire Area Health Authority* [1987] AC 750, which is discussed in Section 5.3

3   See *Wilsher v Essex Area Health Authority* [1988] AC 1074

4   *A County Council v K, D and L* [2005] 1 FLR 851

injury and there are no scientific means of establishing their relative contribution to that injury. (We address 'material contribution' in Industrial Disease claims in Section 6.3 and in Clinical Negligence claims in Section 8.7.)

6.1.3 Distinguishing the Approach to the Past and to the Future

We have seen in Chapter 5 how the balance of probabilities is used to prove past facts. If it is more likely than not that it was the accident that caused the psychiatric illness or the prolapsed intervertebral disc, then for the purposes of the claim, it did. If it is more likely than not that it was the breach of the duty of care of the doctor that caused the myocardial infarction, then for the purposes of the claim, it did. However, once it is proved that damage was caused in the accident, and it is proved on the balance of probabilities what the impact to date has been (compared to what would have occurred in the absence of breach of duty), in addressing the future the law recognises that there are uncertainties as to what will happen and what would have happened in the absence of the accident. The assessment of damages for these future potential effects of the breach of duty will take into account the nature of those future chances or uncertainties.

The law, however, recognises the difficulty there can be in seeking to assess all of these relevant risks and chances when looking into the future to assess the consequences of an injury. Short cuts, such as the use of 'the acceleration method', can be used if this is fair to the claimant and properly reflects the medical evidence (see Section 6.4 below).

6.2 Giving Opinions on Causation

In considering and giving opinion upon each of the claimant's complaints, the medical expert must distinguish clearly between:

1. the present injuries or medical situation and how these would have been but for the accident;

2. the present symptoms and the symptoms as these would have been but for the accident;

3. the present effects (or degree of disability) and what these would have been but for the accident; and

4. the present consequences of the injuries, symptoms and effects on the claimant's daily life, and the consequences as these would have been but for the accident.

Opinions on causation need to be expressed on the period from the accident to the date of the examination or report, and for the future.

> When addressing causation, one such area of confusion for medical experts (and alas many instructing lawyers) is the distinction in the medico-legal use of the terms: *Injury, Symptoms, Effects and Consequences.*

The difficulty of forming opinions on causation is that a claimant may have had some symptoms prior to the accident, on to which the symptoms resulting from the injury have been superimposed. There may be pre-existing degenerative changes, asymptomatic prior to the accident but contributing to the situation since the accident or which might do so in the future. There may also be some other unrelated disease or condition that will affect the future. All of these issues can make causation a challenging principle to apply.

> The greatest failing in medical expert reports is the inability or unwillingness of medical experts to address causation adequately. It is a daily complaint of lawyers that medical experts do not understand the importance of causation: this complaint applies equally to reports in personal injury, clinical negligence and industrial disease claims.

When addressing causation, the medical mind is far more comfortable with giving opinions on the situation as it is now than on giving opinions on what the situation would have been in the absence of (i.e. but for) the accident. The medico-legal mind understands that without the second half of the opinion dealing with the 'but for' position, the opinion is incomplete and the claim cannot be valued.

6.2.1   Causation Graphs

A straightforward way to think about causation is to use a 'causation graph', where the X-axis represents the progression of time and the Y-axis deals with the severity of injuries/symptoms/effects. A typical graph for a claimant injured in a road traffic accident is presented below.

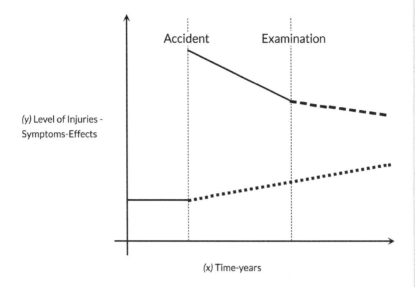

CAUSATION GRAPH #1: Actual and Predicted Recovery from Injuries

Accident   Examination

(y) Level of Injuries - Symptoms-Effects

(x) Time-years

The solid line illustrates a very low-level of injury/symptoms/effects experienced by the claimant before the accident, with a sudden uplift as the claimant is injured in the accident. Following the accident, there is a gradual improvement in the claimant's situation as the injuries heal and the symptoms diminish. Initially, he returns to work part time before returning to full time work. At the examination date, the medical expert's opinion is that the claimant's medical situation in the future will continue to gradually improve – this is represented by the dashed line – with fewer effects on his activities of daily living.

To deal properly with causation and the consequential loss arising, the medical expert also has to give opinion on the claimant's situation in the absence of the accident, to the date of the report and into the future – this opinion is represented by the lower dotted line. The opinion of the expert as represented on this graph is that there would have been a gradual worsening of the claimant's pre-existing condition over time. The expert will need to consider whether the two lines dealing with the projected future (dashed and dotted post examination date) would eventually meet, which would be the moment when the symptoms that the claimant is likely to suffer as a result of the accident will be equivalent to those that he would have suffered without ('but for') the accident.

The upper and lower lines on the causation graph will be different in every case. If the upper and lower lines meet, either because the claimant's condition improves sufficiently or because of a likely deterioration of a pre-existing condition, then this will be the time-limit for the compensation claim – i.e. the claimant will be back in the position he/she would have been in but for the accident and the 100% Recovery principle[5] will have been met.

In a personal injury claim, the essential questions to be addressed are:

> To what extent, and in what way, has the accident affected the claimant's (actual) situation with regard to the injuries, symptoms and effects he/she has suffered and the consequential restrictions on employment and his/her activities of daily living, since the accident and for the future? [Top line]

> But for the accident, what would have been the claimant's (hypothetical) situation with regard to his/her pre-accident condition from the accident date and into the future (i.e. injuries/symptoms) and in regard to any effects and consequences resulting from his/her pre-accident condition over the same period? [Bottom line]

> How much worse off, in terms of consequences, has the claimant been since the accident, is presently, and will be for the future, than would have been the situation in the absence of the accident? [To answer this, the expert describes the differences in injuries/symptom/effects that the space between the top and bottom lines represents and then gives opinion on the consequences that arise from these differences.]

The expert's approach in forming opinions on these questions therefore, as illustrated by the causation graph, is to:

1. identify the situation until now and for the future; (Top line)

2. identify what the situation would have been until now and for the future, but for the accident; (Bottom line)

3. consider if the difference is caused by or attributable to the accident;

4. describe the difference in terms of injuries/symptoms/effects; (the area between the two lines)

5. interpret the difference the accident has made in terms of consequences: pain, suffering and loss of amenity, restrictions or limitations in activity and consequential restrictions in terms of daily living, employment and special needs[6].

---

5   See Section 2.5

6   We recommend that this final element of the opinion, regarding the consequences of the injury be dealt with in its own section. See discussion of consequences in Section 6.6.2, report templates in Chapter 11 and Notes to the templates in Appendix 1.

Experts can apply this approach to causation to any factual situation in a claim. Consider the following examples:

> A claimant with a painful arthritic hip injures the same hip in an accident and 12 months afterwards undergoes a total hip replacement. What additional pain and restriction in activity and what treatment did the claimant experience over that which would have occurred "but for" the accident? By what period, if any, was the need for the hip replacement brought forward?

> A claimant in his 60's suffers from noise induced hearing loss caused by exposure to excessive noise in the workplace. As a result, his hearing thresholds at particular frequencies are raised. What is the likely impact of this hearing loss in terms of everyday activities (conversation, watching TV, speaking on the telephone) and what is the need for hearing aids? How does that compare with likely age-related hearing loss in the absence of the noise induced hearing loss? When would hearing aids probably have been required in any event?

> A claimant suffers a 4th degree perineal tear in childbirth, which is neither recognised nor appropriately treated following the birth. This results in the need for subsequent surgery including a colostomy and persisting residual symptoms. What treatment would have been appropriate had the situation been recognised at the time? How would that treatment compare with the treatment in fact required as a result of the failure to diagnose and treat? How does the current situation and future consequences compare with what would probably have been the situation with appropriate treatment?

Whatever the factual situation, the same logical approach applies. The expert needs to identify and report on the difference that the accident or adverse event has made.

> In assessing which, if any, injuries have been caused by the accident, it is often helpful in less clear-cut cases for the expert to consider whether the likely mechanism of the accident would have caused the injuries complained of and whether the level of symptoms reported by the claimant is consistent with the injuries identified by the expert as having been caused by the accident.

6.2.2   'Egg-Shell Skull' Principle and Causation

The 'Egg-Shell Skull' principle means that someone who causes injury to another person must take that other person as they are. If, therefore, the injured person has a particular vulnerability, which means that the impact of the accident or injury on them is more severe than would normally be expected, the person who causes the injury is responsible for all of the consequences. Common examples of this might include the impact of a traumatic experience on someone with a vulnerable personality as a result of a history of depression, a soft tissue knee injury in the case of someone still recovering from a previous similar injury or a prolapsed lumbar disc following an accident in someone with degenerative disease of the spine. In each case, the person causing the injury cannot avoid liability for the consequences being greater than would normally have been expected in a person of reasonable fortitude or constitution. Indeed, in an extreme case it may be that no significant injury would have been sustained, or injury of a different kind only would have been sustained, but for the pre-existing vulnerability. Nevertheless, the person causing the injury will still be liable for the full consequences of his/her act on the victim assuming that some injury, however minor, was foreseeable.

This principle is also relevant to cases where the consequence of the injury is greater because of a pre-existing condition, as for example a one-eyed person who is significantly worse off as a result of an injury causing loss of the remaining eye than if the injury to the eye was sustained by a person with normal binocular vision. Similarly it has been said that "it is much worse to be totally deaf than half deaf, and the additional hearing loss (from half to totally deaf) causes greater damage than the initial hearing loss (from full hearing to half deaf)."[7]

A recent example is the case of *Reaney v University Hospital of North Staffordshire NHS Trust*[8] in which the claimant had contracted transverse myelitis, causing damage to the spinal cord and what was effectively T7 paraplegia. Through the negligence of the defendant during hospitalisation, she developed a number of deep pressure sores with consequent osteomyelitis, flexion contractures and hip dislocation. The combined effect of these disabilities was that the claimant would now require two carers on a 24/7 basis for life and larger accommodation to house the carers, whereas she would have managed on the basis of 7 hours professional care a week supplemented by modest amounts of family support. She was entitled to damages to fund that additional level of care which she would not otherwise have required but which arose because of the effect of the hospital's negligence on top of her pre-existing condition.

However, these same egg-shell skull issues will be relevant to the question of causation – i.e. what injury or loss resulted from the accident and how that compares with what would probably have occurred in any event. In our example above, the person with the vulnerable personality might have suffered some further relapses of depression in any event. The claimant with the injured knee might not have

---

7   An example from *Clerk & Lindsell on Torts* 20th Ed at para 2.31

8   [2014] EWHC 3016

been able to return to skiing or working as a carpet layer even in the absence of the second accident. The disc prolapse might well have occurred in any event even in the absence of the second accident so that the subsequent surgery would still have been necessary.

It follows that the medical expert need not be directly concerned with the eggshell skull principle, but will be concerned with how in the particular case the consequences of the injury, in terms of the claimant's medical condition, can be attributed to the accident and will be concerned with any such vulnerabilities when considering what would have been the situation but for the accident.

6.2.3   Use of Percentages to Describe or Apportion Injury

The expert should always describe in words the difference an accident has made. It is unlikely to be useful for a medical expert to express this difference in terms of a percentage that reflects the difference between aspects of the situation now and the situation as it would have been but for the accident. A common and incorrect approach is for a medical expert to write, for example, that 50% of the symptoms (or pain or discomfort or disability) is attributable to the accident and the balance to the pre-existing condition. While this could be said to address the issue of causation of injury, it wholly fails to address the difference that the accident has made and therefore does not help the lawyers to establish a value for the claim.

The difficulty for the lawyers seeking to value the claim on the basis of a percentage contribution becomes obvious when we consider the following example. Take a claimant with low back pain. The expert's opinion is that 50% of the claimant's symptoms are attributable to the accident and 50% are attributable to his preexisting condition and would have been present in any event.

1.   Does the expert mean that the claimant now has twice as much pain?

2.   Does the expert mean that the claimant can only walk half as far?

3.   Does the expert mean the claimant can only lift half as much?

This opinion expressed as a percentage could mean that the claimant receives virtually no damages, or that the claimant receives nearly 100% of the damages claimed. If the first 50% (from the pre-existing condition) would not have affected the claimant's ability to work or any activities of daily living at all, or only occasionally, while the second 50% (from the accident) affected the claimant so that he can now no longer work or do anything useful around the home, then the first 50% will have little relevance in terms of damages recovered, whilst the second 50% will attract almost a full award of damages. In contrast, if the first 50% had resulted in the claimant losing employment and being largely unemployable because of the resulting restrictions in activity, the second 50% may actually add very little to the restrictions and the recoverable damages may be extremely small.

An opinion that 50% of the symptoms are attributable to the accident simply does not mean that he will recover 50% of the damages that he would have recovered had 100% been attributable to the accident. The expert must explain the differences between the situation as it now is (and will be for the future) and the situation as it would have been but for the accident and how these differences affect the claimant's life. The lawyers, often in larger cases with the aid of quantum experts, can then assess the loss that results from the symptoms that are attributable to the accident.

A lawyer would find the following opinions **unhelpful** because the evidence does not address in grounded and pragmatic language the difference that the accident has made and so prevents the lawyers from valuing the claim:

> Of his present problems 60% can be attributed to the low back while 40% can be attributed to symptoms and signs in his right lower limb. Of the overall disability arising from the low back and right lower limb, 20% might have been expected to occur even if this accident had not taken place but 80% of his residual symptoms can be attributed to the accident.

> She has a past history of suffering from anxiety symptoms. On each occasion this was treated successfully with short term treatment involving anxiolytic medication. She recovered completely from these symptoms. Having had anxiety symptoms in the past this should be viewed as a vulnerability factor to her developing depressive disorder due to the pain and restrictions arising from the accident. I would attribute up to 20% of the causality of the depressive disorder to this pre-existing vulnerability and 80% to the pain and restriction in activities arising from the accident.

> I would estimate that of the severity of his low back symptoms at the 5 year point after his accident, two-thirds will be attributable to his long-standing low back problems whereas one-third of the severity will be as a result of the accident and would not have been present if this accident had not occurred. Therefore there will be, at the 5 year point, an increase of 50% in the severity of his symptoms, solely as a result of the accident.

> In my opinion, 60-70% of the trouble that he is having in his thoracolumbar spine is attributable to the accident. The treatment he now requires is attributable to the accident and to the pre-existing degenerative changes in the spine. In my opinion, 60-70% of the treatment he now requires to his thoracolumbar spine is attributable to the accident.

A lawyer would find the following opinions **helpful** because the evidence makes clear the difference the accident has made and so helps the lawyers to value the claim:

> She has a past history of suffering from anxiety symptoms. On each occasion these were treated successfully, with full recovery after short term treatments involving anxiolytic medication. By 2007, she seems to have recovered completely from these symptoms. Having had anxiety symptoms in the past, this should be viewed as a vulnerability factor to her developing depressive disorder in the future.

> In the absence of the accident, it was highly probable that she would suffer a further depressive disorder at some time in the light of further stressors and adverse life events. In my opinion, any such depressive disorder caused by adverse life events would have been readily amenable to further similar treatment and recovery. However, it is the pain and restriction in activities arising from the accident that both initiated and perpetuated the current depressive disorder, which is of a far greater magnitude in terms of its physical and emotional impact and from which she has still not yet fully recovered.

> As a result of the accident, he continues to suffer symptoms in his low back and right lower limb, resulting in the restrictions in activity described above. I consider his complaints of residual symptoms to be reasonable and within the expected range given the severity of the accident. My impression is that, while all of his symptoms do impact on his everyday life, it is probably his back symptoms that undermine his quality of life and are the fundamental cause of his continuing disability. In my opinion, his restrictions are attributable to the accident and I do not consider it likely that he would have experienced any of these restrictions in the absence of the accident.

> … in the absence of the accident, he would probably have developed minor symptoms involving occasional and intermittent low back pain. This would likely have been managed with occasional use of over-the-counter painkillers and perhaps very occasional physiotherapy, but would not have significantly interfered with his work or activities of daily living. There is no indication that he would have developed any lower limb symptoms in the absence of the accident.

> An opinion that 50% of the symptoms are attributable to the accident simply does not mean that he will recover 50% of the damages that he would have recovered had 100% been attributable to the accident.

6.2.4   Questions about Percentages

In particular circumstances, the court may choose to apportion damages between two or more defendants on a percentage basis. This may be done where two or more defendants are responsible for the same injury or where the court cannot distinguish which specific accident or adverse event has caused what specific damage. This is normally done without the input of medical experts.

Some examples of such apportionment are:

1. A claimant suffers a psychiatric injury as a result of the combined effects of a vicious assault in which he suffered damage to his eye - for which assault his employer was liable - and a subsequent clinical negligence, which resulted in the loss of vision in that eye. Aspects of the damages recovered were apportioned between the defendants to reflect their relative contributions to the condition.

   As the different aspects of his subsequent mental problems could not be readily attributed to the two separate incidents (the assault and the surgical operation) an apportionment was made based on the rough and ready assessment of their likely contribution. Neither defendant was found to have caused the whole injury, some being caused mainly by one, some mainly by the other, and some by their combined effect, so that neither could properly have been held liable for the whole.

2. A claimant suffered three road traffic accidents, in each of which a whiplash injury was suffered. After the third accident, the claimant was forced to retire.

   The two medical experts giving evidence at the trial agreed that the effects of the accidents were cumulative and were responsible for the chronic pain state from which the claimant subsequently suffered. The judge held that it was this 'cumulative effect' that resulted in the retirement and the court apportioned damages resulting from the retirement and for the long term consequences between the three defendants. (The first two defendants had sought to argue that it was the third accident that caused the retirement and without it the claimant would not have retired.)

In both of these situations[9], the medical expert's role was to describe the consequences of the accident or injury in relation to which he/she is instructed – i.e. the effect of the assault or of the clinical negligence or the effect of the first, second, third or all three of the road traffic accidents. The expert will only address the proportions by which each breach of duty is responsible for the whole after first considering the effects of each individual breach and then only if specifically instructed to do so.

---

9   From *Rahman v Arearose Ltd* [2001] QB 351 and *Pearce v Lindfield* [2003] EWCA Civ 647

6.3 Industrial Disease Claims and 'Material Contribution'

In limited circumstances, the law permits the claimant to establish causation of damage to a lower standard, on the basis that the breach of duty made a 'material contribution' to the injury suffered by the claimant. In these cases, it is not possible to establish that 'but for' the negligence or other breach of duty of the defendant, the injury (including within the term 'injury' both medical conditions and diseases) would not have occurred. The most common application of this material contribution principle is in industrial disease claims in which the claimant is exposed to a harmful substance or agent, although it has also been applied in other fields including clinical negligence[10].

In this difficult area of law, the expert should always seek clear instructions from the instructing solicitor as to which of the tests of causation needs to be applied. However, it is useful for experts to understand the important distinguishing factors in all cases where the material contribution causation test should be applied.

There are three factors that distinguish these cases:

1. the agent responsible for causing the disease or condition is the same in each of several periods of exposure;

2. the mechanism by which that agent is applied to the claimant is the same; and

3. medical science cannot prove which period of exposure caused the injury.

So for example, the material contribution test would be applied in a case where a claimant demonstrates symptoms of noise induced hearing loss having been exposed to excessive noise by each of a number of employers as well as in his pastime of clay pigeon shooting. Or in the case of a claimant who used hand vibrating tools in several periods of employment – some as a self-employed contractor – who now suffers from vibration white finger.

However, where the agent that may have caused the condition could be one of several different agents – i.e. there are competing causes for the condition – the claimant will still have to establish which of the agents did, on the balance of probabilities, cause the condition and the lawyers will seek evidence from the medical experts on the 'but for' basis. For example, smoking and certain chemicals are major risk factors for bladder cancer. So, a claimant who smokes and who develops bladder cancer after exposure to aromatic amines from dyes will have to prove that this latter exposure more than doubled his risk of developing such a cancer as a result of smoking in order to demonstrate that the aromatic amines were the more likely cause[11].

---

10   See for example *Bailey v Ministry of Defence* [2009] 1 WLR 1062 and Section 8.7

11   *Novartis Grimsby Ltd v Cookson* [2007] EWCA Civ 1261

6.3.1 Application of Material Contribution Test to Complex Factual Situations

There are a variety of complex factual situations that create difficulty for lawyers and experts alike when seeking to address causation using the material contribution test. We discuss these difficult situations below and then explain how the medical expert must deal with these issues in the report.

Scientific Impossibility or Factual Difficulty

The law distinguishes between cases where the difficulty or impossibility of proof is as a result of an inability on the part of medical science to answer the causation question and those cases where it is as a result of a problem in establishing what the facts are (or were). The medical expert must therefore be able to distinguish between these two situations.

Only in the situation where there is an inability on the part of medical science to answer the causation question on the 'but for' basis is the material contribution test applicable:

A turkey plucker, who was provided with gloves and an apron, contracted campylobacter enteritis. She alleged that she had been infected as a result of her employer's failure to protect her from the risk of infection from handling dead poultry. The judge hearing the case held that the employer was negligent and in breach of statutory duty in failing to warn her of the risk of exposure to the bacterium and to advise her as to the precautions she should take to minimise the risk of infection. He went on to find that it was not possible to establish if those breaches had caused the infection, that is, that the infection would not have occurred had there been no such breaches. Therefore, he went on, the 'but for' test was not applicable and the claim succeeded because the breaches had materially increased the risk of infection.

On appeal, it was pointed out that the judge's difficulties with the 'but for' test were the result of a failure by him to make crucial findings of fact, for example, as to whether if properly warned the claimant would have avoided touching her face, or would not have discarded her gloves, or whether the risk of contact with the bacterium from contact with door handles would have been reduced or avoided. Had such findings been made it would have been open to him to hold that on the balance of probabilities the claimant would not have been infected if the employer had fulfilled its obligations. Therefore, it was not impossible for the claimant to prove causation on the usual 'but for' basis and it was not appropriate to apply the material contribution test instead. This was not a case where medical science was unable to establish the probability that the claimant would suffer the injury as a result of the employer's breaches of duty[12].

12   *Sanderson v Hull* [2008] EWCA Civ 1211

Some Exposure Culpable/Some Non-Culpable

A claimant may be able to prove that he/she has suffered injury as the result of cumulative exposure to a substance that is now known to be hazardous. Although all of the exposure may have been during employment with one employer, some of the exposure was culpable (i.e. negligent exposure or in breach of duty) and some was not. This situation arises where, for example, the state of knowledge about a substance has advanced, so that its hazardous nature is discovered or the level of what was previously regarded as safe exposure is reconsidered at a time when employees had previously been exposed to it without such knowledge. The situation also arises where there are statutory regulations that prohibit one activity that would result in such exposure, but not another activity that would also result in exposure.

In these cases, it is impossible to prove whether it was the culpable, or so-called "guilty" exposure, or the non-culpable or "innocent" exposure that caused the injury. The claimant may then establish liability arising from the employer's culpable exposure if it can be proved that this exposure made a material contribution to the cause of the injury:

A claimant contracted pneumoconiosis from being exposed to harmful silica dust at work with one employer. Some of the dust came from using swing grinders, and some from use of a pneumatic hammer. Owing to the regulations that applied at the time, the former was exposure for which liability arose (it was culpable), the latter was not. In the absence of detailed evidence as to the relative proportions of dust inhaled by the claimant arising from those 2 processes, the employer was held liable as the 'guilty' dust – that for which the employer was legally liable – had made a material contribution to the causation of the disease[13].

Cumulative Exposure where the Mechanism of Exposure is Unclear

The material contribution test also applies in claims where there is cumulative exposure to a substance capable of causing injury, but where medical science cannot prove the precise mechanism by which the injury was caused and therefore which period of exposure was responsible for the injury:

An employee contracted dermatitis from brick dust. He was exposed to brick dust while working in pipe kilns but also was exposed to the dust when he went home in his dusty work clothes. The employer was not liable for exposure in the pipe kilns but was under a duty to provide facilities to enable the employee to wash off the dust before going home. The precise mechanism by which the dermatitis was caused could not be proved by medical science at that time and it could not be proved whether it was the

---

13   *Bonnington Castings v Wardlaw* [1956] AC 613

dust in the kilns or the dust on the clothes taken home that caused the dermatitis. However, the claimant was permitted to recover in full for his condition against his employer on proof that there was a significant increase in the risk of contracting that disease as a result of the 'guilty' exposure[14].

Cumulative Exposure: Two or More Culpable Exposers

The material contribution test is also applied to claims in which there are two (or more) potential defendants liable to the claimant for cumulative exposure to a substance that is capable of causing injury, but where medical science cannot prove which of the defendants has in fact caused the injury.

Where the condition is dose-related, so that the greater the exposure, the worse the condition will be (as might be the case with pneumoconiosis, asbestosis or noise induced hearing loss), then the condition will probably have arisen to some extent as a result of each period of exposure, and each period of exposure can be said to have materially contributed to the final condition. Each employer responsible for a 'more than minimal exposure' will be liable to the claimant for causing the condition.

Where it is not possible scientifically to say which of the periods of exposure by the successive employers resulted in the disease (as for example in the development of mesothelioma from exposure to asbestos) then any of the employers who had been responsible for 'materially increasing the risk' of contracting the disease will be liable[15]. Therefore, in this limited category of cases, liability will be established where it is proved that exposure by one defendant resulted in a material increase in the risk of the injury being caused.

Cumulative Exposure: 'But For' Test Applicable

In contrast to the above situations, it may be that the claimant has been exposed to a single substance or agent capable of causing harm by several employers, but that it is still possible to address causation on the usual 'but for' basis.

For example, it may be proved that in the absence of the exposure by the last employer, the claimant would not have developed the condition at all. This could be argued where the threshold for the development of symptoms had not been reached until the exposure by the last employer, in which case, the other employers may be able to avoid liability on the usual 'but for' basis. Typically, this situation may arise in relation to a cumulative condition such as vibration white finger where, had the claimant's exposure to vibration ceased with the penultimate employer, the condition would not, on the balance of probabilities, have developed.

---

14   *McGhee v National Coal Board* [1973] 1 WLR 1

15   *Fairchild v Glenhaven Funeral Services* [2003] 1 AC 32; *Barker v Corus Plc* [2006] UKHL 20

6.3.2   Apportionment of Damages

A further issue that arises in claims involving concurrent and cumulative causes of injury is the extent to which a defendant should be liable for the total damage and loss suffered by the claimant. If three employers exposed the claimant to asbestos and he subsequently contracts asbestosis or mesothelioma, with damages assessed at say £100,000, how is that liability to be divided between the employers? Further, where one of those employers was not culpable (for example, owing to the state of knowledge during that period of employment as to the dangers from the inhaling asbestos dust) or cannot now be identified or has no insurance or assets, how then is the liability to pay damages divided?

'Divisible' and 'Non-Divisible' Conditions

Where the condition that the claimant contracts or develops is dose-related, such as with noise induced hearing loss or asbestosis, then each defendant is liable for its contribution towards the condition. Lawyers call such injury 'divisible', meaning that the seriousness of the medical condition is related to the degree of exposure to the agent causing it. The defendant is only liable for the part of the overall injury that its culpable exposure caused. Where there is a period of exposure that does not result in liability being established against anyone (for example because of non-culpable exposure) that contribution is also taken into account in such a 'divisible' injury claim, thereby reducing the liability of the liable employers. Also, where there is a period of exposure for which the claimant him/herself is responsible, for example during a period of self-employment, then this contribution is also taken into account, reducing the amount of damages to be paid by the liable employers.

If the injury is not dose-related and is therefore 'indivisible', so that it is not possible on the basis of medical science to say how much contribution the exposure by any one defendant has made to the injury or condition (other than that it is more than minimal), then the traditional approach has been that it is inappropriate to apportion the damages between the defendants and non-culpable exposers. Each defendant will be liable to the claimant for the whole (although entitled to a contribution from each of the other defendants)[16].

Where the condition is not dose-related but liability is established on the basis of a material contribution to an increase in the risk of the injury occurring, for example in the case of the development of mesothelioma from exposure to asbestos, the law is that the liability is shared according to 'the contribution to the risk' of contracting the disease[17]. However, in the specific case of mesothelioma (and only in this case) the law has been changed by statute to provide that each of the culpable employers is liable for the whole of the damages, although each is entitled to seek a contribution from each of the other culpable employers[18]. The argument as to the

---

16   *Dickins v O2 Plc* [2008] EWCA Civ 1144; *Bailey v Ministry of Defence* [2009] 1 WLR 1062

17   *Barker v Corus Plc* [2006] UKHL 20

18   Section 3(2) Compensation Act 2006

correct approach to apportionment of damages in the case of lung cancer found to have been caused by exposure to asbestos is currently working its way through the courts. At the present time (June 2015), where there are multiple exposers none of whom can be shown to have individually doubled the risk of lung cancer, damages are apportioned according to the contribution to total dose of asbestos for which each exposer is responsible, as if the condition were divisible, although traditionally cancer would have been regarded as an indivisible injury[19].

Where apportionment of damage is required, to avoid a complicated and time-consuming process of assessment of the contributions made, the court will often fall back on a time-exposed basis to assess the contributions. Each liable party will pay as its share of damages that proportion which the period of exposure for which that party is liable bears to the total period of exposure.

Where, for example, a claimant is exposed to asbestos dust by several employers and subsequently develops asbestosis, each employer will be liable to contribute to the damages recoverable for that condition to the extent of their contribution to the condition by exposure to the dust. The apportionment is a question of assessment of time exposure by the defendants or possibly by the intensity of such exposure, but this is a matter for assessment by an engineering expert rather than a medical expert.[20]

6.3.3　Approach to the Evidence

When faced with a claim in which the material contribution test needs to be applied, it is important for the expert to adopt a logical approach in assessing the evidence to ensure that the material contribution test is applied appropriately to the issues in dispute.

Culpable and Non-Culpable Exposure

Where there is a single period of both culpable and non-culpable exposure, the medical expert should address two questions.

1. Would the injury probably have occurred as a result of the non-culpable exposure in any event?

If the answer is that the injury would have occurred in any event, then 'but for' the culpable exposure, the injury would still have occurred. Therefore, the claimant would fail to prove causation of injury as a result of the culpable exposure. Where the answer is that it would not have occurred in any event, then 'but for' the culpable exposure, the injury would probably not have occurred. Therefore, the claimant would succeed in proving causation of injury as a result of the culpable exposure.

2. If the medical expert is unable to answer the above question because medi-

---

19   *Heneghan v Manchester Dry Docks et al* [2014] EWHC 4190

20   See *Holtby v Brigham & Cowan* [2000] 3 All ER 421

cal science cannot establish the probability that 'but for' the contribution of the culpable exposure the injury would not have occurred, then the second question for the expert to address is, was the contribution of the culpable exposure more than minimal?

Where the answer is that the contribution of the culpable exposure was more than minimal, the 'but for' test is modified to the assessment of 'material contribution'. Therefore, the claimant would succeed in proving causation from the culpable exposure. Where the answer is that the contribution was not more than minimal, causation would not be established and the claimant would fail.

Periods of Culpable Exposure

Where there are periods of culpable exposure by more than one potential defendant, the medical expert should assist by addressing two questions, which would need to be considered in relation to each potential defendant.

1. Would the injury in its totality probably have occurred as a result of the exposure by one, some, or all of the other potential defendants in any event?

If the answer is that the injury in its totality would probably have occurred in any event, then 'but for' the potential defendant's exposure the injury would still have occurred. Therefore, the claimant would fail to prove causation of injury against that potential defendant. Where the answer is that the injury in its totality would probably not have occurred 'but for' the exposure by that defendant, the claimant would succeed against that defendant. However, if the medical expert is unable to answer the question because medical science cannot establish the probability that 'but for' the contribution of the defendant the injury would or would not have occurred, then the expert must then consider the second question.

2. Can medical science establish that the contribution of the culpable exposure by that defendant was more than minimal?

If the answer is that the contribution of the culpable exposure was more than minimal, then the 'but for' test is modified. Therefore, the claimant would succeed against that potential defendant. Where the answer is that the contribution is not more than minimal, causation would not be established and the claimant would fail to prove the claim against that defendant.

Therefore, where it is impossible medically to say which of the several defendants' actions or failures caused the injury, but that in each case the mechanism of exposure would have been the same, then the medical expert should express an opinion as to whether each defendant's actions or failures made a material contribution to the risk of developing the injury.

Apportionment

Having expressed an opinion that the defendant has made a material contribution to the cause of a dose-related injury or a material increase in the risk of an injury (except in the case of mesothelioma), what the lawyer then requires is an opinion as to the extent of the contribution made by that defendant to the resulting injury. Where to do so would be outside the expert's field of expertise, then he/she should indicate this in the report and signpost for the lawyers the need to instruct a suitable expert to address the question.

6.4 'Acceleration' and 'Exacerbation' (a classic case of 'Foot-Wearing')[21]

The terms 'Acceleration' and 'Exacerbation' are not strictly medical or legal terms of art. These terms exist in the medico-legal sphere as a shorthand description of the relationship between the situation since an accident when compared to the likely progression of a pre-existing condition (i.e. the top and bottom line on the causation graph). Experts and lawyers alike talk about "a 3-year acceleration case" as one where the level of symptoms the claimant is now suffering has been brought forward in time by three years. Similarly, experts and lawyers will discuss an increase in symptoms following an injury as "an exacerbation of a pre-existing condition".

Although well established as medico-legal terms, the medical basis for opinions based on the underlying principles these terms signify is beginning to be challenged by some medical experts. Indeed, for some experts and lawyers, these terms are simply a fiction to enable an award of damages to be calculated and have no basis in science at all. For others, the use of these terms represents the best approach available for predicting what would have happened to the claimant in the absence of the accident and so represents the only sensible way of calculating an award of damages.

For a few experts, however, the use of these terms appears to be a way to humour lawyers and their obsession with quantification:

> We have come to slightly differing opinions with regard to the period of advancement of symptoms as a result of the index event. I suggest 9 – 12 months; Mr S suggests a somewhat wider range of 12 – 24 months.
>
> However, given that the whole concept of advancement or acceleration is an artificial one that cannot be accurately quantified and is a concept that we introduce in cases of this nature to try to help the legal profession in the quantification of damages, we should simply produce these figures as a guide for the court and would not see them as an area of significant disagreement.

---

21   For an explanation of 'Foot-Wearing' see Authors' Note

6.4.1 The Legal Basis for Acceleration

The law also recognises the somewhat tenuous nature of the 'acceleration method' for assessing future loss[22] but sees it as, in appropriate cases, a convenient and fair approach. In the case of *Smithurst v Sealant Construction Services Ltd* [23] the claimant suffered a disc prolapse after handling heavy weights at work. Medical evidence indicated that he was more at risk of such a prolapse than the majority of the population. The court had to consider the correct way to assess damages allowing for that risk and therefore the chance that the consequences of the disc prolapse would be experienced by the claimant at some uncertain date in any event. On the basis of strict legal principle, if there was, in the absence of the accident, a 25% risk of prolapse in 5 years, a 50% risk in 10 years and say a 75% risk in 15 years, then the losses now suffered as the result of the prolapse would be discounted by a proportion of the loss for each of those periods to reflect that risk:

> 'Our attention was ... drawn to the case of Hanks v Ministry of Defence[24] in which Royce J. in the course of assessing damages did consider the risks that certain events would happen in the future and made different assessments in relation to different events relevant to different heads of loss. However, I do not think it follows that that is the only permissible method to adopt. The assessment of damages is to some extent inevitably imprecise; what is required is that the judge adopt a method of assessment that is fair to the claimant and takes proper account of the evidence before the court and the way in which the case was presented. Although in principle when considering what the future would have held for the claimant had he not been injured by the defendant the court should approach the matter by assessing the relevant risks or chances, that may call for a much more sophisticated enquiry than the court is equipped to perform. ... In many cases the acceleration method, although less refined, will be fair to the claimant if it properly reflects the medical evidence.'

The court went on to consider how to assess damages in this case:

> '[The medical expert evidence] supports the conclusion that the chances of Mr. Smithurst's suffering a very similar injury in the future existed as from the moment of the accident and rose progressively to near certainty by the end of two years. A detailed evaluation of the chances that Mr. Smithurst would have suffered a similar injury at any given point in his working life might lead to a different award of damages, but that does not mean that it is wrong to adopt the acceleration approach. ... The acceleration method would involve an element of swings and roundabouts, under which Mr. Smithurst would recover damages calculated at the full rate over two years but nothing thereafter, rather than damages calculated at a progressively diminishing rate over a longer period. I do not think that an excessively analytical approach to the

---

22   The correct approach to the use of the term 'Acceleration' is set out in Section 6.5

23   *Smithurst v Sealant Construction Services Ltd* [2011] EWCA Civ 1277

24   [2007] EWHC 966 (QB)

> *assessment of damages is to be encouraged in cases of this kind and where the medical experts have not attempted to forecast in statistical terms the chances that a similar injury would have occurred at different times in the future the judge will not have been provided with the means to carry out a proper assessment of the risks involved. In those circumstances, provided the judge is careful to ensure that the cut-off date fairly reflects the medical evidence, the acceleration approach can in my view properly be adopted.'*

It should be noted that this case addressed the situation where an identical event (in this case a disc prolapse) precipitated in different circumstances would have occurred. This was not the comparison of the impact of an acute onset following an accident with a slow development of a degenerative condition which would have occurred in any event but with a different impact on the claimant. That situation is likely to result in an even more difficult task if the risks involved in the equivalent development of the condition or of symptoms were to be accurately assessed and timed.

'Acceleration' is therefore condoned by the courts as an unsophisticated and not unduly analytical approach to a common situation in injury claims. That does not, however, mean that the term should be used without any analysis by the expert as to what the situation on which he or she reports and expresses an opinion really is.

6.4.2   The Need to Explain 'Acceleration'

Whatever an expert's professional opinion on the conceptual validity of these terms – and it seems that this argument may become more contentious in the next several years – there is no doubt that in most cases these terms are either used inappropriately or without an appropriate level of explanation, to the point where the accuracy of the evidence is lost. A very serious problem arises when experts in their reports use these terms as a shorthand description, because experts and lawyers alike have forgotten (or never knew) what the terms actually mean and so use the terms without making clear what in fact they mean by them.

What is required is a comparison of the likely situation as it would have been but for the accident and the situation as it now is and is likely to be in the future. The expert is required to assist in that exercise by applying his/her expertise to the evidence to provide an opinion as to the likely difference(s) of onset – both temporal and qualitative – of the symptoms as the result of the accident and the differences in consequences for the claimant as the result of the accident. (We first introduced this issue in Section 5.5 in the discussion of 'Proof'.)

Even though medical experts generally find this approach to be artificial and not based in medical science, for lawyers this is a pragmatic approach to calculating the appropriate level of compensation, as *Smithurst v Sealant Construction Services Ltd*[25] demonstrates. In many cases where acceleration and exacerbation are relevant issues, medical experts often reach very different opinions without a strong basis from which an opposing opinion can be challenged.

---

25   *Smithurst v Sealant Construction Services Ltd* [2011] EWCA Civ 1277 discussed in detail in the previous Section

Such differences of opinion would have to be discussed at an experts' meeting and the basis of the difference explained. The outcome of the discussion then allows the lawyers or the court to reach a judgement on the matter. For the valuation of the claim, these differences of opinion can be extremely important, so the more help experts can offer in relation to the likely progression of a pre-existing condition, the more helpful the evidence will be to the lawyers and the court.

Let us turn once more to the causation graph to understand precisely what the terms 'acceleration' and 'exacerbation' mean:

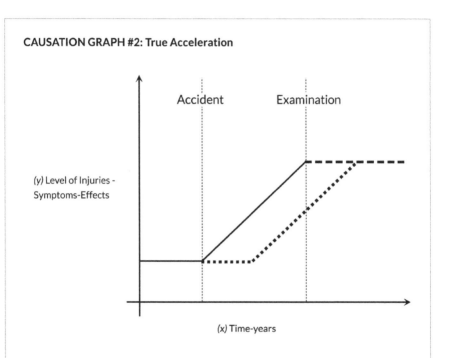

CAUSATION GRAPH #2: True Acceleration

Accident   Examination

(y) Level of Injuries -
Symptoms-Effects

(x) Time-years

The accurate use of the term acceleration would require that the injuries, symptoms and effects that the claimant suffered as a result of the accident are *exactly the same* as those that the claimant would have suffered in the absence of the accident, but are experienced earlier as a result of the accident. On the causation graph, this means that the line moves to the left on the X-axis (i.e. brought forward in time) but its shape does not change.

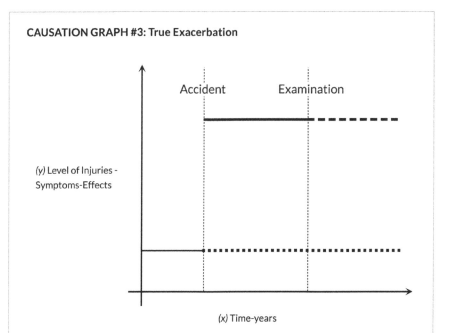

CAUSATION GRAPH #3: True Exacerbation

Accident   Examination

(y) Level of Injuries -
Symptoms-Effects

(x) Time-years

The accurate use of the term exacerbation would require that the injuries, symptoms and effects that the claimant suffered as a result of the accident are of *exactly the same type* as those that the claimant would have suffered in the absence of the accident, but are now more severe as a result of the accident. On the causation graph, this means that the injuries/symptoms/effects line moves upwards on the Y-axis (i.e. increasing the severity) but its relation to time does not change.

Therefore, where the onset of a condition caused by an accident is different to what would have otherwise been the case, this is not "an acceleration case". Where more injuries have been suffered than would otherwise been the case, this is not "an exacerbation case". If an expert chooses to use the shorthand terms acceleration or exacerbation, then it is essential to also explain what is meant in terms of the injuries, symptoms, effects and consequences for the claimant. Otherwise, there is the considerable danger that the expert will not communicate to the lawyer with any accuracy what he/she in fact means.

The use of the terms acceleration and exacerbation alone is not sufficient or precise enough to communicate clearly the situation to the court. The expert must, therefore, avoid the terms altogether or use them only as the starting point for a clear description of the situation. It may be appropriate to indicate that there has been an acceleration of the onset of symptoms, but it is then necessary to describe (and if appropriate to contrast) the differing onsets: the actual and the hypothetical onset but for the accident.

Therefore, a lawyer would find the following opinions **unhelpful** because the evidence does not address whether the symptoms are identical to those that would have been suffered in any event, whether the onset of symptoms is identical or what the rationale is for the opinion (a guess in the first example and unstated empirical evidence in the second being unacceptable):

It must be emphasised that the issue of acceleration in a case such as this is essentially speculative. It is quite possible that different colleagues might take significantly different views regarding the length of time of the acceleration periods, some preferring a longer period and others a shorter period. My guess, and it can be no more than that, is an acceleration period of 3 years.

He is a 59 year old man with evidence of degenerative change in his spine and a reasonable suggestion is that he would be experiencing symptoms probably within 2 to 3 years of this material incident. This is a purely speculative suggestion based on no valid scientific evidence and is very much empirical in nature.

A lawyer would find the following opinions **helpful** as the evidence deals effectively with both the recovery from the accident and the 'but for' the accident situation:

The back and neck symptoms and pain that Mr X suffered following the accident were initially severe and incapacitating. These began to diminish gradually in the weeks following the accident, so that six weeks on from the accident, Mr X was able to spend short periods out of bed and to move short distances around the ward. He returned home after 10 weeks in hospital. His neck pain and stiffness gradually resolved within 12 months of the accident, leaving him with residual back symptoms and pain that continued to settle over the next 6 months (i.e. 18 months post-accident). At that time, he was able to begin part time work in office based employment, though he continues to suffer pain and stiffness that require analgesics and occasional days off work.

In the absence of the accident, Mr X would probably have suffered a gradual increase in back symptoms and pain as a result of the natural progression of the pre-existing deterioration in his lumbar spine. It is my opinion that, in the absence of the accident, the pain and restriction that he would have experienced within a period of 3-6 years in any event would have been commensurate with the level of residual symptoms that remains 18 months after the accident.

However, there is a both a qualitative and quantitative difference between a sudden onset of symptoms and pain as a result of trauma and the gradual onset of symptoms and pain as a result of the deterioration of a pre-existing condition. First, a sudden onset of symptoms as the result of a trauma removes any possibility that the injured person can make adjustments to ameliorate the effects resulting from the symptoms and pain. Second, the injured person, once recovered (to the fullest extent possible) usually feels more vulnerable to further injury and tends to be more risk averse in his day-to-day activities. This leads to a greater level of restriction than would be the case with similar symptoms from a pre-existing condition.

In the case of Mr X, it is probable that in the absence of the accident, with appropriate treatment and reasonable adjustments, he would have been able to continue in his full time manual employment until about...

The issue of acceleration inevitably requires a degree of speculation. In forming an opinion on the acceleration of his pre-existing condition, I have taken into account the following factors:

1. the nature of the accident and the injuries he sustained;

2. his age and previous medical history;

3. his working and recreational activities over of the last 20 years; and

4. the nature and extent of degenerative changes shown on X-ray and MRI.

I am of the opinion that whilst it is probable that Mr Q would have developed similar symptoms in any event in due course, such symptoms almost certainly would not have commenced before his 50th birthday and probably not until his mid-fifties, which is some 10-15 years after the accident. I am therefore of the opinion that the accident has probably resulted in his suffering symptoms some 10 to 15 years earlier than would otherwise have been the case. So far as the nature and effect of those symptoms is concerned...

In the case of Mr X, it is probable that in the absence of the accident, with appropriate treatment and reasonable adjustments, he would have been able to continue in his full time manual employment until about...

> The use of the terms acceleration and exacerbation alone is not sufficient or precise enough to communicate clearly the situation to the court. The expert must, therefore, avoid the terms altogether or use them only as the starting point for a clear description of the situation.

6.4.3   Differences in Valuation

In an "acceleration case", where the accident has brought forward symptoms from a pre-existing condition, the lawyers need to know, on the balance of probabilities, when it would have been that the claimant would have suffered such symptoms and restrictions in activities in any event in the absence of the accident and therefore by how many years the accident has brought forward those symptoms. The lawyers also need to know the relative onsets of the consequences arising from both the accident and the projected onset of the pre-existing condition. The lawyers require that the expert addresses causation of injury in this way so that they can calculate the loss caused by the injury. The alternative approach is to address the degree of probability of differing levels of symptoms and consequential loss at several points in the timeline, as discussed in the case of *Smithurst* above.

> As an example, let us take what may initially have been described as a 4 to 6 year acceleration case that could, following a more detailed description of the onset of symptoms, lead to an unexpected outcome:
>
> *Following the accident, a 54-year old claimant (with a normal retirement age of 65) was unable to return to work. Therefore, the accident led to his medical retirement within 6 months of the accident when he was 55. The medical expert's opinion is that, but for the accident, the symptoms from a pre-existing previously asymptomatic degenerative condition would probably have developed 4 to 6 years later.*
>
> Based on this evidence of a '4-6 year acceleration case' the lawyers may value the loss of earnings in the case as follows:
>
> *Limited to say 5 years: (i.e. at age 60, his situation would have been as it is now). Therefore loss of earnings = 5 x annual net earnings.*
>
> *Say:*
>
> *£15,000 x 5 = £75,000*
>
> Had the medical expert reported in more detail on the gradual onset of symptoms after 4-6 years, the consequences for the claimant may have altered. The expert may actually consider that a gradual onset of symptoms from his pre-existing condition would have allowed the claimant to adapt to his back condition more successfully - the gradual onset of symptoms allowing the claimant time to adapt to the requirements of his work, to take appropriate medication, to receive physiotherapy when necessary and to take short periods off work when his symptoms were at their worst.
>
> If this were to be the situation, then the claimant would probably have been able to continue in employment perhaps until his normal retirement age after another 5 years. Therefore, on the balance of probabilities, the claim-

ant has not lost 4 to 6 years' earnings (the period of acceleration of symptoms) but has in fact lost 9 to 10 years' earnings (the period of acceleration, plus the 5 years he would probably have managed to continue working during the gradual onset of the symptoms) together with the additional pension he would have earned in that time.

Based on this assessment the valuation for loss of earnings alone would be:

Limited to 10 years: (i.e. at age 65, his situation would be as it is now). Therefore loss of earnings = 10 x annual net earnings.

Say:

£15,000 x 10 = £150,000

In reality, most cases in which pre-existing conditions (whether symptomatic or asymptomatic) are relevant contain both an element of acceleration and an element of exacerbation of symptoms. Symptoms are usually worse in the initial period following the accident than they would have been with a gradual onset. Also, the effects and consequences are often more severe because of the trauma that precipitates the sudden onset. These are important issues that the expert must consider when expressing opinions on causation.

Take another look at causation graph #1[26] for a typical injury situation and compare it to the acceleration and exacerbation graphs. These graphs have fundamentally different shapes and therefore would probably result in markedly different consequences for the claimant and markedly different assessments of financial award for the injury.

To return briefly to the sign outside the temple in Mandalay, if what the expert intends to communicate is the equivalent of 'Wear nothing on your feet', then the expert should avoid using the phrase 'No Foot-Wearing'. If symptoms have been brought on earlier by the accident and have been made worse for some or all of the time as a result, describe the situation – do not simply state that the symptoms have been accelerated.

---

26 See Section 6.2.1. Please remember, the causation graphs we have discussed in this section are an aid to clear thinking; such graphs have no place within the expert report itself - a medical expert's opinion should be expressed in words and not illustrated with graphs.

6.5   Prognosis and Future Risk

In relation to a claim, lawyers are only interested in the future for one purpose – to value the damages recoverable. The questions that the lawyers want to have answered are (typically):

1.   will the claimant be able to continue in his current employment, or in any employment, until normal retirement age?

2.   what assistance is the claimant likely to need in the future? and

3.   will further costs be incurred?

Lawyers do not ask these questions in order to be able to empathise with the claimant's plight, but rather in order to calculate the total value of damages claimed. The law seeks to provide suitable compensation for the future in order to put the claimant in the same position that he/she would have been in but for the accident, so far as it is possible to do so in monetary terms.

We saw at Section 2.6.4 that an award of provisional damages may be made in circumstances where there is a chance in the future of the claimant developing a serious disease or serious deterioration as the result of the injuries sustained. It is necessary for the medical expert to identify when such a chance arises and to address the degree of chance, the timing of onset of such disease or deterioration and its consequences.

6.5.1   Use of Percentages

Lawyers deal with the future in terms of the degree of risk of something occurring over a time period. This is because damages will be awarded as a proportion of the full value, to reflect the degree of risk and when the loss related to that risk is likely to occur. The best way to express the degree of risk is by the use of percentages.

For the court to award damages for a future complication or deterioration it must be established:

1.   that as a consequence of the accident or adverse event, a risk now exists of a future complication or deterioration (a risk that would not otherwise have existed); and

2.   what degree of risk the claimant now has of suffering such a complication or deterioration that leads to a future financial loss or of incurring future expense.

The risk should be assessed, so far as it is possible to do so, in terms of a percentage (or a range of percentages) and the point in time at which (or the period within which) the risk is likely to occur. Therefore, the medical expert has first to consider whether the injury has resulted in there being a risk of some kind of degeneration of the current condition. If there is such a risk, then the medical expert has to go on to assess the degree of risk.

Where, for example, a fracture has marginally affected a joint, the expert may conclude that it does give rise to a risk of deterioration:

> There is a 20-30% chance that he will need a hip replacement within 4 to 6 years.

If the injury did not involve the joint, then the expert may conclude there is no material risk:

> This injury will not have any effect on the hip joint in the future.

Prognosis can be presented on an injury by injury basis, with a separate prognosis given for each injury in turn, or a prognosis for all the injuries can be presented after causation for each of the injuries has been addressed. The approach of giving a prognosis for each injury in turn encourages the expert to provide a detailed prognosis on each of the injuries – nothing is left out. However, it may be necessary to consider an injury in relation to other injuries that the claimant has suffered and so writing the prognosis for all the injuries together may be more appropriate in some cases.

Whichever approach is adopted, the prognosis must deal clearly with the medical and the medico-legal issues: the likely progression of the injuries/symptoms/effects in the future and what the likely situation would have been without the accident, particularly as we have seen in respect of the onset of symptoms from a pre-existing condition[27]. The prognosis of injuries is essential for helping the lawyers to establish the end point of the claim. All calculations of future loss are calibrated by the timeline established in the prognosis.

Once the opinion is clear, the lawyers will be able to value the loss:

> The claimant's lawyers are provided with the cost today of joint replacement surgery. Adding this to loss of earnings prior to and following the surgery gives a total loss of £30,000. In the opinion of the expert, the risk of the claimant needing this surgery is around 25% and the date the surgery will be required will be in about 5 years.
>
> The claimant expert's opinion establishes that a risk of requiring this surgery consequent upon the injury exists. The damages recovered will be proportionate to the degree of risk of needing the surgery as assessed by reference to the medical expert's opinion. The expert's opinion is that there is a risk of around 25% that the claimant will require the surgery. On that

---

27   See the discussion of Acceleration and Exacerbation in Section 6.4

> basis the loss is reduced to approximately £7,500 (25% of £30,000). A further adjustment will be made to reflect the fact that the sum is to be paid now and will not be required (if at all) for around 5 years. Therefore, the sum is discounted in accordance with actuarial tables by a factor of 0.8839 to £6,629 (or thereabouts).

It will, therefore, make a considerable difference in the damages recovered whether the risk is 'small', so that only a small fraction of the full potential value will be awarded, or if the risk is 'substantial', in which case most of the full potential value will be awarded. We return to this issue in Section 6.5.4 below.

> Future risk should be assessed, so far as it is possible to do so, in terms of a percentage (or a range of percentages) and the point in time at which (or the period within which) the risk is likely to occur.

6.5.2   Use of Dates

An issue that often arises is when the expert offers a prognosis without making clear which date the prognosis is to be calculated from – the examination date or the accident date:

> In my opinion, it is likely that Mr S's back pain is due to damage to the soft tissues and ligaments of his lower lumbar spine. I expect his pain to settle in around 18 months and that he will be pain free within two years.

It is important that the expert makes clear which date is being used as the baseline and the expert can make the report even clearer by giving the date or range of dates in the future which the time period indicates:

> In my opinion, his pain will settle in around 18 months from the accident date, after which time he will be able to carry out all of his normal daily activities, with only occasional episodes of mild back pain. My opinion is that he will be pain free within two years of the accident date, that is, by about April 2010.

6.5.3   Clinician's Approach to the Future

The medical mind approaches the future in a very different way to the legal mind. There is often a sensible reluctance to fill a patient's mind with problems, which may develop but also may not. Clinicians seek to avoid causing unnecessary worry and potentially causing a patient to interpret symptoms in an exaggerated manner and so undermine his/her chances of making a full recovery. Having completed complex treatment or therapy to a standard that clinicians would normally regard as successful, the treating clinician may also be reluctant to sit down with the patient to spell out everything that could now go wrong and the possible time scales for such potential problems.

The 'tactful honesty' and optimism of a doctor in the role of treating clinician and the assessment of a medical expert are often at odds with each other. It is not good enough for the purposes of a medical expert report to provide the following as a prognosis, however true it may be as a statement. A lawyer would find the following evidence **unhelpful**:

> All that can be said about prognosis is that symptoms may last indefinitely. That is not the same as saying that symptoms may last forever, but rather that it is impossible to give a meaningful prognosis. Some patients may improve by 2 years from the index event, others may take longer.

Lawyers will, in this context, tend to treat 'indefinitely' as meaning 'forever'. Similarly, something likely to continue into the foreseeable future is in a lawyer's eyes likely to continue indefinitely. The issue that the lawyers want to have addressed is "what the prognosis is for this particular claimant". What the lawyers require is a reasoned opinion based on the medical expertise and experience of the expert. A lawyer would find the following evidence **helpful**:

> In assessing the prognosis for the symptoms Mr T is currently experiencing, there are no relevant scientific studies that I can rely upon. In clinical practice, approximately 10% of patients continue to experience symptoms of neck and back pain that do not improve with time. However, given the gradual improvement and settling in Mr T's symptoms over the last 12 months, his recent return to work and his obvious determination to get his life 'back to normal', my prognosis is that his symptoms will continue to improve in the future, achieving an almost full recovery within 2-3 years. During this period, I expect he will benefit from 6 sessions of physiotherapy per year, and will require treatment with analgesics and a few days of bed rest, up to four times per year.
>
> After this 2-3 year initial recovery period, there is a high probability (70-80%) that he will continue to suffer with intermittent residual symptoms of neck and shoulder stiffness, which would need to be treated with analgesics, a few days of bed rest, and occasional physiotherapy - perhaps 2-3 sessions per year. I expect such episodes of residual symptoms to happen once or twice per year, for 5-7 years, after the initial recovery period.

Most medical experts do not like to quantify risks in terms of percentages over time. Forming opinions about the future often causes the medical mind to experience an elevated level of anxiety. The obvious lack of a scientific basis for the opinion leaves the expert feeling exposed and vulnerable. What good medical experts realise is that they are the ones best placed to identify the level of risk and the period of time within which any such risks would manifest and so they are not afraid to provide a reasoned estimate of the risk.

6.5.4   Using Percentages in Opinions on Prognosis

As we have seen, the clearest way of describing future risk is by giving a percentage risk within an appropriate time period. We set out in the table below expressions typically used by medical experts when describing future risk. Try completing the 'percentage' column for each expression, and then ask some of your colleagues (in no particular order and without showing them the table or your own quantification for each expression) what percentage they would assign to each of these expressions:

EXPRESSION	PERCENTAGE
a small risk	%
some risk	%
a risk	%
a real risk	%
a substantial risk	%
a high risk	%
a very high risk	%

If we consider what is meant by these expressions, in terms of the percentage degree of risk, it becomes clear that no single or consistent interpretation exists. Therefore, no single interpretation will be agreed by the parties, their lawyers, the medical experts or the judge at trial. Each person hearing these expressions will form his/her own interpretation. The interpretation will vary in different contexts: doctors with their natural reluctance to worry a patient unduly, lawyers seeking the best outcome for their clients, and the common use of understatement in British English ("it's a bit hot"; "the traffic is none too good"; "it wasn't a great weekend").

Without a quantified description of the risk, there is a real danger that many of these phrases will fail to convey to the listener or reader the assessment of risk made by the expert. The words will convey no objective measure of risk and so the claim cannot be properly and appropriately valued.

It may sound, at first read, reasonable to give a prognosis as follows, but a lawyer would find the following evidence **unhelpful**:

> In the accident, Mr B sustained a whiplash injury to his neck. The residual symptoms are likely to improve with physiotherapy. However, he may be left with some symptoms of pain and stiffness which could occur permanently on an intermittent basis.

However, if we assume that the symptoms are interfering with the claimant's ability to manage his employment, how can the value of his claim be assessed on the basis of this description? Leaving aside issues as to how intermittent the symptoms may be and what interference with employment may result from symptoms of inconvenience, the question still remains as to how likely it is that the symptoms will persist – what is the risk?

The difficulty in communicating what is meant when describing the risk can only be overcome by the expert's use of a clear and understandable scale and then communicating the percentage risk associated with that scale in the report. Inevitably, there will usually be a range of possible percentages to describe the risk, so it is generally more appropriate to indicate a range of percentages in the report:

- 'there is a 10-15% risk'
- 'there is a 70-80% risk'.

There is then no possibility that the lawyers will fail to understand the indicated level of risk or have to seek clarification of it. The expert's opinion is clear, and the lawyer can value that risk appropriately.

A lawyer would find the following evidence **helpful**:

> In the accident, Mr B sustained a whiplash injury to his neck. There is a good chance (70-80%) that his residual symptoms will improve with physiotherapy. However, he may be left with some symptoms of pain and stiffness on perhaps 2 or 3 occasions a year, and I put the chances of this occurring at about 30-40%.

This approach also applies if there is a chance of improvement, as this would justify a reduction in damages to reflect that possibility. In circumstances where a claimant's symptoms are improving, the lawyers will apply an appropriate discount to reflect the situation. To say that the claimant 'might improve with time' gives little indication of the likelihood of the improvement taking place and over what period of time, and does little to assist in valuing the claim.

The medical expert should therefore consider, and express reasoned opinions in the report on, the following matters:

- Is there a chance that at some definite or indefinite time in the future the

claimant's condition may deteriorate or improve?
- What is the percentage chance of the future occurrence?
- Over what period of time may this deterioration or improvement take place?
- What would be the likely consequence of such deterioration or improvement on the claimant and on activities of daily living?

In order to address the possibility of a provisional award of damages[28] the lawyers need to know specifically whether there is a chance that at some definite or indefinite time in the future the claimant may develop some serious disease or some serious deterioration in his/her physical or mental condition as a result of the matters arising from the incident/ accident/exposure to noxious substance the subject of the claim. It is therefore important that the medical expert describes and quantifies the nature of such future disease or deterioration and its potential impact on the claimant so that its seriousness can be assessed by the lawyers and the court.

> To say 'There is a real risk that further major surgery will be necessary' is equivalent to 'No Foot-Wearing'. To stop the reader guessing as to the meaning, the expert should state unambiguously what he/she really means by 'a real risk'.

6.5.5   Life Expectancy[29]

In contrast with future complications, life expectancy is decided 'on the balance of probabilities'. The issue to be answered is to what age, or for what period, is the claimant more likely than not to survive. This is established as a present fact, not as a future risk. Life expectancy is based on the present known facts – there is in fact no risk of death, only a certainty of death. The only issue is when it will occur.

To a lawyer, if on the balance of probabilities death is likely in five years, then that date of death is treated as a fact. This period of life expectancy will almost certainly be wrong – the claimant will either die sooner or later, but this lack of certainty is of no concern to the lawyers. It is for this reason that the court, in compensating for continuing future loss, can now award periodical payments instead of lump sum damages in certain circumstances, so that the damages in fact paid will continue until the death of the claimant and will be the correct amount for that period of life. However, periodical payments are not always awarded and calculations of lump sum payments continue to be made on the basis of the probable life expectancy of the claimant.

In some cases, establishing the life expectancy of a claimant is an essential part of the assessment of future loss as part of the damages to be awarded. It may have

---

28   See Section 2.6.4

29   See also the earlier discussion in relation to the balance of probabilities at Section 5.3 above

most significance in clinical negligence claims, such as those involving serious birth injury - because of the ongoing substantial cost of care – but will also arise in claims for a failure to diagnose or treat a condition as a result of which life expectancy is significantly reduced. Issues of life expectancy do arise in personal injury cases as well, for example, because of catastrophic injuries or in claims for a cancer resulting from exposure to substances in breach of duty or to establish the future period for which care and assistance is required where there are some future sequelae.

In many cases, published 'life tables' can be used to establish a figure for life expectancy, or sources such as *Brackenridge's Medical Selection of Life Risks* (now in its 5th edition published in 2006), with appropriate adjustments, as necessary, for particular factors such as smoking or cardiac history. However, if the claimant is outside the cohort for whom the life tables are applicable, then the question for the expert to address is 'to what age or for what period will 50% of the claimant's cohort survive'. It is at this point that it cannot be said that the claimant is more likely than not to survive and therefore the claimant cannot prove on the balance of probabilities that he would live that long (or any longer). Life expectancy in cases involving cancers (whether caused by breach of duty or missed through negligence or poor management) can often be assisted by the prognostic tools now available and from references to published papers on survival rates.

By applying medical expertise and knowledge to the particular facts of the case, a medical expert should be able to identify a range of opinion as to probable life expectancy and narrow that range down by reference to the particular facts of the case. This is not and is not thought by the lawyers to be anything more than an opinion reached on the balance of probabilities.

In some cases, it is not only the life expectancy of the claimant that is important. If the claimant is married then it may be necessary to know for how long it is probable that he/she would have continued to support the spouse in the absence of the breach of duty and resulting shortened life expectancy, and therefore which of them would have had the longer life expectancy must also be proved.

> In contrast with future complications, life expectancy is decided 'on the balance of probabilities'. The issue to be answered is to what age, or for what period, is the claimant more likely than not to survive.

6.6 Consequences of Injuries

Many experts are unaware of the importance of addressing in detail the consequences of the claimant's injuries. The medical expert report provides the basis for the assessment of the damages claimed by the claimant and therefore has an essential role in helping the lawyers to value cases appropriately. It is essential that the medical expert gives opinions on all of the consequences of an accident. This includes all the consequences that arise along the accident timeline, beginning at the accident date and continuing until the claimant makes a full recovery or reaches the point where no further improvement or deterioration is likely to occur.

We deal in Section 10 specifically with matters relating to care and other therapeutic needs and how these should be addressed by such experts. The emphasis in this Section is on the approach to be taken by medical experts in providing the framework within which the care and other needs experts can provide their opinions. There is an area of overlap as in some areas of speciality and in some situations the medical expert will need to express an opinion not only on specific needs but on how those needs should be met, as for example in the case of spinal cord injuries.

6.6.1   Addressing Consequential Loss

CPR 35.3(1) requires an expert only to comment on matters within his/her expertise. This requirement guides us to the approach that the expert needs to adopt when assessing the consequences of an injury to the claimant. Most medical experts are aware that they are in no way qualified to comment on the type of job that an injured claimant unable to return to his previous employment would be able to manage. Nor would many claim any expertise in assessing how many hours of help with housework would be required if a claimant can no longer do the cleaning. These questions would perhaps require the expertise of an employment expert or care consultant.

However, employment experts and care consultants will be instructed only where the cost of doing so is proportionate to the value of the claim; otherwise, the parties will have to manage as best they can based on a medical expert's opinion. Where employment experts and care consultants are instructed, they usually have little or no medical expertise and so will also base their assessment of the claimant's likely restrictions upon the medical expert's opinion.

Essentially, the expert needs to address whether, on the balance of probabilities:

1.   the consequences claimed are medically supportable given the levels of injuries/symptoms/effects, and are therefore 'attributable' to the accident; and

2.   the consequences claimed are within the expected range given the levels of injuries/symptoms/effects, and are therefore 'reasonable'.

The key to addressing whether a consequence is attributable and reasonable, while staying within medical expertise, is to concentrate on identifying the restrictions on activities that the claimant now has or will be likely to experience in the future. Specifically, the court needs to know the nature of tasks that are now likely to be impossible or difficult as a consequence of the accident. The lawyers would find the following evidence **helpful**:

Work

Since the accident, Mr J says he has been unable to do any work activity that requires heavy lifting, stretching or repeated bending. He says that at work his role has been limited to light duties such as fixing fuses and sockets and excludes re-wiring and the fitting of appliances. In my opinion, his level of ongoing restriction is in all probability to be permanent and is both reasonable and attributable to the accident.

The disc-prolapse operation in Sep 08 has meant that he has less pain, but Mr J tells me that it did not improve his capacity to do heavy work. At present, he tells me that he has an agreement with his employers to continue with light duties at work. As I do not consider that there will be any improvement in his condition, in my opinion were this agreement to be discontinued he would be limited in the open labour market to maintenance roles that did not require him to do heavy lifting, stretching or repeated bending.

Domestic

Between the accident and the operation in Sep 08, Mr J says he was restricted in carrying out household duties. In my opinion, this is reasonable and attributable to the accident. During this period, any task that would have required him to use more than minimal force, such as is required when vacuuming or cleaning, would have been too difficult for him.

Transportation

[...]

Medical experts can avoid the temptation of becoming pseudo-employment or care consultant by expressing opinions only upon the type and level of restriction the claimant is likely to have in the future, rather than the types of job the claimant will be able to do.

Notice that in this example the expert uses mundane description of the restrictions that the claimant is facing, '...that did not require him to do heavy lifting, stretching or repeated bending.' Any form of abstract description of restriction, such as using percentages when describing restrictions, is not helpful.

> The medical expert report provides the basis for the assessment of the damages claimed by the claimant and therefore has an essential role in helping the lawyers to value cases appropriately.

6.6.2   Consequences to Assess

The best evidence as to whether the consequences of an injury claimed by the claimant are attributable to the accident and reasonable given the level of injuries sustained will come from the medical expert. The evidence of a medical expert carries much greater weight than anything that the claimant can say, owing to the medical expert's expertise and independence. As an independent expert, with a duty to assist the court with matters within his/her expertise, the medical expert is not seen as benefiting from (and therefore not influenced by) the litigation.

Consequences relevant to a personal injury claim may be found in some or all of the following heads of claim arising from the injury[30]:

- pain and suffering, and loss of amenity;
- medical or therapeutic treatment;
- care and assistance;
- current employment;
- future employment;
- life expectancy;
- additional housing, mobility or transportation needs;
- restrictions on activities of daily living; and
- restrictions on domestic, recreational, social or sporting activities.

If any of these heads of claim are clearly not relevant to the case, then there is no need for the expert to comment on them. Otherwise the expert should deal with all the consequences that arise in the relevant categories.

6.6.3   Pain and Suffering, and Loss of Amenity

The judge will look closely at the medical expert report in assessing damages for the injury itself (i.e. damages for 'pain and suffering and loss of amenity'). The medical expert report should therefore:

- summarise the likely continuing effects of an injury, in terms of disability, pain and suffering;
- predict whether this situation is likely to change over time, in terms of deterioration or recovery, and the consequential level of disability; and
- provide a comparison of the situation that would have existed but for the accident and the situation following the accident, identifying what difference the accident has made.

6.6.4   Medical or Therapeutic Treatment

If there has been medical or therapeutic treatment, or if there is likely to be such treatment in the future, then the medical expert report should:

---

30   See Section 2.6 and 2.7 for further discussion of heads of claim

- identify what treatment there has been;
- where past treatment has been outside the NHS[31], address whether it was reasonable and attributable to the accident;
- identify the likelihood of the need for treatment in the future, giving some indication of the percentage risk of that need (if at all possible), and provide an indication of when in the future it will be needed;
- give some indication of the likely cost of such future treatment if carried out privately - at today's values - and give some indication of any other material implications of such treatment: for example, the need to take time off work or the need for significant quantities of post-operation care or domestic assistance; and
- provide a comparison of the situation that would have existed but for the accident with the situation following the accident, identifying what difference the accident has made.

As a claimant is under a duty to take reasonable steps to mitigate his/her loss or damage, if there is treatment that the claimant is reluctant to undergo or if potential treatment is risky or may have adverse consequences, the nature of any such risk that might reasonably affect the claimant's decision to undergo the treatment should be addressed in the report. This may also be relevant to whether there has been a break in the chain of causation (see Section 7.8).

6.6.5   Care and Assistance

Medical experts are not care experts. A medical expert will not generally be expected to assess the amount of care and assistance necessary to enable the claimant to live a normal (pre-accident) life. However, the medical expert is often in a much better position than the lawyers or the judge (or even the care expert) to indicate what level of restriction is relevant to the need for care and assistance that a claimant has or is likely to suffer in the future, as a consequence of his/her injuries.

If there has been a claimed need for care and assistance, or if there is likely to be such a need in the future, then the medical expert report should:

- express an opinion as to the nature of help that it would have been reasonable to need, or continues to be needed, or which the claimant will be likely to need in future – for example, help with dressing or washing, applying dressings, general housework, heavier domestic tasks, home maintenance and DIY or gardening; and
- provide a comparison of the situation that would have existed but for the accident with the situation that exists following the accident, identifying what difference the accident has made.

---

31   The cost of such treatment, whether funded by the claimant or by his medical insurers, will form part of the damages claimed. A claimant is entitled to choose to be treated privately – Section 2(4) Law Reform (Personal Injuries) Act 1948

6.6.6　Current Employment

The effect of an accident on a claimant's earning capacity is likely to be a significant aspect of the damages claimed. Frequently, it is the largest item of claim. Whilst a medical expert is not an employment expert or an occupational therapist, the medical expert report should assist in identifying:

- the ability of the claimant to continue in his pre-accident employment since the accident and in the future;
- the time for which it was reasonable to be off work;
- the general nature of the work that the claimant is now incapable of doing;
- any limitations or restrictions on future working by reference, for example, to activities which could or could not reasonably be managed until the intended retirement age; and
- provide a comparison of the situation that would have existed but for the accident with the situation following the accident, identifying what difference the accident has made.

A lawyer would find each of the following opinions **unhelpful** because the evidence does not address the practical restrictions arising from the injuries:

> Ms T will be at a disadvantage in finding suitable employment in future because of the effects of the accident on her.

> He is 56 years of age, and his opportunities on the open labour market are essentially non-existent.

> Mr G is not at a significant disadvantage on the employment market.

> His psychiatric status is not altogether incompatible with the acceptance of the responsibilities of employment.

A lawyer would find the following opinions **helpful** because the evidence addresses the practical restrictions that the claimant will have:

> Mr G can no longer lift or carry heavy weights or bend repeatedly, and therefore will be unable to return to manual work such as he was performing prior to the accident. There is however no reason why he should not continue in work such as that in which he is currently employed and which he has described to me as a factory storeman role.

Given these restrictions it is unlikely that in his present psychiatric state he would be capable of returning to full time work in his pre-accident office environment. With a graduated return to work in 12 – 24 months' time he would probably manage to work part time in a less demanding and less stressful environment, but he would be prone to further periods of stress-related absences from time to time, perhaps needing several days off work once or twice a year during these episodes.

He would not now be capable of employment that required him to walk any more than very short distances, to stand or sit for protracted periods, and lift or carry anything of any significant weight. The effect of the injuries and the continuing symptoms and restrictions is that he could not now return to his previous work as a school caretaker.

Given the restrictions in activities set out above, were Ms T to seek to return to the employment market in the future she would no longer be able to manage a job that required her to spend much of the working day at a keyboard or in any employment requiring repetitive movements of the fingers or wrists. However, subject to those limitations, there is no reason why she would not be able to manage more general and varied office work or light manual work.

Miss C is currently employed within the local authority's education department in an advisory role. She has no contact with young people at work and is not required to partake in or observe classroom activities. She appears to be managing this role well. She has made good progress since the index event and would no longer fulfil the criteria for diagnosis of Major Depressive Episode or Panic Disorder. However, despite the treatment she has received, in my opinion there would be a very high risk that a return to working in a classroom would initiate further panic attacks. In the future, she is very unlikely to be able to cope with any situation in which she would be exposed to large numbers of people and therefore she is most unlikely ever to be able to return to the classroom setting.

6.6.7   Future Employment and 'the Ogden Tables'

Where an injury affects the claimant's ability to secure future employment, this can form part of the claim. Where the claimant is likely to face a disadvantage in looking for further work, then the medical expert report should assist the lawyers in identifying:

- any disadvantage the claimant may suffer in the future on the open labour market by reference, for example, to relevant restrictions in activities that would otherwise reasonably be expected; and
- provide a comparison of the situation that would have existed but for the accident with the situation following the accident, identifying what difference the accident has made.

Where a claimant is disabled as a result of the accident, the lawyers may seek to assess the value of the future impact on employment using the 'Ogden Tables', actuarial tables provided for the assessment of future loss[32]. In what lawyers informally refer to as an 'Ogden calculation'[33], it is possible to compare, on an actuarial basis, the likely future earnings of someone with and without disability. For this purpose, it is necessary to establish whether or not the claimant is 'disabled' and the extent of such disability. The medical expert is therefore likely to be asked to assist in this assessment.

The notes to the Ogden Tables contain the following guidance as to when a claimant is to be regarded as 'disabled':

> Disabled:
>
> A person is classified as being disabled if all three of the following conditions in relation to the ill-health or disability are met:
>
> > (i) the person has an illness or a disability which has lasted or is expected to last for over a year or is a progressive illness,
> >
> > (ii) the person satisfies the Equality Act 2010 definition that the impact of the disability substantially limits the person's ability to carry out normal day-to-day activities, and
> >
> > (iii) their condition affects either the kind **or** the amount of paid work they can do.
>
> Normal day-to-day activities are those which are carried out by most people on a daily basis, and we are interested in disabilities/health problems which have a substantial adverse effect on the respondent's ability to carry out these activities.
>
> There are several ways in which a disability or health problem may affect the respondent's day-to-day activities:
>
> Mobility - for example, unable to travel short journeys as a passenger in a car, unable to walk other than at a slow pace or with jerky movements,

---

32   See Section 2.7.3

33   This basis of calculation first appeared in the 6th edition of the Ogden Tables in March 2007. We are currently using the 7th edition from 2012.

difficulty in negotiating stairs, unable to use one or more forms of public transport, unable to go out of doors unaccompanied.

Manual dexterity - for example, loss of functioning in one or both hands, inability to use a knife or fork at the same time, or difficulty in pressing buttons on a keyboard.

Physical co-ordination - for example, the inability to feed or dress oneself, or to pour liquid from one vessel to another except with unusual slowness or concentration.

Problems with bowel/bladder control - for example, frequent or regular loss of control of the bladder or bowel. Occasional bedwetting is not considered a disability.

Ability to lift, carry or otherwise move everyday objects (for example, books, kettles, light furniture) - for example, inability to pick up a weight with one hand but not the other, or to carry a tray steadily.

Speech - for example, unable to communicate (clearly) orally with others, taking significantly longer to say things. A minor stutter, difficulty in speaking in front of an audience, or inability to speak a foreign language would not be considered impairments.

Hearing - for example, not being able to hear without the use of a hearing aid, the inability to understand speech under normal conditions or over the telephone.

Eyesight - for example, while wearing spectacles or contact lenses - being unable to pass the standard driving eyesight test, total inability to distinguish colours (excluding ordinary red/green colour blindness), or inability to read newsprint.

Memory or ability to concentrate, learn or understand - for example, intermittent loss of consciousness or confused behaviour, inability to remember names of family or friends, unable to write a cheque without assistance, or an inability to follow a recipe.

Perception of risk of physical danger - for example, reckless behaviour putting oneself or others at risk, mobility to cross the road safely. This excludes (significant) fear of heights or underestimating risk of dangerous hobbies.

Condition (i) is not normally controversial. To enable the lawyers to establish whether or not the claimant is disabled for these purposes the medical expert will need to express an opinion, within his/her area of expertise, as to whether:

1. there is a substantial adverse effect on the claimant's ability to carry out normal daily activities; and

2. there is an effect on the kind of paid work the claimant can do.

To do this the expert will need to address the restrictions in relevant activities that the claimant has presently and will reasonably experience as a result of the injury sustained.

6.6.8   Life Expectancy

Where the claimant's life expectancy has reduced as a consequence of the accident, then the claimant, or the claimant's estate or dependants, can claim for consequential losses resulting from the probable shortening of his/her life. The potential losses that arise as a consequence of losing many years of a working life may make the assessment of life expectancy an important one. The medical expert report should either address the issue directly or where this assessment is beyond the area of expertise of the expert should indicate the need for an appropriate expert to consider the issue.

6.6.9   Additional Housing, Mobility or Transportation Needs

Where a claimant is likely to suffer mobility restrictions, the medical expert report should assist in terms of likely restrictions relevant to housing, mobility or transportation needs. This may involve matters such as:

- the walking distance of which the claimant is reasonably capable;
- the ability reasonably to use public transport;
- the need for adaptations to a car;
- difficulty with stairs and therefore the need for single floor accommodation, adaptations to the home or a stair lift;
- difficulty with bathing or the need to install a shower; and
- the need for residential adaptations.

The medical evidence will deal with the nature of the likely restrictions and the impact on housing, mobility or transportation. A suitably qualified expert will then be used, if it is considered appropriate by the lawyers, to advise as to the details and cost of the adaptations required.

6.6.10   Restrictions on Activities of Daily Living

In a case involving serious disability, a suitably qualified care expert will be instructed to assess the restrictions on daily self-care activities and the need for care and assistance. The care expert will benefit from an assessment of the restrictions as assessed by the medical expert. In less serious cases, the assessment of the degree of impact on activities of daily living and the cost of assisting the claimant will be based on the lawyers' and the judge's assessment of the impact, which will in turn be based on the medical expert report and the evidence of the claimant and his/her witnesses.

Therefore it is important to address in the medical expert report:

- the extent to which any continuing restrictions are likely to affect the claimant's ability to manage activities of daily living, such as dressing, undressing, washing/bathing/showering, using the toilet and preparing and eating meals; and
- how these restrictions compare with restrictions which would have existed in the absence of the accident.

6.6.11 Restrictions on Domestic, Recreational, Social or Sporting Activities

To the extent that these are not covered in an assessment of restrictions on activities of daily living, the medical expert should describe the restrictions likely and reasonably to impact on other everyday activities. This will include:

- housework (from dusting to spring cleaning);
- window cleaning;
- home decoration inside and outside;
- other home maintenance tasks specific to the claimant's pre-accident life (from changing light bulbs to building house extensions);
- gardening (from pruning roses to laying a patio and hedge trimming);
- shopping;
- dog walking and jam making;
- sexual activity[34]; and
- sporting and other physical activities such as dancing, football or swimming.

The assessment of damages for such loss of activity will, where appropriate, be based on the cost of getting others to perform these activities for the claimant. The loss of an ability to participate in social or sporting activities will not generally be compensated for by an award based on financial loss or financial costs. Any compensation will form part of the award for general damages for pain, suffering and loss of amenity.

---

34 Medical experts are often concerned with how to deal with claimant's restrictions in respect of sexual activity. While loss of fertility and its consequences may be readily identified, the effects and consequences of long-term or permanent impotence on relationships and the potential costs of medical treatment or medication should not be omitted. Where appropriate recommendations for opinions from other suitable experts should be included in the expert report.

6.6.12 The Reasonableness of Provision

Experts with the relevant expertise to express an opinion on what assistance or equipment is reasonably required as the result of an injury should not confuse their role when making recommendations in that regard for a patient where financial provision is to be made by a local authority or the NHS, taking into account financial and other limitations in that regard, with the role when providing an opinion in the context of litigation where the object of damages is, so far as is possible, to put the injured party back into the position they would have been in had they not been injured. That difference is illustrated by the following:

> 'Doubtless because of his extensive experience in dealing with paraplegics in many situations, in some of which he will be asked to prepare a report for medico-legal purposes and in others where he will be asked to recommend to a local authority what may be required for someone not in a position to claim compensation, Mr Gardner effectively said that what might be a reasonable and realistic claim in one context may not be so in the other. I have little doubt that that is correct in practice, particularly in times when local authority provision involves so much emphasis on the allocation of scarce resources. However, much as the practical distinction needs to be recognised, I do not think it truly informs the role of the court in assessing what may be claimed. The example relied upon by [counsel for the defendant] for the purposes of his submissions was the view expressed by Mr Gardner that "in medico-legal terms" it would have been reasonable to claim on the Claimant's behalf for a "roll-in vehicle" ..., but "in clinical terms" it was not reasonably justified and he did not think that she would have been awarded such a vehicle. He had also said something similar in relation to the care package. As I have said, it is tolerably clear that these distinctions can be made for practical purposes and helpful to know how an expert is approaching the issue, but I do not consider that much, if any, weight can be attached to them other than to say that it serves to confirm that it is ultimately for the court (assisted, but not dictated to, by the opinions of experienced experts) that drives the appropriate conclusion about what may "reasonably be required" in a particular claimant's case.'[35]

Conclusion

Writing clear and supported expert opinion is essential if an expert is to perform his/her required duties to an acceptable standard. The opinions that the lawyers require medical experts to address move beyond those that are ordinarily required to be addressed in medical practice. A medical expert must express opinions on all medico-legal issues that fall within his/her area of expertise – specifically these relate to causation, prognosis and future risk, and the consequences arising from a claimant's injuries.

---

35   *Reaney v University Hospital of North Staffordshire NHS Trust* [2014] EWHC 3016 at para 52

Key-Point Summary

1. It is important to differentiate the use of the terms 'injury', 'symptoms', 'effects' and 'consequences' when addressing causation.

2. Lawyers do not generally appreciate the difference between the medical use of the terms 'signs' and 'symptoms', so it is important that the expert makes clear what the sign is and what it shows and how it supports or does not support particular aspects of the claimant's claim.

3. Expressing opinions on causation involves a two-stage analysis: on the balance of probabilities, were the claimed injuries caused by the accident or negligence of the defendant? And in the absence of the accident or negligence, what would the situation have been in any event?

4. Causation graphs are a useful tool for analysing cases in terms of the difference a breach of duty has made to the claimant, especially so in more difficult cases. These graphs should not, however, be used in the report itself – these graphs are an aid to thinking not reporting.

5. The cases in which 'material contribution' needs to be assessed – most often relating to industrial disease – are those where there is more than one relevant period of exposure to an agent responsible for the disease or injury and medical science cannot establish causation on the 'but for' basis.

6. 'Acceleration' and 'exacerbation' are terms that are both misused and misinterpreted by experts and lawyers alike. Experts should only use these terms in conjunction with a clear explanation of the underlying factual/opinion matters. The sudden versus gradual onset of symptoms following an accident is a crucial issue that medical experts, and as a consequence their instructing lawyers, often fail to consider.

7. Expressing opinion on prognosis and future risk involves a two-stage analysis: is there a risk of deterioration or improvement in the claimant's condition? And having described this deterioration or improvement, what is the likelihood of this occurring and within what period?

8. Wherever possible, prognosis and future risk should be expressed as percentages (or a range of percentages) over a specific number of years or a specific time period.

9. Medical experts play an important role in identifying the consequences of an injury, both to the date of the report and for the future. This requires the expert to ask appropriate questions of the claimant to ascertain what consequences are being asserted as part of the claim.

10. The likely consequences for the claimant are best expressed in terms of the restrictions that the claimant will experience. These opinions are the starting point for care and other needs experts who may be instructed in the claim at a later stage.

11. Where future treatment is likely to improve the claimant's condition and prognosis, the expert should indicate this in his/her report. The claimant is under a duty to mitigate his/her loss.

12. Expressing opinions on the consequences of the injuries claimed involves considering two related issues: are the consequences claimed 'attributable' to the accident and are they 'reasonable' given the severity of the injuries/ symptoms/effects caused by the accident.

Next Steps

In the next chapter, we will explore complex claims, where experts and lawyers alike face difficulties in dealing with the issues in dispute.

7

Opinion Evidence in Complex Claims

Introduction

Once the basic principles underlying medical expert evidence have been understood, the vast majority of personal injury claims are straightforward and do not pose fundamental difficulties. However, there are complex claims that are intrinsically difficult for everyone who is concerned with achieving settlement or preparing for trial. In such claims, the expert has to show a greater level of awareness and skill in applying his/her medical expertise within the medico-legal context. In these complex claims, the expert must truly engage his/her medico-legal mind to give coherent opinion on what are often extremely difficult issues.

Chapter Outline

In this chapter, we will discuss eleven categories of complex claim. In each category, there are specific approaches that will help the expert to provide coherent expert evidence when reporting. The eleven categories are as follows:

1. difficulties in diagnosis;

2. linking the injury to its cause;

3. competing factual scenarios;

4. exaggeration and malingering;

5. surveillance evidence;

6. seat belts and contributory negligence;

7. multi-accident claims;

8. breaking the chain of causation;

9. criticism of medical treatment in a personal injury claim;

10. mental capacity; and

11. cases that rely on expertise.

In claims falling into any of these categories, the medical expert must apply exactly the same medico-legal principles that we have already discussed, in order to achieve a consistent and coherent approach to all the issues that arise. However, the care and skill with which these principles need to be applied create a qualitative difference in the evidence.

7.1   Difficulties in Diagnosis

In some claims, claimants present with complex or even paradoxical complaints on which the medical expert has to report. It may be that a single area of expertise, be this in a physical or a psychological field, cannot on its own fully explain the situation. Further, a minority of claimants seem to suffer worse symptoms and effects than the vast majority of claimants who present with similar injuries. This may be a by-product of the litigation itself, the particular circumstances or nature of the accident or solely as a result of the claimant's physiological or psychological makeup – or it may be that the claimant is dishonestly attempting to manipulate the level of compensation that he/she hopes to be awarded. Any and all of these possibilities need to be considered by the expert.

It is easy to assign the motive of financial gain to these claimants – and without doubt for some claimants this is entirely justified. However, as with all opinion evidence, experts must take care to assess all possible causes for the complaints and to give reasons for any conclusion reached, not least because abnormal illness behaviour is commonly seen in surgeries and consulting rooms across the country in the absence of any claim for damages.

7.1.1 Approach to the Evidence

When dealing with such cases, while staying within his/her area of expertise, the expert should seek to explain the situation as far as is possible and in so doing assist the lawyers in understanding the key medical issues in the case:

1.   what is probably wrong with the claimant, if anything?

2.   what probably caused this condition?

3.   what would the situation probably have been in the absence of the accident?

4.   what is likely to happen to this claimant in the future? and

5.   what are the probable consequences for this claimant?

These issues are the same as for any other claim; what changes is the level of certainty that the expert has when expressing opinions. It is entirely appropriate for the expert to express the difficulty of the case openly in the Opinion section of the report:

> The range and severity of symptoms that Mrs J is experiencing are not commensurate with the injuries she sustained in the accident. I can find no physiological basis for the ongoing pain and physical restrictions with which she presents. However, in my opinion, on the balance of probabilities, Mrs J does have a genuine restriction in her ability to twist, bend and stretch and is genuinely in pain.

The expert can then discuss the range of possible causes for these symptoms and give opinion on the likelihood of each being caused by the accident. The need for an assessment from another expert can also be indicated in the report, for example, by recommending a referral to a psychiatrist or pain consultant. This may enable progress towards a diagnosis to be made. Alternatively, where another expert report has already been obtained, an expert is entitled to rely on this opinion evidence, suitably referenced, in reaching his/her own opinion.

Experts, when faced with paradoxical symptoms that no single area of expertise seems capable of explaining, are sometimes faced with having to give an opinion as to whether the accident has caused the claimant's symptoms, whilst acknowledging that the diagnosis for the injury itself remains uncertain:

> Given the findings on MRI, I am uncertain as to why Mrs D has such severe leg pain with signs of nerve root irritation. It may be that Mrs D sustained nerve root damage at the time that her disc tear occurred in March 2006 and this might be the cause of ongoing neuropathic pain. I would not however expect her to have the very reduced straight leg raising that she has on the basis of her MRI scan, and indeed I would not expect her to have such restrictive back movements given the extent of her degenerative disc disease and her only moderate paravertebral spasm.
>
> The absence of anatomical abnormality commensurate with the symptoms she is reporting does not imply that her complaints of pain and disability are disingenuous but may reflect the fact that our understanding of the mechanisms of the initiation and perpetuation of pain are poorly understood and that our techniques of investigation are limited. Although her pain symptoms seem out of proportion to the MRI finding, the GP records contain no indication that she experienced pain or psychological problems prior to the accident…
>
> Therefore I identify the following possible causes for her continuing pain and disability:
>
> 1. conscious exaggeration;
>
> 2. unidentified damage to structures causing pain;
>
> 3. unconscious exaggeration (psychological or psychiatric component).
>
> In respect of conscious exaggeration, testing of Mrs D by myself and other practitioners has been consistent and no practitioner has raised doubts about Mrs D's veracity. While recognising that this is a matter for the court to decide, given the assessments by myself and others, I consider it unlikely that Mrs D is consciously exaggerating her symptoms.
>
> Unidentified additional damage to structures causing ongoing pain and disability is a possible explanation. Any such damage would almost certainly have been caused by injury sustained in the accident given the absence of any previous history of pain in the medical records. However, given the current state of medical understanding I am unable to say that such damage probably exists – this is a possible explanation.
>
> In my opinion, the most likely explanation is psychological or psychiatric factors, which are wholly responsible for, or contributing to, an exaggerated sense of pain and disability. However, it would require the opinion of an expert in either of these disciplines to address this issue.

In these difficult claims, experts must pay particular attention to the boundaries of their expertise. For example, if chronic pain comes within the particular expertise of an orthopaedic surgeon or rheumatologist, then he/she can give opinion relating to chronic pain. However, the expert's qualifications and relevant experience set out at the beginning of the report should give details of this particular expertise, so that the lawyers understand the basis on which the opinion is given. If such expertise is beyond the expertise of the expert, then defining the limits of expertise and suggesting a referral is the appropriate approach.

7.2   Linking the Injury to its Cause

In the vast majority of claims, it is obvious that the accident caused the injury of which the claimant complains, even if the full extent of that injury may not be so clear. However, in some claims, the connection is less clear and the medical expert can and should express an opinion on the 'attribution' of the injury to the accident or adverse event. In such cases, the expert has to identify factors that may or may not connect the claimant's presenting condition with the accident.

The following are examples of situations in which an expert should express an opinion on the attribution of the injury to its alleged cause, and give reasons for that opinion whether for or against the attribution:

1.   complaints of symptoms or of loss of function that cannot readily be attributed to the accident;

2.   symptoms, effects and consequences that are on a scale larger than might normally be expected from such an accident;

3.   work related upper limb disorders or other 'repetitive strain' type of claims;

4.   industrial disease claims; or

5.   stress related or other psychiatric injury claims.

> A minority of claimants seem to suffer worse symptoms and effects than the vast majority of claimants who present with similar injuries. This may be a by-product of the litigation itself, the particular circumstances or nature of the accident or solely as a result of the claimant's physiological or psychological makeup – or it may be that the claimant is dishonestly attempting to manipulate the level of compensation that he/she hopes to be awarded.

7.2.1   Approach to the Evidence

In 1 above, the claimant may complain of symptoms such as pain or of some loss of function that cannot readily be causally linked to the accident or adverse event.

The expert must consider whether there is any other possible cause to which these complaints can be attributed, whether in the claimant's make-up or pre-accident condition or in the treatment that the claimant has received because of the accident. The elimination of alternative causes is as important to the lawyers as the identification of a cause.

In 2, symptoms, effects and consequences may be on a scale larger than might normally be expected. These claims may arise, for example, out of a low-impact collision or a relatively minor lifting incident. The expert must consider whether the symptoms complained of are beyond the possible range of injuries and symptoms that could be caused by the forces involved in the accident or whether the symptoms might be explained by, and be consistent with, those forces given what is known about the claimant's previous medical history or condition. Findings on examination may be consistent with the expected range of injuries and symptoms that could be caused by the forces in the accident, even though the general description of symptoms and limitations given by the claimant appears to be of an apparently more serious nature than would be expected. The medical expert needs to explain the rationale underlying his/her opinion on these matters.

In 3, when reporting on cases involving work-related upper limb disorders or 'repetitive strain' type cases, the expert should express an opinion as to whether the particular condition that has developed can be attributed to the precipitating activity described or the movements or position of the claimant's body as reported to the expert, and whether there are other possible causes of the condition, whether it is possible to express an opinion as to which is the more likely cause.

In 4, in industrial disease claims involving, for example, complaints of noise induced hearing loss or the development of a condition (such as dermatitis or asthma) as a result of exposure to a substance at work, the expert should be able to express an opinion as to whether the findings in relation to the condition are supportive of a connection with the alleged causative agent. Other possible causes should be considered and if possible an opinion expressed as to the more likely cause.

In 5, the development of a recognised psychiatric condition (whether claimed to be as a result of exposure to the trauma of an accident or the effects of an accident or stress at work) may be multi-factorial and may be related to the nature of the precipitating event or the claimant's previous psychiatric history. The expert should address whether the development of the condition is consistent with, and capable of being attributed to, the precipitating event. This may require consideration of more than one account of the factual context in which the condition developed. Again, other possible causes should be considered and where possible an opinion expressed as to the more likely cause.

In each of these five types of claim, it is essential that the expert only expresses an opinion consistent with the his/her own area of expertise, and if that is not possible, then provides a signpost to the appropriate expert to address the issue. The last three are also examples of situations where the expert should express an opinion as to whether the injury sustained by the claimant is of a type, if not an extent, reasonably to be foreseen from a medical point of view in such a situation.

A lawyer would find the following evidence **helpful** because the experts delineate possible causes and provide a rationale for the opinions expressed:

Miss Q, who is left hand dominant and uses a computer mouse in her left hand, has developed both left carpal tunnel syndrome and de Quervain's syndrome at the left wrist. Both of these conditions arise spontaneously throughout the population, but it is widely acknowledged by specialists that both can on occasions be caused by excessive or inappropriate use of the hands. As a result, these conditions can be caused by activities at work.

In Miss Q's case, despite a probable pre-existing vulnerability, she appears to have had no difficulties with her keyboard work for about 3 years. She reports that her problems began when the intensity of her work increased in March 2008. She describes a clear association between her work and her symptoms, with an improvement when not at work, deterioration later in the working day, and deterioration with increased intensity of work. Despite a work station assessment and various adjustments to her workstation, the symptoms have persisted.

Based on the facts before me, I am of the opinion that should it be found that there is a close association between her symptoms and the increased intensity of her work, both de Quervain's syndrome and carpal tunnel syndrome were in her case probably caused by her work and did not develop spontaneously.

There are two possible causes of Mr H's condition. The first is long term low-level exposure to di-isocyanates. The second is a history of heavy smoking. In this case, Mr H's work history of low-level exposure to di-isocyanates would not commonly result in his developing the severe condition from which he now suffers. However, the medical literature referred to above supports a causal link between low-level exposure over a long period of time and severe presentations of the condition.

There is uncertainty about Mr H's smoking history. If he were found to have a history of heavy smoking, then I consider the more likely cause of his condition would be his smoking rather than his occupational exposure. However, if he were found to be a light smoker, then it is unlikely that his smoking has any causal link with his condition. In the latter case, in the absence of evidence of any other non-occupational exposures to irritants, on the balance of probabilities his condition was the result of his occupational exposure to di-isocyanates.

It is now two years since the accident, which occurred in August 2008. Mr J gives a clear and consistent account of the accident without obvious distress. The accident was understandably a very traumatic experience and given his pre-existing psychological vulnerability, it is unsurprising that he coped badly in the months that followed. His relationship and work difficulties then emerged, resulting in a significant deterioration in his mental state some 12 months after the accident.

The current symptoms Mr J describes to me are spread across the neurotic spectrum, involving obsessional thinking, depression and anxiety. He describes ruminations about death, anxiety and depressive symptoms and also flashbacks to the accident.

In my opinion, Mr J is currently suffering (1) ongoing symptoms of PTSD and (2) depression with moderate levels of anxiety. I deal with these symptoms below:

1. His ongoing symptoms of PTSD are caused by the accident. These symptoms of PTSD have now begun to diminish, such that at 2 years post-accident Mr J now reports that his symptoms of flashbacks and heightened feelings of anxiety and dread are occurring with less intensity, perhaps two or three times per week.

    In my opinion, given the progress Mr J has made, particularly in the last six months, there is a high probability that his symptoms of PTSD will continue to diminish to a point where they would be classed as minor residual symptoms within the next 12 months (i.e. 3 years post-accident).

2. Mr J is suffering from depression with moderate levels of anxiety. He has a 10-year history of depressive illness prior to the accident, which the accident has exacerbated in the last two years, increasing the number of issues with which Mr J feels unable to cope and adding to the intensity of his depression and anxiety.

    In my opinion, the injuries he sustained in the accident and his ongoing symptoms of PTSD materially contributed to his depression and anxiety and were contributory factors in his work and marital relationship difficulties that occurred 12 months post-accident.

As his symptoms of PTSD have begun to diminish, the level of his depressive illness appears to be returning to its pre-accident intensity, such that it is likely that over the next 12 months (3 years post-accident) his symptoms of depression and anxiety will have returned to their pre-accident levels, At that stage Mr J will be back in the position he would have been in the absence of the accident and any ongoing symptoms will be as they would have been in any event.

7.3   Competing Factual Scenarios

An expert opinion will often depend on which facts are accepted by the expert as being probably correct (see for instance the example relating to Mr H in Section 7.2.1 above). It is for this reason that the expert is required to make clear in reaching the opinion:

- the facts that have been relied upon;
- the facts that the expert knows to be true and those which the expert assumes to be true; and
- any asserted facts that the expert has rejected as improbable and why the expert has rejected them as improbable[1].

However, there is more than one side to every claim, so if the expert expresses an opinion based on one of two sets of inconsistent facts, and this set of facts is rejected by the judge, the expert is effectively left expressing no relevant opinion. It is therefore necessary, and required, for the expert to express an alternative opinion on each alternative set of facts:

> Guidance   58   Where there are material facts in dispute experts should express separate opinions on each hypothesis put forward. They should not express a view in favour of one or other disputed version of the facts unless, as a result of particular expertise and experience, they consider one set of facts as being improbable or less probable, in which case they may express that view and should give reasons for holding it.

7.3.1   Approach to the Evidence

Where the expert does not express an opinion in favour of one or other set of facts, the expert simply sets out the factual dispute and gives an opinion on each set of facts. A lawyer would find the following evidence **helpful**:

> If Mr D is correct and the past shoulder problems had resolved completely prior to the accident, then the accident caused a further episode of impingement syndrome which continues. However, for the reasons set out above, significant symptomatic impingement syndrome would probably have commenced in any event within about 2 years of the date of the accident, reaching the level of symptoms he experienced after the accident within a few months. At this point, 30 months on from the accident, the situation is most probably as it would have been in the absence of the accident, with the need for treatment and finally surgery being brought forward by a similar period.
>
> However, if, as the GP records suggest, the court finds that Mr D had not

---

1   Guidance 57 and 58 and see Sections 4.2.7 and 4.2.10

> recovered from the past shoulder pain at the time of the accident then it is probable that the accident caused an exacerbation for a few months of the symptoms already present but that otherwise the course of the shoulder symptoms and the treatment has not been affected by the accident.

Where the expert is able to express an opinion in favour of one or other disputed set of facts, as a result of his/her particular expertise, the expert is permitted to express an opinion that one set of facts is 'improbable or less probable'[2]. Once again, if the expert expresses such an opinion, then he/she should still express an opinion on the other set of facts[3].

In some areas of expertise, the diagnosis rests on a finding of fact in the absence of which there would be no satisfactory evidence of injury, as in the following example, which a lawyer would find **helpful**:

> During my examination of the claimant, he stated that he has severe and continuing tinnitus. In contrast to what he told me, there is no reference to tinnitus in any previous assessment or in the medical records. This condition is not susceptible to objective assessment. If the court finds that the description given to me by him is correct, then in my opinion, his condition is probably caused by exposure to excessive noise at work and his condition is likely to be permanent. This opinion on causation is however dependent upon the court's finding that he does indeed suffer tinnitus as described. Conversely, if the court does not accept his evidence, then there is no other evidence to substantiate that he does in fact suffer from tinnitus.

7.4   Exaggeration and Malingering

When dealing with cases where there is a suspicion of 'Exaggeration' or 'Malingering', an expert should first define how these terms are being used in the report or avoid their use altogether, as neither term has a legal definition.

7.4.1   Exaggeration

Exaggeration suggests that complaints, descriptions of symptoms, behaviour or apparent restrictions have been enlarged or altered beyond what is normal or expected, or to an extent that is out of proportion in some manner to the injuries sustained.

---

2   Guidance 58

3   We discuss competing factual scenarios in the context of clinical negligence claims in Section 8.5 and 9.3.3

From the medico-legal perspective, the significance of exaggeration is whether it is conscious or not. The claimant is entitled to recover for all of the genuine injuries, symptoms and effects of the accident and for the genuine consequences. If the exaggeration is probably not conscious, then the claimant will recover damages for all the additional symptoms, effects and consequences experienced beyond what would objectively be expected given the organic findings. Although the claimant can recover damages for the actual impact of the injury as he/she perceives it, the fact that there is an element of non-conscious exaggeration may be relevant to prognosis and therefore to assessing damages for future loss.

7.4.2   Malingering

If exaggeration is conscious then it is considered by the courts to be malingering. The definition of malingering used in DSM-5[4] is a useful one for our purposes:

> 'The essential feature of malingering is the intentional production of false or grossly exaggerated physical or psychological symptoms, motivated by external incentives such as … avoiding work, obtaining financial compensation …'

The emphasis is on intentional falsehood and external motivation. The malingering claimant is trying to extract money from the defendant through false (and therefore dishonest) pretences – a criminal offence. If there is probably conscious exaggeration, then that exaggeration is taken out of consideration in assessing damages, but the claimant is still entitled to damages for the genuine effects and consequences of the injury. However, the claimant, having lost credibility as a witness, may well have difficulty proving the probable (and genuine) impact of the injury.

There may also be implications in terms of any costs order that the court might make and the claimant might lose the protection of QOCS if found to have made a claim which is 'fundamentally dishonest'. Further a recent change in the law means that even if the claimant would be entitled to some damages, if the he/she is found to be have been 'fundamentally dishonest' in relation to the claim then the claimant will not be able to recover any damages at all, unless the court finds that the claimant would suffer substantial injustice if the claim is dismissed[5].

Some experts identify different categories of conscious exaggeration. Sometimes a claimant will exaggerate when motivated by a desire to be taken seriously as someone with pain or disability. Although this is probably in the conscious category of exaggeration, experts often see such claimants in a different light to the 'malingerer'.

Lawyers and experts alike often use exaggeration and malingering to mean different things, resulting in miscommunication and confusion. The medical expert

---

4   DSM-5: *Diagnostic and Statistical Manual of Mental Disorders - 5th edition* (2013). Washington DC: American Psychiatric Association

5   Section 57 Criminal Justice and Courts Act 2015. The term 'fundamentally dishonest' is not defined in the Act.

must describe accurately what he/she actually means when using these expressions and not merely use these expressions as a shorthand description.

To state that the claimant 'is clearly exaggerating' is an example of Foot-Wearing. The expert must make clear if such exaggeration is in the expert's opinion conscious or unconscious and give reasons.

7.4.3   Approach to the Evidence

The medical expert may consider that there is exaggeration of symptoms, or that the claimant is altogether fabricating them. However, whether or not there is conscious fabrication by the claimant is strictly a matter for the judge to determine, not the medical expert. The honesty or dishonesty of witnesses is a legal matter not a medical matter. The medical expert may be able, as a result of particular expertise, to provide factual or opinion evidence that can assist the judge in coming to a decision. However, there are likely to be few occasions when the medical expert can properly express an opinion, based on medical expertise alone, that a claimant is lying about his condition.

Interestingly, experts often put all difficulties relating to the previous medical history down to the claimant's attempt to manipulate the situation and give scant regard to any other issue, including the expert's own ability to communicate effectively. Claimants report that they are often unclear about what information the expert actually wants to be told.

One expert told us that he had asked a claimant if he had ever had any "spinal problems", to which the claimant gave an emphatic, "No". Later looking through the medical records, the expert found a 20-year history of back pain and so wrote in his report that the claimant had attempted to present a misleading previous medical history. Three days after issuing the report, the expert received a call from the instructing solicitor requesting that the report be amended, because the claimant had not realised that the expert's question about his "spinal problems" meant that he should tell the expert about his periodic back ache.

Whether this claimant misunderstood the expert or used the claimed misunderstanding to try to cover up for a lack of frankness, the medical expert must ensure that in communication with the claimant there is no room for any such misunderstandings. Similar issues arise when a claimant may not connect a question about "previous mental health issues" with having been prescribed tablets "to help" during a messy divorce.

For these reasons, we recommend that medical records are read before interview, so that any factual conflicts can be explored with the claimant before the report is written. If during such exploration the claimant refuses to deal honestly with his/her previous medical history, then the expert is under an obligation to express an opinion on the conduct of the claimant in the Opinion section of the report.

7.4.4   Observations Outside the Medical Examination

This and the following Section deal with observations outside and within a medical examination. The discussion is equally applicable to care and other needs experts who carry out any assessment involving the claimant for the purposes of their report.

The medical expert may make observations outside the formal medical examination, which he/she considers relevant to the question of the genuineness of the claimant's presentation or reported symptoms or observed restrictions. A lawyer would find the following evidence **helpful**:

> From my consulting room window, I witnessed Mr R get out of his car without any apparent discomfort or difficulty, walk quickly to the boot and take out his crutches. He then proceeded to use his crutches to slowly cross the car park with an expression of intense discomfort on his face.
>
> On examination, Mr R was unable to perform physical movements that I had already witnessed him performing without difficulty in the car park. This complete change in physical function I attribute to a conscious exaggeration of his symptoms (malingering).

Other less dramatic examples of such observations would include observations as to the wear on shoes or of the rubber ferrules on crutches or walking sticks (which might be considered inconsistent with the claimant's reported disability or use of aids), or the state of a splint (one reported to be needed "all of the time" but which appears in a pristine condition) or the state of a claimant's hands (where there is a complaint of being unable to carry out various tasks but the state of the claimant's hands appears to suggest otherwise). Such observations can also be potentially supportive of the claimant's case (for example wear on shoes or ferrules consistent with a limp, a well-worn splint or soft clean hands and nails).

In these situations, the medical expert must appreciate that he/she has become a witness of fact in relation to such observations, in the same way as an undercover surveillance operative would be. Where such observations are disputed (in their entirety or even just in certain relevant details) the expert will be submitted to cross-examination in relation to the precise circumstances of the observations and precisely what was seen.

The observations could also be the subject of detailed written questions[6]. A detailed contemporaneous note recording the observations and the circumstances

---

6   Under CPR 35.6 – see Section 4.4

in which they were made is therefore essential. Those notes should record such matters as:

1. precisely what was seen and when;

2. from where the observations were made;

3. at what distance;

4. what light conditions were; and

5. the period of such observations.

In the case of subtler observations, it is usually appropriate, having recorded the claimant's account, to put the apparent inconsistency to the claimant for comment and possible explanation (for example, the claimant may have worn new shoes for the trip to the medical expert or the old splint has fallen apart and has just been replaced).

Should the medical expert's observations successfully be put into doubt under cross-examination, or in the light of other contradictory evidence, then it is likely that the medical expert's evidence as a whole – including the medical opinions within it – would also be thrown into doubt.

7.4.5 Observations Within the Medical Examination

It may be that as a result of an expert's particular expertise or experience he/she is able to say that facts put forward by the claimant are improbable, for example, as to the nature of the claimant's symptoms or restriction in activity or loss of faculty. A lawyer would find the following evidence **helpful**:

> In the course of examination of Mr V, I elicited pain on axial loading, pain on simulated rotation and straight-leg raising of 90° when extending the knee when Mr V was seated, in contrast to the 60° when he was lying supine on the couch. These findings do not have an organic cause or explanation. These positive responses to 3 of the so-called Waddell signs indicate a non-organic component to his complaints. Such findings could be explained by Mr V's heightened emotional state as demonstrated by his crying as he described to me the effects of the accident on his daily life. An alternative explanation is conscious exaggeration.
>
> Waddell himself emphasised that psychological factors needed to be considered when positive signs are elicited, and that on their own such findings were not a test of credibility or faking. Given the consistency of Mr V's presentation during my examination and in previous examinations by other medical practitioners not involved in the litigation, at this stage I consider it probable that Mr V is genuine in his complaints. I recommend that a psychological assessment should be obtained to explore possible psychological factors contributing to his presentation.

The results of the psychometric tests suggest that Mr B has pronounced intellectual deficits, significant memory problems, poor naming skills and impaired executive and visuospatial functions. However, it is unlikely that the results accurately represent his true abilities for the following reasons:

1. His working memory for digits was unusually short, a result pointing to the operation of functional factors.

2. When cued to facilitate recall, his performance deteriorated significantly, whereas performance usually is maintained or improves with prompting.

3. Mr B performed normally on one symptom's validity task, but his performance on another was worse than found among those with conditions such as Alzheimer's or vascular dementia, indicating that he did not apply proper effort.

4. The results are inconsistent with Mr B's everyday level of functioning as related by himself and his mother, which indicates independence in activities of daily living.

5. When assessed by Dr N in 2009 using many of the same tests, his performance was within normal limits. Such deterioration does not fit with the sequelae of a head injury.

6. On a visual recognition memory test Mr B's performance fell significantly below chance. Such a result is inconsistent with a genuine memory disorder and represents unambiguous evidence of dissimulation.

It is therefore highly probable that the results of the tests are invalid and non-credible and that they represent dissimulation.

The expert should only express an opinion as to the improbability of what the claimant says or does where such opinion is based on the expert's particular expertise. If, therefore, the claimed loss of movement or the claimed distribution of a loss of sensation is inconsistent with any physiological or neurological explanation, then this is a matter on which an expert in the appropriate speciality should comment. If pain is apparently experienced during examination as a result of tests that should not induce such pain – such as Waddell's signs on an orthopaedic examination – then this too should be explained clearly. Other examples of such testing would be Erhardt's test for suspected feigned hearing loss or forced choice memory tests for purported cognitive impairment.

Such inconsistency in signs or results on its own may not be evidence of conscious or intentional exaggeration, so the medical expert should report on the inconsistency and list the possible explanations. Waddell himself wrote of his tests that 'Isolated signs should not be over-interpreted. Multiple signs suggest that the patient does not have (only) a straightforward physical problem, but that psychological factors also need to be considered […] Behavioural signs are not on their own a test of credibility or faking[7].

The medical expert will be more effective if he/she lists those matters that give rise to questions about appropriate responses, consistency or honesty. Only in the clearest of cases should the expert go further to express his/her opinion on the credibility of the claimant, as it is beyond the role of the expert in reporting to the court. It is best to leave it to the judge (or the lawyers) to form a conclusion' on the basis of all of the available evidence. A lawyer would find the following evidence **helpful**:

> Mr W sustained an injury to the cervical spine. Given the nature of the accident and the investigations detailed above this is the kind of accident which would be expected to result in some neck symptoms but would generally be expected to resolve in 6 to 12 months.
>
> Mr W presents in an exaggerated fashion. The examination and presentation do not fit the clinical picture. He demonstrates virtually no range of movements of his neck or right shoulder girdle but despite this apparent disability is able to wash and dress himself (including putting on shoes, socks and trousers), shave and maintain his appearance. He is showing gross signs of inappropriate illness behaviour and is either consciously or unconsciously magnifying his symptoms.
>
> As I observe his behaviour and his general demeanour, my opinion is that it is probable that he is unconsciously exaggerating his symptoms and that his main disability is therefore psychological. I recommend that Mr W undergoes formal psychological and psychiatric assessment and recommend that his admission into a multi-disciplinary rehabilitation programme be considered.

> The inconsistencies between the history given to me by Mr A in relation to his previous spinal problems and what was disclosed in the medical records as well as the inconsistency on examination in respect of his ability to dress raise serious questions as to his reliability as a witness. In particular, the ease with which he picked up his shoes and put on his socks after the examination and ran the fingers of his right hand through his hair after dressing lead me to suspect conscious exaggeration of his symptoms. Those instructing me might well wish to carry out further investigations as to Mr A's true level of disability.

---

7   Main, C.J. & Waddell, G. (1998) 'Behavioural responses to examination. A reappraisal of the interpretation of "nonorganic signs"' *Spine* 23(21):2367-71; Waddell, G., McCulloch, J.A., Kummel E., & Venner R.M., (1980) 'Nonorganic physical signs in low-back pain.' *Spine* 5(2):117-25.

The medical expert's observations of the claimant are extremely important, so these must be accurately described and their potential significance explained in simple terms.

> The medical expert may become a witness of fact in relation to observations outside or within the medical examination and may be subjected to cross-examination in relation to the precise circumstances of the observations and what the expert actually saw or heard.

7.5 Surveillance Evidence

When defendant insurers suspect that an exaggerated or false claim is being made, surveillance of the claimant is one approach to disproving the claim. Typically, a claimant is followed for several days or weeks (on occasions, over a period of years) in an attempt to video behaviour that is at odds with the account given to the medical experts on examination. This surveillance usually results in an edited video recording, and mostly showing mundane and inconsequential behaviour. This is normally supplied to the expert on DVD. It is good practice to watch the DVD before reading any written commentary provided with the footage. The commentary can be read subsequently and considered in the light of the expert's uninfluenced response to the footage.

When shown surveillance evidence that appears to contradict the evidence obtained during the medical examination, medical experts should avoid reacting to feelings of betrayal or professional embarrassment at having apparently been misled by the claimant. It is essential to move beyond such emotions before considering the issues from the independent and impartial standpoint required of the medical expert.

> Let us consider a claim where a claimant reports at interview that he has a significant degree of disability, consistent with an inability to carry out various activities. The expert's findings support the claimant's account and the medical expert reports on these findings in the usual way. Several weeks later, surveillance video is produced showing the claimant partaking freely in such activities that he previously claimed were impossible for him to do.
>
> This video is clearly evidence upon which the medical expert must give an opinion. However, before giving such an opinion the questions the medical expert needs to consider are:
>
> 1. is the person in the video actually the claimant?
>
> 2. when and in what context was the video taken? and

3. has any other information (such as a commentary or report) been provided that may influence any interpretation of the video?

The expert should be sure that the person in the video is actually the claimant, and not, for example, a family member. Before making any assessment of the relative abilities of the claimant as reported to the medical experts and as shown in the video, it is important to take proper account of the period during which observations were made and the date in relation to any medical examinations, therapy or other treatment in the case. The expert should also consider if the abilities of the claimant are within an expected range, especially in cases where symptoms may vary in their intensity and where symptoms and restrictions might reasonably vary from time to time.

If the person featured in the video is clearly the claimant and the activities shown on the dates indicated are clearly outside the range of activities that can be reconciled with the history given or the findings on examination, then the expert may give a clear opinion of conscious exaggeration. However, it is sensible to be cautious in less clear-cut cases, remembering that it is the role of the judge to decide on the honesty of witnesses.

When commenting on the surveillance evidence, an expert should consider the following:

1. are the observations for a few minutes, or several hours, on consecutive days or spaced out?

2. are the observations mixed in that some are consistent and some inconsistent with the previous complaints, observations or descriptions of restriction, or are all inconsistent? and

3. is the weather, the time of year, the time of day, the nature of activity or any other factor of potential relevance to an assessment of the relevance of the video?

Where part of the expert's assessment of the video is dependent on a report or commentary provided with it by the investigators, it is essential that the expert makes clear whether it is what is shown in the video or what is described in the accompanying report or commentary that is being relied upon in making the assessment. As is always required under CPR 35, the medical expert must make clear the facts upon which the opinion as to the significance of the surveillance evidence is based.

If the expert is informed that there is a dispute as to the significance of potentially relevant observations of the claimant – for example, that the claimant says that the video shows a "good day" and not a "typical day" or that it was the day after a particularly beneficial therapy or that the observations were only for a short period during the "best part of the day" – then it may be necessary for the expert to express separate opinions on the significance of the evidence on each of the potential versions of the facts[8].

Taking sufficient care to analyse the video in this manner will ensure that the expert's opinion as to its significance can be justified, even under cross-examination, and that the opinion can be evaluated properly by the lawyers involved in the claim.

> It is good practice to watch the DVD before reading any written commentary provided with the footage. The commentary can be read subsequently and considered in the light of the expert's uninfluenced response to the footage.

7.6   Seat Belts and Contributory Negligence

A failure to wear a seat belt in a car may result in the passenger or driver suffering injury that could have been avoided or that is more severe or is of a different kind to that which probably would have been suffered had the seat belt been worn. This failure is regarded in law as 'contributory negligence' on the part of the claimant, which in the most serious case will reduce the damages that would otherwise have been recovered by 25%. This reduction is to reflect the degree of 'blameworthiness' of the claimant for his/her own injuries. The leading judgment, in addressing the judge's task in such cases, gives the following guidance:

> *'Whenever there is an accident, the negligent driver must bear by far the greater share of responsibility. It was his negligence which caused the accident. It also was a prime cause of the whole of the damage. But insofar as the damage might have been avoided or lessened by wearing a seat belt, the injured person must bear some share. But how much should this be? … This question should not be prolonged by an expensive enquiry into the degree of blameworthiness on either side, which would be hotly disputed. Suffice it to assess a share of responsibility which will be just and equitable in the great majority of cases.*

> *Sometimes the evidence will show that the failure made no difference. The damage would have been the same, even if a seat belt had been worn. In such cases, the damages should not be reduced at all. At other times the evidence will show that the failure made all the difference. The damage would have been prevented altogether if a seat belt had been worn. In such cases, I would suggest that the damages should be reduced by 25 per cent. But often enough the evidence will only show that the failure made a considerable difference. Some injuries to the head, for instance, would have been a good deal less*

---

8   See Section 4.2.7

> *severe if a seat belt had been worn, but there would still have been some*
> *injury to the head. In such cases, I would suggest that the damages attribut-*
> *able to the failure to wear a seat belt should be reduced by 15 per cent.'*[9]

The medical expert should not, unless instructed to do so, proffer an opinion on the consequences of such failure to wear a seat belt even where it is apparent that a seat belt has not been worn by the claimant or where there is an issue as to whether or not a seat belt was worn. There are circumstances when the law does not require a seat belt to be worn and therefore in which there will not be criticism of the claimant for not wearing a seat belt (for example taxi drivers and pregnant women). The expert, however, could quite properly signpost in the report the fact that the failure to wear a seat belt may have had an impact on the injuries sustained and await further instructions.

We have however already noted in Section 3.4.1 above how in relation to soft tissue injury claims under the RTA Protocol an expert is required to provide an opinion on the consequences of a failure to wear a seat belt, whether using the prescribed medical report form RTA3 or not, although we have also expressed our reservations as to whether most experts have the expertise to do so.

When instructed to provide an opinion, the medical expert in such cases will need to express an opinion on questions related to the 'but for' scenario. Typically, experts will be asked to address questions about what the situation would have been had a seat belt been worn:

1. what injuries would probably have been sustained?

2. what injuries in fact sustained would probably have been avoided? and

3. what injuries in fact sustained would probably have been significantly different (and describe the difference)?

4. what injuries would probably have been sustained which in fact were not? and based on the above

5. did the absence of wearing a seat belt probably make a significant difference to the injuries sustained, and in general terms, what was that difference?

The law is only interested in a significant or 'considerable' difference[10]. The graver the injuries and the larger the sums in issue in the claim, the more detailed an examination will be called for. In a high value claim, engineering as well as medical expert evidence may well be called for and the expertise of the appropriate medical expert to deal with the issues may be investigated in detail by the parties and the court. In a low value claim, the court is likely to take a more 'broad brush'

---

9   *Froom v Butcher* [1976] QB 286

10   *Stanton v Collinson* [2010] EWCA Civ 81

approach to the assessment on the basis of such expert evidence as is available in preference to carrying out a detailed and costly investigation.

The medical expert, therefore, must be able to justify logically any opinion expressed as to the likely differences in injury and must ensure that sufficient factual information is available (such as accident photos of the vehicle) in order to express such opinion. As with all opinion evidence, the expert should make clear in the report any reservations or qualifications he/she may have in expressing such opinion.

The medical expert will need to make sure that there is an adequate factual basis for expressing such opinion. Information necessary before expressing an opinion would be likely to include, in addition to the medical records, evidence as to the general circumstances of the accident, collision speed and angle, and the damage to the vehicles (or other objects) involved. The expert is likely to want to see the police accident report (if any), witness statements, plans and photographs or other detailed description of the state of the vehicle(s) after the accident.

In some cases, there may be a factual dispute as to whether or not a seat belt was worn. In such cases, the medical expert should express an opinion as above on the probable consequences of any failure to wear a seat belt. In addition, if the expert, as a result of his/her particular expertise or experience, considers it more likely that either the seat belt was or was not being worn, then the expert should express an opinion in favour of one or other proposition, explaining and justifying the basis of that opinion[11]. For example, the expert may be guided by the nature of the injuries sustained.

7.7 Multi-Accident Claims

Reporting on multiple accident claims often causes experts confusion. Although we term these cases 'multi-accident', the same principles apply where one or more, or indeed all, of the 'accidents' are the result of clinical negligence.

The need to instruct a medical expert to deal with a multi-accident claim usually arises in one of three situations:

1. a claimant has suffered injuries in two accidents and the total loss from both accidents needs to be assessed[12];

2. legal liability attaches to a defendant in only one of two accidents, and the loss attributable to that defendant needs to be assessed; or

3. two defendants are in dispute as to what proportion of the damages each is liable to meet.

---

11   Guidance para 58 and see Section 4.2.7

12   In such cases, the claim would be against the same defendant, such as an employer or the same insurance company where different motorists were insured by the same insurer.

In 1 above, the medical expert has to report on what has occurred after both accidents, compared with what would probably have occurred without both accidents.

In 2, the medical expert has to report on what has occurred as a result of the accident to which legal liability attaches compared with what probably would have occurred without that accident.

In 3, the medical expert has to report in two stages: first, on the difference that the first accident has made to the claimant, compared with what would probably have occurred without the 1st and 2nd accidents; secondly, the expert has to report on the difference that the 2nd accident has made when compared to the probable recovery of the claimant from the 1st accident.

7.7.1   Applying Causation Graphs

A useful tool for preparing reports on multi-accident cases is to adapt the causation graph, which we introduced in Chapter 6, to reflect these more complex issues.

(1) Two Accidents - Report on Both (Cumulative Effects)

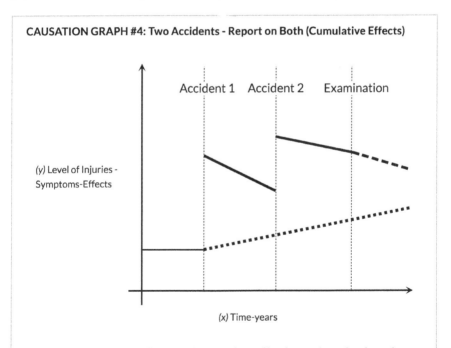

CAUSATION GRAPH #4: Two Accidents - Report on Both (Cumulative Effects)

Accident 1   Accident 2   Examination

(y) Level of Injuries - Symptoms-Effects

(x) Time-years

The expert reports on the cumulative effect of both accidents by describing the situation represented by the solid lines (and the dashes representing the future), then the situation represented by the lower dotted line, and then describing the injuries, symptoms, effects and consequences that create the area between these lines. The situation in the absence of either one of the accidents is irrelevant.

(2a) Two Accidents - Report on First

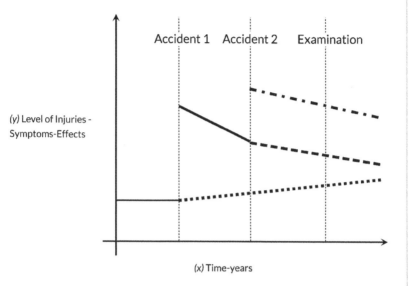

CAUSATION GRAPH #5: Two Accidents - Report on First Accident Only

Accident 1   Accident 2   Examination

(y) Level of Injuries -
Symptoms-Effects

(x) Time-years

When reporting on the first of two accidents, the expert has to describe the situation represented by the solid line (and the dashes representing the projected first accident recovery), the situation represented by the lower dotted line, and the injuries, symptoms, effects and consequences that create the area between these lines. The upper dot-dashed line, the impact of the second accident, is irrelevant.

(2b) Two Accidents - Report on Second

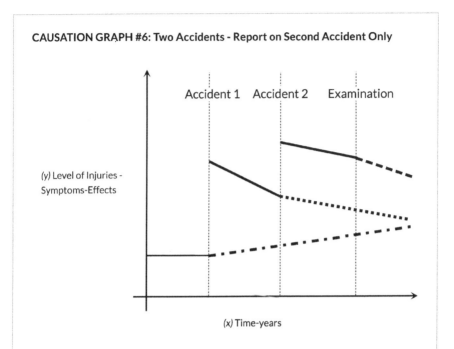

CAUSATION GRAPH #6: Two Accidents - Report on Second Accident Only

Accident 1   Accident 2   Examination

(y) Level of Injuries -
Symptoms-Effects

(x) Time-years

When reporting on the second of two accidents, the expert has to describe the situation represented by the solid line (and the dashed line for the future), the situation represented by the dotted line (the projected first accident recovery) and finally describe the injuries, symptoms, effects and consequences that are represented by the area between the these lines. The situation in the absence of both accidents represented by the dot-dashed line is irrelevant.

(3) Two Accidents - Report on Both (Differentiating Effects)

When the expert has to report on the separate impact of each of two accidents, the expert has first to report on the first accident, in the absence of the second accident. This means that the expert has to project what recovery the claimant would probably have made had the second accident not occurred and contrast this with the without both accidents baseline. Then the expert has to report on the additional loss caused by the second accident beyond the projected recovery from the first accident.

Once again, the expert must address these issues in terms of the additional injuries, symptoms, effects and consequences probably caused by each accident. Causation Graph #6 above can be readily adapted to illustrate this type of report.

In multiple accident claims, the medical expert may find difficulty in establishing an accurate factual basis – namely, the condition of the claimant after the first accident and the recovery that was (or was not) taking place when the second accident occurred. The medical situation that the expert must give opinion upon is also more difficult, with little help from the medical literature available on victims of multiple accidents.

7.7.2   Approach to the Evidence

The expanded long-form opinion structure[13] can be developed to cope with these multi-accident cases, whether the expert is asked to report on the cumulative effect of both accidents, the first accident only, the second accident only, or on the differentiated effects of both accidents. We will take each of these situations in turn.

Report on Both Accidents (Cumulative Effects)

Opinion and Prognosis

1.   Acknowledge the complexity/difficulty.

2.   Identify the claimant's present medical situation.

3.   Identify the specific injuries sustained in the 1st accident and the resulting symptoms/effects and any recovery prior to the 2nd accident.

4.   Identify the additional injuries sustained in the 2nd accident and the resulting symptoms/effects and any recovery prior to the examination date and for the future.

5.   Identify the claimant's medical situation without both accidents to the examination date and for the future.

6.   Express opinion on causation for the present situation (on the difference in injuries/symptoms/effects between the present situation and the situation as it would have been without both accidents).

7.   Contrast the prognosis for the present injuries/symptoms/effects and the projected situation as it would have been without both accidents.

8.   Describe in pragmatic terms the likely consequences now and for the future[14] (the restrictions in activities of daily living arising from the injuries/symptoms/effects suffered in both accidents and the situation as it would have been without both accidents).

---

13   See Sections 7.11.1 and 11.3.3.

14   We recommend that the consequences of injuries be dealt with in a separate section of the report. We include the consequences of injury here to show the underlying logic for the order of the opinion.

Report on 1st of 2 Accidents

Opinion and Prognosis

1. Acknowledge the complexity/difficulty.

2. Identify the claimant's present medical situation.

3. Identify the specific injuries sustained in the 1st accident and the resulting symptoms/effects and any recovery prior to the 2nd accident.

4. Identify the likely progression of the 1st accident injuries/symptoms/effects (without the intervention of the 2nd accident) to the examination date and if necessary into the future (i.e. if the 1st accident injuries/symptoms would not have resolved by the examination date).

5. Establish the 'but for' 1st accident baseline to the examination date and if required projected into the future (and discounting the 2nd accident).

6. Express opinion on causation as at the examination date (on the difference in injuries/symptoms/effects between the projected recovery from the first accident and the situation as it would have been without both accidents) and where possible give medical justification for discounting injuries/symptoms the expert attributes to the 2nd accident.

7. Contrast the prognosis (if required) for the injuries/symptoms/effects from the projected recovery from the 1st accident beyond the examination date and the projected situation as it would have been without both accidents.

8. Describe in pragmatic terms the likely consequences now and for the future (the restrictions in activities of daily living arising from the injuries/symptoms/effects suffered in the 1st accident and the situation as it would have been without both accidents).

Report on 2nd of 2 Accidents

Opinion and Prognosis

1. Acknowledge the complexity/difficulty.

2. Identify the claimant's present medical situation.

3. Identify the specific injuries sustained in the 1st accident and the resulting symptoms/effects and any recovery prior to the 2nd accident.

4. Identify the additional injuries sustained in the 2nd accident and the resulting symptoms/effects and any recovery prior to the examination date and for the future.

5. Identify the likely progression of the 1st accident injuries/symptoms/effects (without the intervention of the 2nd accident) to the examination date and if necessary into the future (i.e. if the 1st accident injuries and symptoms would not have resolved by the examination date).

6. Express opinion on causation as at the examination date (on the difference in injuries/symptoms/effects between the situation as it is now and the projected recovery from the 1st accident) and where possible give medical justification for discounting injuries and symptoms that the expert attributes to the 1st accident.

7. Contrast the prognosis for the present injuries/symptoms/effects and the situation as it would have been without the second accident.

8. Describe in pragmatic terms the likely consequences now and for the future (the restrictions in activities of daily living arising now and for the future from the present injuries/symptoms/effects and the situation as it would have been without the second accident).

Report on Both Accidents (Differentiating Effects)

Opinion and Prognosis

1. Acknowledge the complexity/difficulty.

2. Identify the claimant's present medical situation.

3. Identify the specific injuries sustained in the 1st accident and the resulting symptoms/effects and any recovery prior to the 2nd accident.

4. Identify the additional injuries sustained in the 2nd accident and the resulting symptoms/effects and any recovery prior to the examination date and for the future.

5. Identify the likely progression of the 1st accident injuries/symptoms/effects (without the intervention of the 2nd accident) to the examination date and if necessary into the future (i.e. if the 1st accident injuries and symptoms would not have resolved by the examination date).

6. Identify the claimant's medical situation without the 1st accident to the examination date and if necessary for the future (and discounting the 2nd accident).

7. Express opinion on causation for the 1st accident as at the examination date (on the difference in injuries/symptoms/ effects between the projected recovery from the 1st accident and the situation as it would have been without both accidents) and where possible give medical justification for discounting injuries and symptoms that the expert attributes to the 2nd accident.

8. Contrast the prognosis (if required) for the injuries/symptoms/ effects from the projected recovery from the 1st accident beyond the examination date and the projected situation as it would have been without both accidents.

9. Describe in pragmatic terms the likely consequences now and for the future (the restrictions in activities of daily living arising from the injuries/ symptoms/effects suffered in the 1st accident and the situation as it would have been without both accidents).

10. Express opinion on causation for the 2nd accident as at the examination date (on the difference in injuries/symptoms/effects between the situation as it is now and the projected recovery from the 1st accident).

11. Contrast the prognosis for the present injuries/symptoms/effects and the situation as it would have been without the second accident.

12. Describe in pragmatic terms the likely consequences now and for the future (the restrictions in activities of daily living arising now and for the future from the present injuries/symptoms/effects and the situation as it would have been without the 2nd accident).

A lawyer would find the following evidence **unhelpful** as the expert makes no attempt to differentiate the two injuries and the symptoms, effects and conse-quences arising from them. This opinion will almost certainly lead to questions being sent to the expert from the lawyers so that the claim(s) can be valued:

> It is very difficult to attribute the proportion by which each of these two accidents contributed to the current condition of the ankle. There was not a full recovery following the first accident and I am not sure that one can put everything down to the second accident. I believe therefore that the first accident primed the ankle but the main injury was in the second accident and I would put it in the region of 30% to the first and 70% to the second.

A lawyer would find the following evidence **helpful** as the expert describes the dif-ference that the accident has made both in medical and in practical terms, thereby helping the lawyers to value the claim:

> As the result of the first accident, he suffered a soft tissue injury of the right ankle giving rise to acute pain for about a week and thereafter frequent episodes of aching and stiffness, which interfered only minimally with his activities of daily living. These symptoms were gradually resolving in the 3 months before the second accident.
>
> In the absence of the second accident it is probable that these remaining symptoms from the first accident would have continued to resolve gradu-

ally so that by 12 months on from the first accident it is probable that he would have made a full symptomatic recovery.

As the result of the second accident 4 months after the first accident, when he again suffered a soft tissue injury of the right ankle, the level of symptoms he was experiencing was exacerbated so that he had difficulty walking and required strong painkillers and a prolonged course of physiotherapy. The current symptoms, as described above, are likely to resolve slowly over the next 2 to 3 years from the date of my examination.

Given that the circumstances of the second accident and that the mechanism of injury in the 2 accidents were different, in my opinion the first accident did not contribute to or increase the severity of the subsequent injury and the resulting symptoms and restrictions.

For the first 8 months after the second accident, the first accident contributed a small and reducing element to his symptoms, which was of little or no functional significance. In the absence of either accident there was no reason for him to suffer any symptoms in his ankle.

More Than Two Accidents

In the examples above, we have set out graphs for cases where the claimant has suffered two accidents. Unfortunately, some claimants become serial accidentees and suffer more than two accidents. We hope that by now the reader will be able to extend the X-axis of a causation graph to account for additional accidents and will be able to draw the relevant lines to indicate how causation needs to be addressed.

7.7.3 Cumulative Effects Cases

The most difficult expression of a multi-accident case is when it is impossible, even on the balance of probabilities, to differentiate between the injuries, symptoms and effects of each of the accidents and the loss attributable to each. In this situation, the lawyers need the expert to be as helpful as possible.

The question as to whether the presenting condition since the last accident is attributable to the cumulative effect of both (or all) of the accidents is the essential question that the lawyers need the expert to address. If so, the lawyers will simply divide up the loss between the defendants based on a percentage estimate of the contribution of each accident.

This approach, as far as the medical expert is concerned, should be adopted only when a more detailed approach is simply impossible or where instructions are expressly given to the medical expert not to seek to differentiate between the effects of each accident.

7.8 Breaking the Chain of Causation

We have seen that damages are only recovered for the injuries and loss resulting from the breach of duty on which the claim is based. Therefore, as illustrated by the causation graph, damages are for the difference between what would have been in the absence of (or 'but for') the accident or adverse event and the situation as it now is.

Damages may in certain circumstances also be limited if something happens after the accident that adversely affects the claimant. It is a matter of law whether a subsequent event 'breaks the chain of causation'[15]. The question is whether the law holds that the subsequent event can be regarded as breaking the causal connection between the breach of duty and the damage suffered. If it does, then the original wrongdoer will not be liable for any subsequent damage.

The subsequent event must have such an impact that it is regarded as obliterating the original wrongdoing, and it may take the form of:

- some natural event independent of any human agency;
- the act or omission of someone other than the claimant and the original wrongdoer; or
- the conduct of the claimant him/herself.

In the following five examples, the chain of causation could become an issue in the claim:

1. One year after the accident, and while recovering from it, a claimant suffers a heart attack and dies for reasons totally unconnected with the accident.

In this situation, the heart attack breaks the chain of causation and damages cease on death. Damages for pain and suffering are assessed on the basis of the period of one year. Care needs and loss of income are limited to that same period.

2. One year after suffering severe injury to a leg in an accident, a claimant is involved in a subsequent accident for which no one else is blamed. In this accident he suffers a traumatic amputation of the same leg.

In this situation, the second accident breaks the chain of causation. Pain and suffering arising from the first accident is assessed on the basis of the period of one year and care needs and loss of income are limited to that period.

---

15   Lawyers often refer to an act that breaks the chain of causation as a 'novus actus interveniens' (a new act intervening).

3.   One year after the accident, while still recovering from a severe leg injury, a claimant trips and falls down stairs while carrying something in both hands, sustaining further serious injury.

In this situation, whether or not the chain of causation is broken may be contentious. The resolution of the issue will depend on whether the original breach of duty and injury contributed to the fall.

4.   A claimant refuses to undergo or to continue treatment, which is necessary to assist in the recovery from the original injuries sustained.

Whether or not the chain of causation is broken, thereby relieving the original wrongdoer of liability for an extended period of recovery caused by the absence of treatment, is likely to focus upon the reasonableness of the claimant refusing such treatment.

5.   A claimant is treated in hospital following an accident, but receives care that falls below the standard accepted as proper as a result of which his condition is aggravated.

In this situation, whether the original wrongdoer avoids liability for the impact of the hospital care depends on the nature and degree of the breach of duty in hospital. We consider this issue further in Section 7.9 below.

7.8.1   Approach to the Evidence

It is not appropriate for an expert to refer to such intervening events as breaking, or not breaking, the chain of causation – this is a matter for the lawyers and the court. However, the expert should be aware of the potential issue for the lawyers and where appropriate and from within the expert's area of expertise, address this subsequent event and how it relates to the original injury. If the subsequent event is outside the expert's area of expertise, then the expert should indicate in the report the need for another appropriate expert to deal with the issue.

Therefore, the matters that a medical expert should address would therefore include:

- whether the claimant's subsequent death was related or in some way connected to the accident;
- whether a subsequent medical complication was related to the accident or its consequences;
- whether a subsequent accident might have been caused or contributed to by the effects of the original accident;
- whether there is an explanation for the claimant's refusal to undergo or complete treatment or whether there are reasons why such refusal might be regarded as reasonable generally or in the particular circumstances of the claimant; and

- whether the claimant's condition has been aggravated by his treatment at the hands of the medical profession subsequent to the accident.

It is enough for the medical expert in the first instance to indicate only briefly an opinion on such matters, unless specifically instructed to address the issue. Should issues concerning a possible break in the chain of causation prove to be an important aspect of the case, then it would be for the lawyers to return to the medical expert for greater clarification.

7.9 Criticism of Medical Treatment in a Personal Injury Claim

In preparing a report in a personal injury claim, the medical expert may be critical of the treatment that a claimant received in hospital following the injury. If the treatment to be criticised has resulted in the claimant suffering additional or unnecessary injury, then the claimant may be able to bring a clinical negligence claim in relation to that additional injury and the defendant in the personal injury claim may be able to avoid paying compensation for that additional injury by blaming the healthcare provider. Clinical negligence is dealt with in Chapters 8 and 9.

In a personal injury claim, most claimants and their advisers do not consider it a desirable course of action to add an additional defendant to the claim – the healthcare provider – and to have to launch a concurrent clinical negligence claim. If a concurrent action is launched, the initial claim immediately becomes complicated by the addition of parties and issues. The claim will also become considerably more expensive to run and will take longer, with a less certain outcome. To the defendant, whilst recognising such effects, it may be a way to reduce the financial exposure in the personal injury claim by passing it on to the healthcare provider. However, even investigating the matter will inevitably incur additional costs, which one of the parties will have to bear.

Where medical treatment subsequent to an accident does give rise to a claim in clinical negligence for the additional injury resulting to the claimant, lawyers describe the intervening clinical negligence as "breaking the chain of causation". The injury that has been caused (or part of it) has not been caused by the original wrongdoer's breach of duty and so the original wrongdoer is not liable for it.

Although the basic principle is straightforward, applying the principle to the facts of a case is a difficult area of law. This is because not all negligent treatment that causes a worsening of an injured claimant's condition will give rise to a separate (and additional) claim for clinical negligence against the healthcare provider. To do so within an existing personal injury claim, the medical treatment must be 'grossly negligent', so that its effect is to 'eclipse the original wrongdoing'[16] and

---

16 *Webb v Barclays Bank Plc* [2002] PIQR P161; *Wright v Cambridge Medical Group* [2011] EWCA Civ 669

'extinguish the causative potency of the earlier tort (or wrong)'[17]. After all, it was the original wrongdoer whose actions (or omissions) put the claimant unwillingly into the hands of the medical profession in the first place.

Therefore, even where the medical treatment did fall below an acceptable standard of care, it will not necessarily in law break the chain of causation and make the healthcare provider liable for any resulting damage caused by the unacceptable treatment. Nor necessarily will unacceptable treatment allow the original wrong-doer to avoid paying full compensation to the claimant.

A medical expert is not expected to know when in law treatment comes so far below the appropriate standard of care that the negligence becomes 'gross'. Indeed, it is difficult for a lawyer to identify the line between 'simple negligence' and 'gross negligence'. The expert is expected only to compare the actual care with that reasonably to be expected. In so doing, the expert can probably give some impression as to how far below an appropriate standard the care was, perhaps in a range from 'momentary oversight' to 'inexplicably crass'.

7.9.1   Approach to the Evidence

Expert reports in personal claims are required for the purpose of establishing the causation of injury or damage and in assessing damages. The report will almost certainly address the causation of the injury sustained by the claimant. Where subsequent medical treatment has contributed to the claimant's condition the expert will need to consider the extent to which the situation was worsened by the treatment received from the medical practitioners.

Therefore, where there are issues as to whether the treatment or management of the claimant by the healthcare provider has contributed towards the claimant's current situation or where the expert considers that the claimant would be in a better condition if he/she had received an appropriate standard of care, the opinion on the causation of injury expressed in the report will not be complete without reference to these issues.

The instructions from the lawyers should state 'the purpose of the advice or report'[18] and this will not normally include questions about the standard of medical care in a personal injury claim. Nonetheless, a medical expert minded to be critical of the standard of care given by medical professionals in treating the injury suffered in the accident should consider two important issues:

1.   whether his/her opinion given in the report is 'true and complete'[19] and whether the 'duty to assist the court on matters within his expertise'[20] has been complied with; and

---

17   *Rahman v Arearose Ltd* [2001] QB 351

18   Guidance para 20(c) and see Section 4.2.1

19   See Statement of Truth and PD35 2.4 and see Section 4.2.17

20   CPR 35.3(1)

2. whether the medical expert is of the appropriate expertise properly to give an opinion critical of the treating clinicians.

In the first instance, the expert will have been chosen in order to assist with identifying the injury, its causation and the assessment of damage. The expert is not instructed to address the standard of care applicable to the subsequent treatment and so may not necessarily be the appropriate expert to do so.

The medical expert must be sure of his/her ground to be making criticisms as to the standard of care provided in hospital subsequent to the accident. The expert must also be confident that he/she has seen all relevant documentation on which to base such opinion. Medical experts must only express an opinion on matters within their expertise[21] and must make it clear 'when a question or issue falls outside their expertise; and when they are not able to reach a definite opinion, for example because they have insufficient information'[22].

It is often useful for the expert to discuss his/her concerns regarding the subsequent medical treatment with the instructing solicitor to establish what new instructions, if any, need to be given to the expert and to get advice as to the manner in which the issue needs to be addressed within the report. If the expert's instructions do require, whether expressly or by implication, him/her to consider whether the outcome of treatment may have been worsened by the acts of someone other than the initial wrongdoer (the defendant), then it would be appropriate for the expert to make reference to concerns about the standard of care on the part of the healthcare provider.

Even though a medical expert may not be in a position to express a concluded opinion about the standard of care or may not have the expertise to do so, if genuinely concerned the expert should at least signpost this for the lawyers as an area for possible further consideration. It may also be appropriate to identify the relevant area of expertise by which the standard of such care should properly be considered should the instructing party choose to do so.

In a personal injury claim, most claimants and their advisers do not consider it a desirable course of action to add an additional defendant to the claim – the healthcare provider – and to have to launch a concurrent clinical negligence claim.

---

21   PD35 2.2

22   PD35 2.4 and Section 4.2.11

To state that 'the claimant's current condition has been contributed to by the medical treatment he received following the accident' is an example of Foot-Wearing. The expert must say how and in what way the medical treatment has contributed to the causation of present condition. Only where the expert has the appropriate expertise should the expert address the standard of care provided to the claimant. (see Chapter 8)

7.10 Mental Capacity

The issue of mental capacity of a claimant may arise from a condition pre-dating and independent of the accident or event that is the subject of the claim, or the condition may be the result of the accident or event. The claimant's capacity will need to be considered in cases involving brain injury acquired in an accident, but also, for example, in claims involving the elderly or a person with learning difficulties or any other vulnerable person who suffers an injury.

The implications in a claim for damages for injury of a finding that the claimant lacks capacity are not only personal to the claimant (the need to appoint a 'litigation friend' so that the claimant is no longer able to make decisions in the litigation for him/herself) but results in the requirement that the court has to approve any settlement of the claim. It is also likely to have substantial financial implications because a substantial head of damages will then relate to the resulting costs in respect of the Court of Protection, the case managers and the lawyers to manage the damages which are recovered.

The appropriate expert will generally be a psychiatrist, neurologist or neuro-psychologist. What follows is not a full exposition of the law relating to capacity, but we will consider the test that has to be addressed by an expert in providing a report which deals with the question of capacity[23].

7.10.1 The Law

The test is a statutory test, set out in the Mental Capacity Act 2005. The Act sets out the principles to be applied as follows:

1. The principles

    (i)   The following principles apply for the purposes of this Act.

    (ii) A person must be assumed to have capacity unless it is established that he lacks capacity.

---

23   For more information see texts such as 'Assessment of Mental Capacity A Practical Guide for Doctors and Lawyers', 3rd edition The British Medical Association and the Law Society. General Editor: Penny Letts

(iii) A person is not to be treated as unable to make a decision unless all practicable steps to help him to do so have been taken without success.

(iv) A person is not to be treated as unable to make a decision merely because he makes an unwise decision.

The statutory presumption at section 1(ii) means that it is for the person seeking to establish lack of capacity to prove that lack of capacity. Section 2(iv) below provides that proof must be on the balance of probabilities. It follows from section 1(iii) that the expert will have to consider what steps could be taken to assist the claimant to make a decision – for example, the appointment of a case manager or the support of a parent or spouse. Perhaps more difficult, particularly when dealing with capacity to make decisions in relation to financial matters, is the provision at section 1(iv) that a person is entitled to make an unwise decision without being regarded as lacking capacity. A claimant is entitled to spend his damages on a new Ferrari or a world cruise rather than on the long-term care or support regime or building works for which the damages were assessed. The test is also decision specific, so that in the context of litigation a person may be able to conduct litigation (and so decide for example whether liability issues should be compromised or an offer of settlement accepted) but may lack the capacity to manage a large sum in damages which is recovered.

Section 2 is concerned with the characteristics of the person under consideration.

2. People who lack capacity

(i) For the purposes of this Act, a person lacks capacity in relation to a matter if at the material time he is unable to make a decision for himself in relation to the matter because of an impairment of, or a disturbance in the functioning of, the mind or brain.

(ii) It does not matter whether the impairment or disturbance is permanent or temporary.

(iii) A lack of capacity cannot be established merely by reference to—

(a) a person's age or appearance, or

(b) a condition of his, or an aspect of his behaviour, which might lead others to make unjustified assumptions about his capacity.

(iv) In proceedings under this Act or any other enactment, any question whether a person lacks capacity within the meaning of this Act must be decided on the balance of probabilities.

Capacity i.e. the ability to make a decision for oneself, is to be considered at the time that a decision is to be made and the inability to make a decision must be caused by an impairment or disturbance of the mind or brain, whether permanent or temporary (section 2(i) and 2(ii)). The test is applied regardless of the person's age, appearance, behaviour etc (section 2(iii)). For the avoidance of doubt section 2(iv) states that questions about capacity must be decided on the balance of probabilities (see the discussion of proof in Chapter 5 above).

Further important guidance as to how the inability to make decisions must be assessed is set out in section 3.

3. Inability to make decisions

(i)   For the purposes of section 2, a person is unable to make a decision for himself if he is unable—

(a)   to understand the information relevant to the decision,

(b)   to retain that information,

(c)   to use or weigh that information as part of the process of making the decision, or

(d)   to communicate his decision (whether by talking, using sign language or any other means).

(ii)   A person is not to be regarded as unable to understand the information relevant to a decision if he is able to understand an explanation of it given to him in a way that is appropriate to his circumstances (using simple language, visual aids or any other means).

(iii)   The fact that a person is able to retain the information relevant to a decision for a short period only does not prevent him from being regarded as able to make the decision.

(iv)   The information relevant to a decision includes information about the reasonably foreseeable consequences of—

(a)   deciding one way or another, or

(b)   failing to make the decision.

Section 3(i) sets out the 4-part test which is at the heart of the question of capacity and which is to be applied in assessing the inability to make decisions. Lack of capacity only arises if the person cannot understand the information relevant to the decision, cannot retain that information and cannot use or weigh that information as part of the decision-making process and cannot communicate the decision. The relevant information will include the information as to the reasonably foreseeable consequences of either deciding an issue one way or the other or failing to make a decision (section 3(iv)). Someone who cannot retain information may nonetheless have capacity if the information is retained for long enough in order to make a decision.

7.10.2 Approach to the Evidence

If follows from the law set out in the previous section that when reporting on whether a person has mental capacity in relation to an identified decision to be taken the expert must follow through a series of questions, applying the standard of proof (on the balance of probabilities) before reaching a conclusion as to whether or not the presumption of capacity is rebutted.

- Does the person have an impairment of the mind or brain, or is there some sort of disturbance affecting the way their mind or brain works, whether the impairment or disturbance is temporary or permanent? (the 'diagnostic threshold')
- If so, does that impairment or disturbance mean that the person is unable to make the decision in question at the time it needs to be made? (the 'functional' test)

The expert must then go on to assess the ability to make a decision by answering the following questions:

- Does the person have a general understanding of what decision they need to make and why they need to make it?
- Does the person have a general understanding of the likely consequences of making, or not making, this decision?
- Is the person able to understand, retain, use and weigh up the information relevant to this decision?
- Can the person communicate his or her decision (by talking, using sign language or any other means? It may be that the services of a professional, such as a speech and language therapist, would be helpful)[24]

By working through this series of questions and providing the answers, the expert should be able to provide the required opinion as to whether the person is proved, on the balance of probabilities, to lack capacity in relation to the decision on which the expert's opinion is sought.

7.10.3 Dependent Capacity

In a borderline case it may be that the claimant is considered to retain capacity if, but only if, assisted and supported by family or professional helpers. In such a case the finding of capacity is dependent on the claimant receiving such support.

---

24   See Mental Capacity Act 2005 Code of Practice (issued by the Lord Chancellor on 23 April 2007) P.41

If that is the case, the expert should address that need – its nature and extent – as a claim for such family and/or professional assistance might be made.

7.11 Cases that Rely on Expertise

Some cases rely more heavily on the opinions of experts because the factual basis is incomplete. The court seeks to hear from the medical expert as to the likely factual position. The problem is that when an opinion is difficult to justify on strictly medical or scientific grounds, most experts are less willing to offer a firm opinion – even an opinion based on the balance of probabilities.

In these difficult cases, the often opaque expressions of opinion found in expert reports are an illustration of the discomfort that the expert feels in applying the civil standard of proof to finely balanced issues. The easy option appears to be for the experts to muddy the waters with artfully impenetrable language and hope the case settles. This is, to say the least, an interesting interpretation of an expert's overriding duty to help the court.

In cases where expressing firm opinions is difficult, experts have to apply their medico-legal minds to the medical issues in dispute. Where scientifically supported opinions are not possible, then the next stage is to consider whether a credible opinion can be given 'on the balance of probabilities'. Clearly, the strength of an expert's opinion, in the face of a contrary opinion, will increase as the expert's level of certainty increases. However, if the expert is confident that his/her opinion is correct 'on the balance of probabilities', then the opinion can be - and should be – clearly expressed in the report.

7.11.1 Structure for a 'Difficult' Opinion

When dealing with a difficult opinion, an expanded long-form opinion structure should be used to explain the basis of the opinion and to deal openly with the difficulties of offering a firm opinion. The following structure allows the expert to deal with the difficulty honestly and openly before expressing clear opinions:

1. acknowledge the difficulty of expressing a firm opinion;

2. discuss whether, given the available evidence, an opinion can be expressed on the balance of probabilities; (and if so)

3. identify the important factors;

4. set out the reasoning process; and

5. give a clear conclusion on the balance of probabilities.

In the example below, the expert begins by acknowledging the difficulty in forming an opinion:

> When considering Mr M's chances of improved long term survival had his
> lung disease been diagnosed in March 2008, there are no relevant scientific
> papers on which I can rely in forming an opinion …However, given the
> nature of the disease and its progression in the months leading up to Mr M's
> death in December 2008, I do consider that there is sufficient evidence to
> give an opinion, on the balance of probabilities, on his chances of improved
> long term survival had the diagnosis been made in March 2008…

Here, the expert has acknowledged the difficulty of the lack of scientific evidence
to support the opinion that follows, which is based instead on the expert's expertise and experience:

> … I give substantial weight to the fact that a large tumour had developed
> (as detailed in 4.7 above) in the claimant's neck by June 2008. In my opin-
> ion, this indicates that the disease was probably already present in Mr M's
> lymphatic system in March 2008 and earlier diagnosis and treatment would
> not have been likely to prevent the spread of the disease to other lymph
> nodes, as subsequently occurred. Therefore, on the balance of probabili-
> ties, I conclude that the failure to diagnose the lung disease in March 2008
> made no material difference to the claimant's chances of long term survival.

Acknowledging the inherent difficulty of giving an opinion is likely to draw a challenge to the opinion should the matter reach court. However, such a challenge is
going to happen in any event and an acknowledgement of difficulty by the expert
demonstrates an open and honest (and therefore, independent) approach to the
issues. Beyond this, the expert's willingness to align in the grammar his/her professional credibility with the opinion expressed – by using the first person singular
– shows a level of commitment and professional responsibility that a court would
be likely to find impressive.

Conclusion

The principles to be applied in a complex claim are exactly the same as those that
must be applied in all claims. By focussing on these basic principles, the expert
will be able to deal with all the issues in the claim appropriately. In many complex
claims, the level of proof that the expert needs to apply to his/her opinions is far
closer to the civil standard of proof than most medical experts find to be comfortable. But this should not deter the expert from giving clear and concise opinions,
explaining clearly the basis on which the opinion is made and the rationale that
supports the conclusion reached.

Key-Point Summary

1. Every expert opinion has to be based on a logical and reasoned approach to the evidence. Experts should always take the time to consider all the possible causes for a presentation – it is a mistake to rush to judgement on what are often very difficult issues.

2. Where there is difficulty in linking an injury to its cause, the expert should consider the question as to whether the injury is capable of being attributed to the accident, even though a direct causal link is difficult to establish, and then go on to apply the balance of probabilities to the attribution.

3. Experts should consider factual disputes very carefully and express opinions on both possible sets of facts, unless there is a clear technical justification for preferring one or other set of facts.

4. The terms 'exaggeration' and 'malingering' do not have a legal definition and lawyers and experts apply these terms in different ways. The medical expert should explain what he/she means when using these terms.

5. When reporting on observations outside of the clinical examination, the expert becomes a witness to fact and so should make careful contemporaneous notes of any observations made and the circumstances in which these were made.

6. Surveillance evidence should be considered very carefully and all issues raised should be considered in the light of all the available evidence. The expert should always make sure the person in the video is actually the claimant and should watch the footage before reading any commentary supplied with it.

7. Cases involving road traffic accidents where there is an allegation or a real possibility that the claimant was not wearing a seatbelt require the medical expert to consider what the claimant's injuries would have been but for the failure to wear a seatbelt and then to compare the situation as it is with the situation as it would have been but for that failure.

8. Multiple-accident claims often involve the expert in reporting on a projected recovery from an accident in order to properly consider issues of causation. All involved in such cases recognise the difficulty of the task, so a logical and reasoned approach to the issue is essential.

9. Some post-accident events 'break the chain of causation' and experts should be aware of this issue when considering causation, though whether an event does or does not break the chain of causation is a matter for the lawyers and the court.

10. When considering possible clinical negligence within a personal injury report, it is important to consider whether an expert in another discipline would actually be the appropriate expert to consider the matter. It is often useful to seek advice from the instructing solicitor when issues arise concerning the quality of medical treatment following an accident.

11. Experts should not shy away from expressing clear opinions in difficult cases, but should explain clearly the basis of and rationale for the conclusions reached.

Next Steps

In the next chapter, we will explore the law as it relates to clinical negligence and the additional issues that experts have to consider when reporting on clinical negligence claims.

8

Clinical Negligence –
Legal Principles

Introduction

The legal principles applied in clinical negligence claims are exactly the same as the principles applied in all personal injury claims. The court still has to decide issues of breach of duty, causation, damage, and condition and prognosis. However, there is no doubt that the medical and legal issues in clinical negligence are more complex and require more careful analysis by all the professionals involved in the claim. There are also differences in the legal issues that the medical expert is required to address in the expert report, in particular the question as to whether there has been a breach of the duty of care owed by the treating clinicians to the claimant.

Chapter Outline

In this chapter, we will explore the essential legal principles that are relevant to clinical negligence claims. We will examine the legal tests to be applied in assessing issues of breach of duty and the specific issues relating to consent, failures to warn and failures to treat. We will also address the difference between the court's approach to disputes in factual evidence and disputes as to the appropriate standard of care. Finally, we will consider causation in clinical negligence claims.

8.1   Legal Principles in Clinical Negligence Claims

A claim for damages for the consequences of an adverse event in clinical practice requires proof of 'negligence'. Negligence has been defined by the court as:

> '...the omission to do something which a reasonable man, guided upon those considerations which ordinarily regulate the conduct of human affairs, would do, or doing something which a prudent and reasonable man would not do.'[1]

8.1.1   The 'Bolam Test'

The general definition of negligence is refined where the issue is whether a person with a particular skill - such as a doctor - is guilty of negligence.

In *Bolam v Friern Hospital Management Committee*[2] the judge in summing up to a jury[3] explained negligence in the context of clinical practice as follows:

> 'I must tell you what in law we mean by "negligence". In the ordinary case which does not involve any special skill, negligence in law means this: some failure to do some act which a reasonable man in the circumstances would do, or doing some act which a reasonable man in the circumstances would not do; and if that failure or doing of that act results in injury, then there is a cause of action. How do you test whether this act or failure is negligent? In an ordinary case it is generally said, that you judge that by the action of the man in the street. He is the ordinary man. In one case it has been said that you judge it by the conduct of the man on the top of a Clapham omnibus. He is the ordinary man.
>
> But where you get a situation which involves the use of some special skill or competence, then the test whether there has been negligence or not is not the test of the man on the top of a Clapham omnibus, because he has not got this special skill. The test is the standard of the ordinary skilled man exercising and professing to have that special skill.

---

1   Alderson B in *Blyth v Birmingham Waterworks Co* (1856) 11 Ex Ch 781 at 784

2   [1957] 2 All ER 118. The case concerned the application of ECT to a patient, who had not been given a relaxant drug, who was not restrained, and who had not been warned of the risk of injury from the procedure. During the treatment, the patient fell off the table and sustained bilateral acetabula fractures.

3   In the 1950s, such civil cases were tried by jury.

A man need not possess the highest expert skill at the risk of being found negligent. It is well established law that it is sufficient if he exercises the ordinary skill of an ordinary competent man exercising that particular art. ...A doctor is not guilty of negligence if he has acted in accordance with a practice accepted as proper by a responsible body of medical men skilled in that particular art... Putting it the other way round, a doctor is not negligent, if he is acting in accordance with such a practice, merely because there is a body of opinion that takes a contrary view.

At the same time, that does not mean that a medical man can obstinately and pig-headedly carry on with some old technique if it has been proved to be contrary to what is really substantially the whole of informed medical opinion. Otherwise you might get men today saying: "I don't believe in anaesthetics. I don't believe in antiseptics. I am going to continue to do my surgery in the way it was done in the eighteenth century". That clearly would be wrong.'

Therefore, to establish whether a person with any particular expertise has been negligent, it is necessary to measure his/her actions against the standard reasonably to be expected of a reasonably competent practitioner, not against the very best or even the very worst practitioner in that field. It follows that the standard of care to be expected of a reasonably competent practitioner is effectively set by practitioners in that same field, not by the lawyers or by the court. Negligence will only be established in the light of the expert opinion of a practitioner in that same field on the actions (or inaction) of a fellow practitioner. If no practitioner will say that the standard fell below that reasonably to be expected from a reasonably competent practitioner, it is unlikely that liability can be established.

The legal test to be applied, as set out in *Bolam*, can therefore be summarised as follows:

'A doctor is not guilty of negligence if he has acted in accordance with a practice accepted as proper by a responsible body of medical men skilled in that particular art...'

The judge moved on to explain a finding of non-negligence – an explanation that is particularly helpful, as it places on the expert the duty of explaining the range of opinion across all the responsible bodies of medical opinion, rather than allowing the expert to simply express an opinion based on the practice to which he/she chooses to adhere:

'Putting it the other way round, a doctor is not negligent if he is acting in accordance with such a practice, merely because there is a body of opinion that takes a contrary view.'[4]

---

4   *Bolam* (see above) at 122B

> To establish whether a person with any particular expertise has been negligent, it is necessary to measure his/her actions against the standard reasonably to be expected of a reasonably competent practitioner, not against the very best or even the very worst practitioner in that field.

8.1.2   Approach to the Evidence – Applying the Bolam Test

The Bolam test has been restated in slightly different ways in subsequent cases[5] and to fit different factual situations, but by its nature the test confirms the need for the expert's evidence to define the acceptable standard and to compare the action of the clinician(s) with the standard as defined.

The following expressions of the Bolam test are all statements of exclusion, in that they identify that the actions (or omissions) of the clinician fell below the standard of care reasonably to be expected of a reasonably competent clinician:

- …the doctor failed to act in accordance with a practice accepted as proper by the responsible body of medical practitioners skilled in that particular field at that time…[6]
- …there was a failure to exercise the ordinary skill of a doctor (in the appropriate speciality) at that time…
- …the actions of the doctor were not in accordance with the practice of a reasonably competent doctor (skilled in that particular field) at that time…
- …what was done would not be acceptable to the responsible body of (such medical practitioners) at that time…
- …he is guilty of such failure as no doctor of ordinary skill (in that particular field) would be guilty of if acting with ordinary skill at that time...

Where the medical expert addresses the standard of care only by addressing what a reasonable body of clinicians at the particular time would have done, rather than by addressing the issue in terms of what no reasonable body of clinicians at the particular time would have done, the expert leaves open the question as to whether a particular practice actually fell below the standard of care of a reasonably competent practitioner. In many disciplines, contrary opinions on treatment exist and different practitioners have different opinions. A successful claim cannot be established on the basis that the action of a clinician was not in accord with the practice of a responsible body of practitioners, rather the claimant must establish that no responsible body of practitioners would accord with the practice adopted, by using the phrase 'the responsible body...' (where there is only one body of opinion) or 'any responsible body...' (where there is more than one responsible body of opinion).

---

5   In *Maynard v West Midlands Regional Health Authority* [1984] 1 WLR 634 the word 'respectable' is substituted for 'responsible'.

6   Where there is more than one responsible body of opinion the phrase 'the responsible body' needs to be replaced by 'any responsible body'

Therefore, a lawyer would find the following opinion **unhelpful** because the evidence does not address the question as to whether in this case the laparoscopic approach fell below an acceptable standard of practice for a general surgeon at the time:

> Mr C had a history of bowel surgery, including opening of the bowel, and a subsequent episode of small bowel obstruction requiring laparotomy and symptoms of intermittent small bowel colic. It should therefore have been clear to a surgeon experienced in such surgery that there would be intra-abdominal adhesions at the time of hernia repair and that these would be extensive and would probably have spread to the lower abdomen, so that the risk of injury to the bowel during inguinal hernia repair was significantly increased. …It follows that the preferred technique in this patient would have been the open technique and not the laparoscopic approach in fact used.

A lawyer would find the following opinion **helpful** because the evidence addresses the surgeon's actions in terms of practice that no general surgeon would regard as proper:

> … In my opinion no reasonably competent general surgeon, in practice at the time of this operation (April 2007), who was presented with a simple, uncomplicated and almost symptom-free hernia in a man with this history of bowel problems, would have failed to recognise that a laparoscopic repair of the hernia involved a high degree of risk. He would therefore have offered the patient an open rather than a laparoscopic repair. In proceeding with a laparoscopic repair, the surgeon failed to act in accordance with a practice that would be accepted as proper by a responsible body of general surgeons.

This opposing opinion would also be **helpful** in delineating the dispute:

> … However, while I personally would have proceeded to carry out the repair by open surgery because of the risk of severe adhesions, and would have criticised any registrar in my team who sought to do otherwise, I have to accept that there are responsible general surgeons who would nonetheless have commenced laparoscopically, recognising that it might become necessary to proceed to an open repair if the anatomical structures were damaged by previous surgery. Therefore, I am of the opinion that the standard of care in this case was such that it would be acceptable to a responsible body of surgeons in practice at the time of this operation.

To give an opinion on breach of duty - i.e. negligence - the expert must apply the Bolam test (or in rare cases the test in *Bolitho* – see Section 8.6 below). The phrases used when applying the Bolam test should accurately reflect the test set out by the court and the phrases properly to be used when applying the test should not be substituted for other less precise phrases.

Using the facts in the example above, compare the following expressions of the Bolam test:

1. No reasonably competent general surgeon in April 2007 would have proceeded with the laparoscopic hernia repair on a patient with a history of abdominal surgery and continuing bowel symptoms.

2. To proceed with the laparoscopic hernia repair on a patient with a history of abdominal surgery and continuing bowel symptoms would not be acceptable to any responsible body of general surgeons in practice in April 2007.

3. In proceeding with laparoscopic hernia repair on a patient with a history of abdominal surgery and continuing bowel symptoms, the general surgeon failed to act in accordance with a practice accepted as proper by any responsible body of general surgeons in April 2007.

4. In proceeding with the laparoscopic hernia repair on a patient with a history of abdominal surgery and continuing bowel symptoms, the general surgeon did not provide an acceptable standard of care.

5. Proceeding with the laparoscopic hernia repair on a patient with a history of abdominal surgery and continuing bowel problems was sub-standard care.

Examples 1-3 accurately apply the Bolam test.

Example 4 would probably be acceptable to most lawyers, but does not address all aspects of the Bolam test. Although the standard of care is identified as 'acceptable' (clearly a reference to Bolam), this example does not include the second part of the test that deals with the 'responsible body of medical practitioners' (skilled in that discipline at that time).

Example 5 would be understood by the lawyers and would probably be acceptable to many, but it provides no reassurance that the expert actually understands the Bolam test or has applied it properly. Many lawyers would seek clarification of this opinion.

8.1.3   Use of the Terms 'Negligent' or 'Negligence'

It is for the court to rule whether or not a medical practitioner has been negligent in law. This ruling will be based on the opinions expressed in the medical expert evidence. The medical expert evidence should apply the Bolam test in one of its forms and express an opinion in relation to it. It is not for the expert to rule whether this amounts to negligence in law and therefore the expert should avoid using the legal terms 'negligent' and 'negligence'.

8.2   Level of Skill Required

As we have seen, the standard by which a medical practitioner is judged is that of the reasonably competent practitioner in the relevant field at the particular time. The question that gives rise to is, "what would a reasonably competent practitioner have done in this situation?" The expert therefore has to define that standard – of the body (or bodies) of reasonably competent practitioners in the relevant field – and justify if necessary that definition.

> The court places on doctors the same duty of care that every other professional person has, namely, the degree of skill appropriate to the task being undertaken.

8.2.1   Establishing the Reasonable Standard of Care

By what evidence can the expert establish what a reasonable standard would be? While the starting point might be consideration of what the expert him/herself would do in that situation, that does not of course provide the reasonable standard, particularly if the expert has been chosen for his/her reputation and experience in the field. The expert's standard might well be too high a standard to apply generally. There are, however, a number of factors which may well assist in establishing the reasonable standard below which it can be said with conviction that conduct would be outside the standard reasonably to be expected of such practitioners.

1.   It is important to define the person, with what qualifications or experience, who would be involved in such treatment. It may be that the criticised doctor was carrying out a procedure outside the range of procedures normally carried out by a person with his/her qualifications, training or experience, or with experience insufficient for such a procedure unless under close scrutiny.

2.   There may be guidelines or protocols available against which the doctor's conduct can be assessed. Assistance may also be gained even if those guidelines or protocols were not in use at that particular trust or hospital, and even if they are not precisely applicable to the situation in issue, although their relevance would have to be demonstrated as would also the weight to be given to them. It will be necessary to spell out the respects in which the guidelines or protocols were not met.

3. Text books may contain relevant guidance. The weight to be attached to that source will have to be justified and explained, as will, if not immediately apparent, the relevance. It will be necessary to spell out the respects in which the guidance was not met.

4. It may be possible to demonstrate the training which would have been widely available and which is relevant to the matter in issue. It will be necessary to spell out the respects in which the guidance in the training was not met.

5. The expert's own experience in working in teams or in observing others at work in different situations or locations might also assist in defining the standard applied by the reasonable body, and if the expert is involved in relevant training or education then that may also be relevant as to what should have been known and practised in such circumstances if that training or education was "mainstream".

It should be possible to form a reasoned conclusion from consideration of these factors whether the practice criticised was or was not commonly accepted practice. It should also be possible to define in this way the lowest standard that would be regarded as acceptable, and which therefore could be excused on the basis of the Bolam test.

It has been said that a doctor should have such an awareness as an ordinarily competent practitioner would have of the deficiencies in his knowledge and the limitations on his skill. He must be alert to the hazards and risks of any professional task he undertakes to the extent that other ordinarily competent members of the profession would be alert, and that he should bring to any professional task no less expertise, skill and care than other ordinarily competent members of the profession would bring. The standard is therefore that of the "reasonable average" and a doctor need not be "a paragon combining the qualities of polymath and prophet"[7].

Standards are of course dynamic and change with time. However, a doctor should not lag behind other ordinarily assiduous and intelligent members of the profession in knowledge of new advances, discoveries and developments in his field[8].

8.2.2 Novices

A newly-qualified doctor is assessed against the same standards reasonably expected of all doctors in that speciality. A lack of experience is no defence. A surgeon who is learning the necessary skills to be a competent surgeon will begin by learning how to perform the more straightforward operations, guided and assisted as appropriate by a competent surgical colleague. This enables the surgeon, although still a novice, to carry out the operation to the standard of a reasonably competent practitioner in that field. The standard is not that of the best and

---

7   *Eckersley v Binnie* (1988) 18 Con LR1 (Bingham LJ)

8   *Eckersley v Binnie* (1988) 18 Con LR1 (Bingham LJ)

most experienced surgeon, but it is required to be that of a reasonably competent surgeon. To achieve this standard of reasonable competence, the inexperienced surgeon may require guidance from, the assistance of, or even intervention by a competent surgeon.

In *Wilsher v Essex Area Health Authority*[9] it was argued by the defendant that in the case of the medical profession, the nature of the duty owed by a doctor should vary depending on his degree of training or experience. The defence argued that:

> *'Public hospital medicine has always been organised so that young doctors and nurses learn on the job. If the hospitals abstained from using inexperienced people, they could not staff their wards and theatres, and the junior staff could never learn. The longer-term interests of patients as a whole are best served by maintaining the present system, even if this may diminish the legal rights of the individual patient, for, after all, medicine is about curing, not litigation.'*

However the argument was dealt with in this manner in the Court of Appeal:

> *'I acknowledge the appeal of this argument, and recognise that a young hospital doctor who must get onto the wards in order to qualify without necessarily being able to decide what kind of patient he is going to meet is not in the same position as another professional man who has a real choice whether or not to practice in a particular field. Nevertheless, I cannot accept that there should be a special rule for doctors in public hospitals; I emphasise public, since presumably those employed in private hospitals would be in a different category. Doctors are not the only people who gain their experience, not only from lectures or from watching others perform, but from tackling live clients or customers, and no case was cited to us which suggested that any such variable duty of care was imposed on others in a similar position.*
>
> *To my mind, it would be a false step to subordinate the legitimate expectation of the patient that he will receive from each person concerned with his care a degree of skill appropriate to the task which he undertakes to an understandable wish to minimise the psychological and financial pressures on hardpressed young doctors.'*[10]

The court therefore placed on doctors the same duty of care that every other professional person has, namely, the degree of skill appropriate to the task being undertaken. An under-resourced, under-trained or overtired junior doctor has to perform to the same standard of competence as a colleague at another hospital who does not experience any such lack of resources or training or the need to work unsocial hours.

---

9   [1986] 3 All ER 801

10   [1986] 3 All ER 801 at 813

An expert instructed to consider a question of medical negligence may find it useful to consider the issue from a departmental perspective:

- were suitably experienced doctors in place or available to assist so that the department could achieve the acceptable standard of care?
- were the correct procedures in place to enable an inexperienced doctor to identify the moment when help from more qualified colleagues should be sought and to obtain such help when required?

If the expert concludes that the treating clinician was inexperienced or out of his/her depth (probably while doing his/her less-than-entirely-competent best), then it is appropriate to point out this fact. However, when addressing whether the standard of care shown in managing the patient fell below the required standard, the medical expert assesses the performance of the department, not merely the inexperienced treating doctor.

Given the difficulties of finding the right expert, the solicitor may instruct an expert who is a leader in the particular field in question, with a senior position in a pre-eminent institution, who must give opinion on the practice of a very young practitioner in a remote district hospital facing an emergency situation. Perhaps, the reporting expert is a specialist surgeon reviewing the actions of a general surgeon, who still might reasonably be expected to carry out such surgery. In both of these situations, the standard of practice to be applied is that of the reasonably competent practitioner in that speciality in the situation as it unfolded. It is not the standard expected of an expert in that field in a centre of excellence dealing with a referred case to be treated at comparative leisure.

8.2.3 Specialists

Where the doctor is in a specialist field, the practitioner will be expected to show the ordinary skill to be expected in the speciality:

> 'The language of the Bolam test clearly requires a different degree of skill from a specialist in his own special field than from a general practitioner. In the field of neurosurgery it would be necessary to substitute for [the] phrase "no doctor of ordinary skill" the phrase "no neurosurgeon of ordinary skill".' [11]

As a doctor becomes more specialised – but not as he/she becomes more experienced - in a particular area of practice, so the standard of skill that is expected increases. However, the doctor is only required to reach a reasonable level of skill within the higher range appropriate to his/her specialism.

---

11 *Sidaway v Board of Governors of the Bethlem Royal Hospital and the Maudsley Hospital* [1985] AC 871 at 897C

8.3   Consent and Failure to Warn

Unless a patient has consented to contact from a doctor, or such contact is carried out in an emergency, treatment involving physical contact will amount to a trespass to the person – an assault or a battery. All adults with capacity can give voluntary and informed consent. Different rules apply in relation to children[12] and to those unable to understand the nature of the decisions to be made. Once a patient is informed as to the nature of the procedure which is planned in broad terms, and consents to it, the consent is valid so far as to permit contact that would otherwise be a trespass to the person and no claim based on assault or battery can be made.

If a doctor fails to provide information about all significant risks of a procedure, even though information is provided about the nature of the procedure in broad terms, the patient may have a remedy in a claim in negligence. A doctor is under a duty to take reasonable care to ensure that a patient is aware of any material risks involved in any recommended treatment, and of any reasonable alternative or variant treatments. The test of materiality is whether, in the circumstances, a reasonable person in the patient's position would be likely to attach significance to the risk, or the doctor was or should reasonably be aware that the particular patient would be likely to attach significance to it.

The test set out in the previous paragraph is the law since the Supreme Court decision in 2015 of *Montgomery v Lanarkshire Health Board*[13] changed the law as it was previously understood to be[14], although the new test reflects what was commonly the practice in the lower courts, if not in fact the law. The test, the Court held, needed now to take into account the importance of personal autonomy and the value of self-determination and that, in making a decision which might have a profound effect on her health and well-being, a patient was entitled to information and advice about possible alternative and variant treatments. The *Bolam* test, which was previously applicable to this issue[15], no longer applies.

Therefore, in relation to patients who are competent to give consent, claims rarely arise as to whether consent has been given. However, claims do arise as to whether the information given by the clinician in obtaining consent was adequate. Consent and failure to warn are part of the same issue so far as the doctor's duty of care is concerned.

A doctor is under a duty to take reasonable care to ensure that a patient is aware of any material risks involved in any recommended treatment, and of any reasonable alternative or variant treatments.

---

12   We do not seek to address issues relating to children and others lacking capacity to give consent in this book

13   [2015] UKSC 11

14   *Sidaway v Board of Governors of the Bethlem Royal Hospital and the Maudsley Hospital* [1985] AC 871

15   See *Chatterton v Gerson* [1981] QB 432

A medical practitioner is now under a duty to warn a patient in general terms of possible material or significant risks involved in any proposed course of treatment, the materiality or significance being viewed from the viewpoint of a reasonable person in the patient's position, or in the light of anything known or which should have been known about the particular patient's circumstances. The General Medical Council Guidance *'Consent: patients and doctors making decisions together'* is consistent with Montgomery and provides further useful and relevant guidance in taking reasonable care in obtaining consent and warning a patient of risks.

Further guidance comes from an earlier decision in which the court described the test in these terms:

> *'If there is a significant[16] risk which would affect the judgement of a reasonable patient, then in the normal course it is the responsibility of a doctor to inform the patient of that significant risk, if the information is needed so that the patient can determine for him or herself as to what course he or she would adopt.'[17]*

A consent form will often list a number of known risks and complications of the procedure to be undertaken. Acknowledgment of the risks of the procedure by signing the consent form does not excuse any lack of care in the carrying out of the procedure, even where such lack of care results in the risk that has been acknowledged. Proper consent does not in any way limit the patient's right to competent treatment. Consent is a process for informing the patient of the risks that might occur despite competent treatment so that the patient may reach an informed judgement as to whether to agree to undergo the procedure.

8.3.1   Approach to the Evidence

In contrast to the expert's role when addressing the Bolam test, on consent issues, where *Bolam* no longer applies, the expert needs to consider and address:

- what type of risks are, or should have been known to have been, involved in the proposed course of treatment?
- what is the chance of each risk arising in relation to this patient?
- whether there are any alternative treatments and if so how do the risks in such alternative treatments compare to those in the proposed course of treatment?
- how significant is each risk in relation to a reasonable person in the patient's position?
- was there anything known or which should have been known about the particular patient's circumstances which renders a risk which might not otherwise be considered material or significant, material or significant?

---

16   In court judgments relating to consent, the words 'serious' and 'significant' have both been used to describe the risks that need to be acknowledged.

17   *Pearce v United Bristol Healthcare NHS Trust* [1999] PIQR P53

On the basis of these responses, the expert can then express an opinion as to what this patient should have been told about the proposed treatment and any alternatives in order to fulfil the doctor's duty to the patient, and compare that with the situation as in fact occurred. The GMC Guidance[18] may be relevant as to the manner in which this information is communicated.

8.3.2   The Patient's Lost Opportunity

Where a patient is not made aware of a material risk, then the patient will have lost the opportunity to decide whether to decline the treatment altogether or delay treatment while considering what to do or while taking a second opinion. There are therefore two situations in which a claim for negligence can be brought on the basis of a failure to take reasonable care to ensure a patient is aware of all material risks and reasonable alternative treatments:

1.   Where a patient is not informed of such a material risk when being consented for an operation and in the course of the operation that risk manifests, the medical practitioner will be liable in damages where the patient can prove (on the balance of probabilities) that if properly warned, then he/she would not have agreed to undergo the treatment.

2.   Where the patient would have probably gone ahead with an operation, but once appropriately warned would not have proceeded on that occasion (even though the patient would probably have undergone the operation on a subsequent occasion), the medical practitioner will still be liable for damages if, on the balance of probabilities, on that subsequent occasion the complication of which the patient was not warned would not have occurred[19].

In *Chester v Afshar* it was found that the surgeon had failed to warn the claimant of a small risk in the proposed spinal surgery. Expert opinion was that no matter how well the surgery was performed, there was a risk inherent in the surgery (1-2%) of developing cauda equina syndrome. The claimant agreed to the surgery, which was duly carried out, but unfortunately she did develop the syndrome. The judge found that the claimant, if properly warned, would have sought a second opinion and would not have undergone the surgery at that time. Had the operation taken place on a subsequent occasion, on the balance of probabilities the complication would not then have arisen, the risk being only 1-2%. The claimant was therefore entitled to recover damages for the consequences of the complication that in fact arose.

---

18   *Consent: patients and doctors making decisions together* (GMC)

19   *Chester v Afshar* [2005] 1 AC 134

> Since the injury she sustained was within the scope of the doctor's duty to warn and was the result of the risk of which she was entitled to be warned, the injury was to be regarded as having been caused by the defendant's breach of duty in not informing the patient to the appropriate standard. The court made no finding as to whether or not she would in those circumstances have undergone the surgery on another occasion (with precisely the same degree of risk of the unfortunate outcome on such an occasion).

In cases involving a failure to properly inform or warn a patient of material risks, the judge will have to resolve on the basis of the evidence presented, whether or not if properly informed or warned the claimant would nonetheless have undergone the treatment at the time it in fact took place. The claimant with the benefit of hindsight may well say, and believe, that if warned of the risk he/she would not have undergone the operation at all or at that time.

Expert opinion may be able to assist the court in assessing the claimant's assertion that he/she would have delayed the operation by addressing the situation where a patient is appropriately warned and dealing with issues such as:

1.   what, on the basis of clinical experience, the expert considers a reasonable patient, properly warned, would have done; and

2.   what patients would be told about the implications of not undergoing the treatment.

8.4   Failure to Treat

Commonly, a clinical negligence claim is concerned with whether the positive actions of a doctor were appropriate. Where the matter complained of is an omission – a failure to treat - then expert evidence needs to address three issues:

1.   did the failure to act fall below a reasonable standard of care? and if so

2.   what would the likely treatment have been had there not been a failure to act? and

3.   what would the ultimate outcome have been had the clinician acted in this way?

The first issue requires the medical expert to address the standard of care reasonably to be expected from the practitioner. Once again, the Bolam test needs to be applied: if a doctor of ordinary skill would also have behaved in the same way, then the claim will fail. However, if the failure to act does not meet the expected standard of care, then the second issue is what a doctor of ordinary skill would have done instead. Finally, the expert should consider what the likely outcome would then have been and whether there would have been a difference in the ultimate outcome (i.e. addressing causation).

It may be possible to answer the second question by establishing what a particular identified individual, who would have been the person to act, would probably have done. For example, if there was a failure on the part of nursing staff to call out a doctor, the doctor who would have been on call can give evidence as to what he/she would have done if the call had been made. If this question can only be answered hypothetically, because the person who should have acted cannot be identified or is not available, then the court will apply the Bolam test to the standard of care that would have been applied by a reasonably competent practitioner in the appropriate specialism and therefore assume that the clinician would have acted within the range of acceptable actions[20]. The probable outcome (and therefore causation) would then be assessed on this basis.

An example of this process is given by the case of *Gardner v Northampton General Hospital*[21]. W attended an A & E department at 00.34 in excruciating pain and with what transpired to be necrotising fasciitis. Sepsis was not considered for over 4 hours and the hospital's sepsis protocol was not applied for 8 hours. The court had to decide how W should have been treated by a hypothetically competent medical team and assuming such competent treatment, whether it was probable that emergency surgery could have been carried out in time to save W's life. The judge found the hospital to have been negligent. The presence of infection should have been confirmed by 02.45 to 03.15, a diagnosis and the need for surgery would then have been identified by 04.30 to 05.00, and W would then have been got ready for surgery by between 05.40 and 06.10. It was also found that an operation up to 07.30 would have enabled W to survive. It followed either that such surgery would have enabled W to survive or alternatively that the hospital's negligence had made a material contribution[22] to her death because it led to such a delay that the advance of the infection could not be averted by surgery.

8.5   Conflicting Opinion on Factual Issues

Conflicting opinion evidence on factual issues is dealt with on a different basis to conflicting opinion evidence as to the standard of care. Where conflicts of opinion arise on factual issues, the judge is entitled to prefer for good reason, the expert opinion of one expert over that of another expert.

For example, an important factual dispute in a case may be:

- whether a claimant would or would not have been pyrexial at a particular examination by the doctor;
- whether an x-ray had it been performed at the time of initial contact with the patient would or would not have demonstrated the presence of a fracture; or
- whether a nerve damaged during the course of an operation was in an atypical anatomical position.

---

20   *Bolitho v City and Hackney Health Authority* [1997] 3 WLR 1151

21   [2014] EWHC 4217

22   "Material contribution" is considered at Section 8.7

The judge is entitled, with the assistance of expert opinion, to take into account all of the available evidence and to come to a decision, on the balance of probabilities. The evidence that the judge considers most persuasive may be the opinion evidence of a particular expert, so rejecting that of another expert, but may also be the evidence of lay witnesses or information in documents adduced in evidence. The judge is required to provide the reasoning by which some evidence (expert or otherwise) is accepted, some rejected and the conclusion is reached.

8.6 Conflicting Opinion on Standard of Care

The judge is required to compare the acts or omissions of the treating doctor with what would have happened if a reasonably competent doctor had been faced with similar circumstances. The judge has no relevant expertise as a clinician and in carrying out this comparison is dependent on the expert opinion of an expert similarly qualified to the practitioner being criticised.

When considering conflicting opinion evidence as to the appropriate standard of care, the judge cannot simply prefer the opinion of one competent expert over another. The judge can only reject one expert's opinion and accept an opposing expert's opinion if satisfied that one of the opinions is flawed.

Typical situations where a judge may find an expert's opinion to be flawed would include a finding that an expert lacked appropriate or relevant expertise or lacked credibility as a result of inconsistencies in the evidence or incompetence as an expert witness. However, where the judge is faced with two medical experts of similar expertise and of reasonable competence giving different opinions as to what would have been an acceptable standard of care, two questions arise:

1. can the claimant prove, on the balance of probabilities, that his/her case is more likely to be correct than the defendant's case? and

2. are there any circumstances in which a finding can be made by the court that established practice – a practice that is followed by reasonably competent practitioners as supported by one expert – is nonetheless negligent?

Unless the judge rejects outright the defendant expert's opinion, he/she cannot find for the claimant:

> 'A judge's "preference" for one body of distinguished professional opinion to another also professionally distinguished is not sufficient to establish negligence in a practitioner whose actions have received the seal of approval of those whose opinions, truthfully expressed, honestly held, were not preferred... For in the realm of diagnosis and treatment negligence is not established by preferring one respectable body of professional opinion to another. Failure to exercise the ordinary skill of a doctor (in the appropriate speciality, if he be a specialist) is necessary.'[23]

---

23   *Maynard v West Midlands Regional Health Authority* [1984] 1 WLR 634

However, the judge is entitled to require that opinions have a logical basis:

> 'The court is not bound to hold that a defendant doctor escapes liability for negligent treatment or diagnosis just because he leads evidence from a number of medical experts who are genuinely of opinion that the defendant's treatment or diagnosis accorded with sound medical practice. In the Bolam case itself, the judge stated that the defendant had to have acted in accordance with the practice accepted as proper by a "responsible body of medical men." Later he referred to "a standard of practice recognised as proper by a competent reasonable body of opinion." Again, in Maynard's case Lord Scarman refers to a "respectable" body of professional opinion.
>
> The use of these adjectives — responsible, reasonable and respectable — all show that the court has to be satisfied that the exponents of the body of opinion relied upon can demonstrate that such opinion has a logical basis. In particular in cases involving, as they so often do, the weighing of risks against benefits, the judge before accepting a body of opinion as being responsible, reasonable or respectable, will need to be satisfied that, in forming their views, the experts have directed their minds to the question of comparative risks and benefits and have reached a defensible conclusion on the matter.'[24]

Therefore, a judge can reject the practice of respectable practitioners if he/she concludes that that practice does not properly weigh up comparative risks and benefits. This test, from the case of *Bolitho*, would appear to give a judge some freedom to find against one of two conflicting expert opinions as to the expected standard of care. However, it was also said in *Bolitho* that:

> 'If, in a rare case, it can be demonstrated that the professional opinion is not capable of withstanding logical analysis, the judge is entitled to hold that the body of opinion is not reasonable or responsible.
>
> I emphasise that in my view it will very seldom be right for a judge to reach the conclusion that views genuinely held by a competent medical expert are unreasonable. The assessment of medical risks and benefits is a matter of clinical judgement which a judge would not normally be able to make without expert evidence... it would be wrong to allow such assessment to deteriorate into seeking to persuade the judge to prefer one of two views both of which are capable of being logically supported. It is only where a judge can be satisfied that the body of expert opinion cannot be logically supported at all that such opinion will not provide the benchmark by reference to which the defendant's conduct falls to be assessed.'[25]

Therefore, it will be rare that a judge will find that the opinion of a competent medical expert as to the appropriate standard of care is unreasonable or not logically supported.

---

24   Lord Browne-Wilkinson in *Bolitho v City and Hackney Health Authority* [1997] 3 WLR 1151 at 1158

25   Lord Bridge in *Bolitho v City and Hackney Health Authority* [1997] 3 WLR 1151 at 1160

An example of this test being applied occurred in *Marriott v West Midlands Regional Health Authority*[26] where the trial judge concluded that if the defence expert's evidence did establish that there was a body of GPs who, on the patient presenting with drowsiness and a headache following a history of a head injury, would not have referred the patient to hospital, then such an approach was 'not reasonably prudent'.

> When considering conflicting opinion evidence as to the appropriate standard of care, the judge cannot simply prefer the opinion of one competent expert over another. The judge can only reject one expert's opinion and accept an opposing expert's opinion if satisfied that one of the opinions is flawed.

8.7 Causation and 'Material Contribution'

Causation in clinical negligence claims is often extremely difficult to assess. Establishing what injury has resulted from a failure in the standard of treatment is often the main issue between the parties, rather than whether there has been a failure in the standard of care. Breach of duty may or may not have been admitted by the defendant, but the real battleground remains in relation to causation. Indeed, the claimant is likely to have fallen into the hands of medical practitioners because he/she was already ill or injured and was in need of medical attention. The outcome of such treatment may have been uncertain even in the absence of care that fell below an acceptable standard.

Damages are only recoverable for what can be proved, on the balance of probabilities, to be the difference between the outcome in the absence of a failure in the standard of care and the actual outcome. As we have seen in Chapter 6 above, a further difficulty is that the question to be resolved - and on which an expert opinion is to be expressed - is not one that generally arises in clinical practice. The medical practitioner does not regularly ask himself/herself "what would have been the outcome if I had done this instead of doing that, or if I had not done the other?" Research is not frequently directed at the outcome of care that falls below a reasonable standard, although research comparing different methods of treatment, particularly in different countries, may throw some light on the issue.

The medical expert, therefore, is once again in an area where the issue that he/she is required to address cannot be addressed directly from clinical practice, but can only be answered by an assessment or even an estimate based on medical expertise. That said, it is probably not too difficult for the expert to identify a likely range of answers or possible outcomes to the causation question: "what would have happened if …?" Once this range of answers or possible outcomes has been identified, it should then be possible for the expert to narrow down the range by reference to the particular facts of the case and their relative importance, and then provide an answer on causation, on the balance of probabilities.

---

26   [1999] Lloyd's Rep Med 23

When dealing with a range of opinion, it is necessary to keep in mind the requirements of PD35 3.2(6) and guidance in the Guidance at para 59-60[27], which requires the expert to summarise the range of opinion and to give reasons for the opinion the expert holds.

There may also be other possible causes of a claimant's condition, in addition to the negligence on the part of the treating clinicians. In Section 6.1.1, we considered the case of a premature baby who developed retrolental fibroplasia after being negligently exposed to excessive levels of oxygen. There were several 'innocent' or non-negligent explanations for the development of the condition. The claimant failed because he could not prove that on the balance of probabilities 'but for' the negligent cause the injury would not have been suffered, or in other words could not prove that it was the excess oxygen that more likely than not had caused the damage[28].

The 'but for' test may be modified in clinical negligence claims in the unusual situation where there are cumulative causes of injury rather than different distinct causes of injury.

A patient who developed pancreatitis following an ERCP procedure experienced a subsequent negligent lack of care and in her weakened state suffered a cardiac arrest and resulting brain damage. It was not possible to say that the cardiac arrest was caused by one or other of the two possible causes (that 'but for' the pancreatitis or the lack of care the cardiac arrest would not have occurred) but it was possible to say that each contributed to the weakness which resulted in the cardiac arrest. As the negligent lack of care had made a material contribution (a more than minimal contribution) to the events resulting in the cardiac arrest, the hospital was liable for all of the damages resulting from the patient's brain damage[29].

The material contribution test has been applied in a number of claims in recent years arising out of clinical negligence[30]. The medical expert should be alert to the possibility of applying this alternative test of causation where there are cumulative causes to injury, but unless specifically instructed to report on this basis, should seek guidance from the instructing solicitor before doing so.

---

27 See Section 4.2.12

28 *Wilsher v Essex Area Health Authority* [1988] AC 1074

29 *Bailey v Ministry of Defence* [2009] 1 WLR 1062

30 *Telles v South West Strategic Health Authority* [2008] All ER (D) 389; *Bousted v North West Strategic Health Authority* [2008] EWHC 2375; *Canning-Kishver v Sandwell & West Birmingham Hospitals NHS Trust* [2008] EWHC 2384; *Gardner v Northampton General Hospital NHS Trust* [2014] EWHC 4217

Conclusion

In clinical negligence cases the standard of care reasonably to be expected of the treating clinicians is often a difficult and complex issue to resolve. This difficulty may arise owing to disagreements as to the appropriate standard of care or from an incomplete or contradictory factual picture. However, the main battle ground in clinical negligence actions remains the issue of causation. Even where a breach of duty has been conceded by the defendants, there is often fundamental disagreement about the difference the breach of duty actually made to the outcome for the claimant. Issues of public policy, such as the right to be properly informed before giving consent for a procedure also arise in clinical negligence actions. Ultimately, however, it is medical practitioners themselves who provide the evidence upon which the court will assess the issue of clinical negligence and in cases involving treatment and diagnosis what the appropriate standard of care is, although in relation to consent it is the court (and not the expert) that will decide what risks, identified by the medical practitioners, are such that the patient should have been made aware of them.

Key-Point Summary

1. The principal legal tests used in clinical negligence are set out in the cases of *Bolam, Bolitho* and *Montgomery*.

2. In relation to issues about treatment and diagnosis, the Bolam test focuses on a standard of practice that is acceptable to a 'reasonable', 'responsible' or 'respectable' body of professional opinion. The Bolitho test seeks to ensure that any such body of opinion is capable of withstanding logical analysis when considering the benefits and risks inherent in treatment decisions.

3. Patients have a right to make informed choices about medical treatment and a doctor is under a duty to take reasonable care to ensure a patient is aware of any material risks involved in any recommended treatment, and of any reasonable alternative or variant treatments. A risk is material if a reasonable person in the patient's position would be likely to attach significance to the risk.

4. A finding of negligence in failing to warn a patient of the possible serious risks of a procedure gives rise to a claim in damages if one of those risks manifests itself and the patient would not have undergone the procedure or would have put it off to another day when that risk would not, on the balance of probabilities, have manifested itself.

5. A judge is able to decide facts in the face of conflicting professional opinion about those facts, on the balance of probabilities.

6.   A judge may only choose to prefer one expert opinion on the appropriate standard of care over another where the judge finds one of the opinions to be flawed. It is not the judge's role to decide which of two reasonable medical practices is to be preferred.

7.   The 'but for' test for causation may be modified where there are cumulative, rather than distinct, causes of injury which can be said to have materially contributed to the injury.

Next Steps

In the next chapter, we will explore some of the complex factual and medical issues that make reporting on clinical negligence so challenging for the medical expert.

Reporting in Clinical Negligence Claims

Introduction

In clinical negligence actions, solicitors face a real challenge in identifying and instructing an expert with the appropriate expertise to report on the issues in dispute. In many cases, the solicitor has access to very few choices when instructing an expert, so often instructs experts based on recommendations from other experts or legal colleagues. At the time the instruction is made, it may not be clear to the solicitor which is the best speciality to instruct. This places a responsibility on an expert approached by a solicitor to say whether another speciality or indeed another practitioner within his/her own speciality would be a more suitable expert to instruct. The relationship between the lawyers and the experts in a clinical negligence case is likely to demand far higher levels of communication and engagement than a typical claim for personal injury.

Chapter Outline

In this chapter, we will briefly explore the clinical negligence marketplace and the role of the medical expert in clinical negligence claims. We will then discuss some of the difficult areas in clinical negligence claims that challenge the skills of both the experts and the lawyers involved in these claims.

9.1   Clinical Negligence Marketplace

An overview of the clinical negligence marketplace can be gleaned from National Health Service Litigation Authority (NHSLA) data. In 2014/15, the NHSLA, which manages claims on behalf of NHS trusts, received 11,497 clinical negligence claims, up from 6,652 in 2009/10 but down from 11,945 in 2013/14[1]. However, the number of claims was significantly below the number of adverse incidents reports made within the NHS, which continue to increase. One study has recorded that although 17·7% of 1,047 patients in the study experienced serious adverse events that led to longer hospital stays and increased costs to the patients, only 1·2% (13) of the 1,047 patients made claims for compensation[2].

Claims currently take an average of 1.31 years to be settled[3]. Of the claims received by the NHSLA over a recent 10 year period, 35.3% were abandoned by the claimant, 46.6% were settled, 2.6% were concluded in court (including approval of settlements of claims on behalf of minors or patients and protected parties) and 15.5% were outstanding[4]. In 2014/15, 46% of claims were reported as being concluded with no damages being paid, the NHSLA paid out £1,044.4m in respect of clinical negligence claims against the NHS (in damages and legal costs), up from £650m in 2009/10 but down from £1,117.7m in 2012/13, and paid £395,142m in legal costs in relation to claims that year[5].

---

1   The NHS Litigation Authority Annual report and accounts for the relevant years

2   Andrews, L.B. *et al.* 'An alternative strategy for studying adverse events in medical care' *The Lancet*, 349, 9048 pp. 309 - 313

3   The NHS Litigation Authority Annual report and accounts 2014/15

4   The NHS Litigation Authority (2012) *Factsheet 3: information on claims 20011/12*

5   The NHS Litigation Authority Annual report and accounts 2014/15

9.2 Purpose of Expert Reports in Clinical Negligence Cases

Providing medical expert reports in clinical negligence claims is often more challenging, and requires more detailed analysis and assessment than in a typical personal injury claim. Depending on the nature of the case, an expert may be instructed to address issues of:

- breach of duty (i.e. whether the treatment has been negligent);
- causation of injury;
- injury, loss and damage;
- condition and prognosis.

Such opinions are given in the context of what are often, at least for the non-medically trained lawyer, complicated medical and factual issues. The issues, which are normally dealt with in more than one report because they are disclosed to the other side at different stages in the claim[6], must be expressed in a manner that assists the lawyers in understanding the issues in the dispute.

The scope of the instructions given to a particular expert will depend upon the nature of the case and the issues that are likely to arise. Sometimes, issues of breach of duty and causation will be dealt with by the same expert, while on other occasions different experts will need to address the different aspects of the claim.

For example, if the criticism is of a hip replacement operation, then it is likely that an orthopaedic surgeon would be able to deal with breach of duty and causation of injury, and (in a separate report) with condition and prognosis. However, a case may require experts to be instructed in several specialities so as to deal effectively with all of the legal issues. Where the events in an A & E department are under scrutiny, it may require an A & E consultant to address the standard of care reasonably to be expected in the first instance, with another expert in a different speciality to deal with the causation issues relating to the outcome of the treatment and to address whether the outcome would have been any different had the actions in A & E been different.

The distinction between the different aspects of a claim for clinical negligence that medical experts have to address can be seen in the example below. This is the conclusion to a report addressing breach of duty and causation, as well as (and a little unusually) the claimant's condition and prognosis. We have placed in square brackets the legal issues that the evidence addresses.

---

6   A report on condition and prognosis must be served with proceedings [PD16(4.2)] while the reports on breach of duty and causation will normally be exchanged in accordance with directions of the court at a later stage

Conclusions

In failing to identify the extent of Mrs Z's perineal injury after the birth of her first child – that she had a fourth degree perineal tear - the standard of care shown fell below that reasonably to be expected in a reasonably competent maternity department at the material time. [**Breach of duty**]

Had the extent of the perineal injury been correctly identified, then Mrs Z would have undergone repair in an operating theatre under regional anaesthesia by an experienced practitioner. With correct and immediate repair, it is more likely than not that Mrs Z would have avoided the subsequent surgery she underwent, the de-functioning colostomy and the secondary perineal repair. She would have been continent of faeces and would have had normal bowel function. With correct classification and repair of the perineal injury Mrs Z would have been able to undergo further spontaneous vaginal deliveries. [**Causation of injury and damage**]

As the result of the failure in the standard of care, Mrs Z underwent the further treatment and is left with significant continuing and permanent symptoms and has been correctly advised that if she does become pregnant again she would be well advised to deliver by caesarean section. As a result of these events she has expressed great reluctance to consider a further pregnancy, which is a reasonable response given the effects and consequences arising from the original failure to diagnose and treat appropriately. [**Condition and prognosis**]

9.3 Areas of Potential Difficulty in Clinical Negligence Cases

We identify five areas of potential difficulty in reporting that have the potential to make producing reports in clinical negligence claims more demanding on the medical expert:

1. dealing with issues of hindsight or outcome bias and focus bias;

2. identifying within the factual basis of the claim whether the key issue is a factual dispute or a dispute about the standard of care;

3. reporting on factual disputes;

4. assessing a series of treatment events over an extended time period; and

5. dealing with complex medical issues.

We address each of these issues in the sections below.

9.3.1   Hindsight and Focus Bias

In assessing and giving opinion on the standard of care shown by other practitioners in treating a patient, the expert must place him/herself so far as is possible in the position of the clinician whose actions or inaction at the time are being criticised.

Maintaining Objectivity

A fundamental issue in clinical negligence claims is to identify an expert who is able to report objectively on the issues in dispute. Consciously or unconsciously, a medical expert may have sympathy for the plight of the claimant or for the clinicians who are the focus of the claim. The expert may be concerned that the claimant should have the funds to be able to receive the care and treatment now required to live a bearable life or conversely that the NHS should not have to use its finances in dealing with such claims rather than in treating patients.

Perhaps an error may have been made in the course of difficult life-saving surgery, where on one view the claimant should be grateful still to be alive at all, but on another view the outcome should have been markedly more beneficial to the claimant. The expert may disapprove of the approach or practice of the clinician and those who still follow it or may have great respect for the hospital or department (or head of department) at which the adverse event occurred. There are many opportunities for the medical expert in a clinical negligence claim to lose an objective mindset when approaching the evidence.

Hindsight or Outcome Bias

The expert is always reporting retrospectively on medical treatment. This creates a difficulty in that the expert needs to see the situation as the treating clinician would - or would have been expected to - have seen it at the material time. The expert has to remove from his/her assessment of the evidence the outcome of the actions, which are now known but were not known at the time. The so called 'retrospectoscope' has long been recognised to give a distorted view of the past when applied to the actions of people at the time.

'Hindsight' or 'outcome' bias has been demonstrated to have a significant effect on the objectivity of doctors. Studies have shown that knowledge of an adverse outcome in a case affects the opinions given by medical experts as to the appropriateness of clinical treatment[7]. Having knowledge of a poor outcome may, for example, cause an expert to minimise the management dilemmas facing the doctor at the time and to overlook the uncertainties inherent in diagnosis and treatment[8]. The expert must also avoid the potential pitfalls of reviewing treatment from the past - perhaps from just a few years ago when practice, knowledge or protocols may have

---

7   Hugh, T.B. and Tracy, G.D., 'Hindsight bias in medico-legal expert reports' *MedJ* Aug 2002: 176(6)

8   Cook R.I., Woods D.D. (1994) 'Operating at the sharp end: the complexity of human error', in Bognor M.S. (ed) *Human Error in Medicine*. Hillsdale, NJ: Lawrence Erlbaum Associates, pp. 255-310

been different - using the present state of knowledge that may have advanced since the time when the treatment was carried out.

In the vast majority of cases, it is impractical for the instructing lawyers to attempt to withhold information as to outcome of treatment from the expert. Further, it is impossible to ask an expert for an opinion on past clinical practice in a manner that does not influence, in some way, the expert's perception of the facts he/she must address. Simply asking for an opinion already indicates the need to take a position in a possible dispute, the outcome of which is likely to have considerable importance for the parties involved.

Focus Bias

There may be difficulties for the expert in maintaining appropriate objectivity when reviewing the actions of a clinician who is following a particular practice that the expert does not favour, but at the material time that he/she cannot say is (or was) inappropriate. An expert may have been following a particular practice for many years and indeed may have justified reservations about alternative approaches. An expert may also have had lengthy discussions with other colleagues about the merits of the approach he/she prefers. All of these circumstances mean that the expert has potentially become focussed on a particular way of thinking about issues in relation to this practice. An instruction to give evidence on a claim relating to the alternative approach can become an opportunity for the expert to present, knowingly or unknowingly, an assessment of the evidence that is focussed on the unsound nature of that alternative approach. However, to comply with the requirements of PD35 3.2(6), the expert still has to consider whether a responsible body of clinicians would support the actions of the clinician, even though the expert does not, and has to report on this point.

Returning to the case concerning the laparoscopic repair, consider the following opinion:

> A reasonable body of surgical opinion would hold that a patient who presents with a single uncomplicated and almost symptom-free hernia, who had had repeated previous abdominal surgery and a history of bowel obstruction, was at a high risk of adhesions and therefore should be offered an open rather than a laparoscopic repair. It follows that the preferred technique in this patient would have been the open and not the laparoscopic approach. It follows that the decision was irrational and not in the patient's best interest.

Drafting such as this creates the opportunity of a challenge to the witness's objectivity. First, the expert has addressed the standard of care incorrectly. By stating what a reasonable body might do, rather than addressing what no reasonable body would do, the expert leaves open the question as to whether this practice actually fell below a reasonable standard of care. Therefore, the opinion that the decision of the surgeon was wrong is not supported by the opinion evidence of the expert as to the appropriate standard of care.

Secondly, the use of the phrases 'irrational' and 'not in the patient's best interest' give the impression of a less than measured - and so less than fully objective - approach to the issue. This is especially so when the treating clinicians' witness statements, which could contain further explanations of the background to the clinical decisions made, may not have been seen by the expert.

Approach to the Evidence

All of these factors, whether conscious or unconscious, which may potentially and adversely affect the validity of the assessment being made of the standard of care, must be recognised by the expert and put aside. This can only happen through self-reflection and the willingness to explore other legitimate points of view.

In my opinion, it was unwise to perform the laparoscopy through a sub-umbilical incision given her history including previous abdominal surgery and the significant risk of adhesions in this area (under the umbilicus), and therefore the risk of penetrating the bowel. However, I recognise that a significant number of responsible gynaecologists would have performed a laparoscopy in such a case and in such circumstances damage to the bowel by insertion of the primary trocar was probably unavoidable.

However, the bowel injury caused by the insertion of the primary trocar should have been detected at that time. Bowel injury is extremely difficult to identify with the laparoscope unless it is inserted at a separate position such as a secondary port. The RCOG guideline suggests that if there is concern that bowel may be adherent under the umbilicus then on completion of the procedure the laparoscope should be used to check that there has not been a "through and through" injury to the bowel under the umbilicus by visual inspection from a secondary port with a laparoscope.

In my opinion, a failure in these circumstances to insert the laparoscope through a secondary port site prior to completion of the procedure fell below the standard to be expected of a reasonably competent gynaecologist. Had the laparoscope been inserted through a secondary port site prior to completion of the procedure then, on the balance of probabilities, the injury to the bowel would have been seen and appropriate action could have been taken then and the development of peritonitis avoided.

If a truly valid and objective opinion as to the standard of care and the effects of any failure of standard of care is to be provided, the expert must carefully consider the evidence, following step-by-step the events as they unfolded, and must consider the situation that the clinician(s) faced, having successfully excluded any hindsight, outcome or focus bias. The expert must assess the treatment decisions made against a reasonable standard of care rather than a standard consistent with the expert's own preferred approach and level of expertise.

> A fundamental issue in clinical negligence claims is to identify an expert who is able to report objectively on the issues in dispute. Consciously or unconsciously, a medical expert may have sympathy for the plight of the claimant or for the clinicians who are the focus of the claim.

9.3.2 Establishing the Factual Basis of the Claim

It is not possible for a medical expert to express an opinion on the appropriate standard of care until the facts material to the opinion have been identified. It may not be apparent to the lawyer, with no or limited knowledge or understanding of the medical issues involved, which of the facts are material to the dispute. Without an explanation from the expert of what the material facts are (and in more complicated cases, why these are material), the lawyer may be unable to understand the basis upon which the expert expresses the opinion he/she does and will be unable to assess the strength of the case or the strength of the opposing side's case. The lawyer will also be handicapped in the exercise of seeking to clarify or strengthen the case or to attack the opposing side's case by seeking, for example, further evidence or documentation.

Where the material facts are uncertain or cannot be ascertained from the material before the expert, it is essential that the medical expert makes this clear and where possible indicates the possible means of clarifying or ascertaining the facts. This may involve the expert indicating to the lawyers that there appears to be missing medical records, test results, x-rays or scans and providing sufficient information to enable the lawyer to make proper enquiries as to their whereabouts. Further, it may be important to know whether the hospital concerned used a particular protocol or the expert may need to ask the lawyers to obtain fresh photocopies of medical records that have been badly copied. Sometimes, the medical expert may indicate particular questions that need to be asked of the claimant or a witness or potential witness.

Often, a very large number of medical records are provided to the expert and frequently these appear to have been jumbled up and placed out of chronological or any other form of order, whether by the health care provider, the person with the task of photocopying the notes or someone else in preparing the claim. Normally, only very few pages are at the heart of the investigation and relevant to the key issue that the expert is seeking to address. The clarity of the report and the ease with which the lawyers are able to understand and engage with the key issues will often be assisted by the expert producing a 'mini-bundle' (or 'core bundle') consisting of just those key pages in the records. These can be attached to the report or provided with it. This mini-bundle can then form the key reference document for the instructing lawyers, in conference with the barrister or at a joint discussion with an opposing expert and at trial. It will also make a subsequent consideration of the case by the expert much easier and will save an immense amount of time (and therefore costs) for all involved thereafter.

Some experts have taken to scanning documents from the medical records and inserting the scan in the report. This can on occasion be a useful way of drawing attention to a key document. However, it is likely that if the original was hand-written, then it is not easily read or interpreted and would in any event benefit from being transcribed in the report so that it can more readily be understood. In that case, little is gained by inserting a scanned copy. Alternatively, only part of the document is directly relevant to the expert's analysis, so that the report would be better focussed, and the reader's time better spent, if only that relevant part is transcribed. However attaching the key documents to the report (scanned or photocopied) for ease of reference may be helpful to the reader.

9.3.3   Factual Disputes in the Evidence

It is common in clinical negligence claims to find conflicts in the evidence between what the treating clinicians recall that they saw, heard or said and what the claimant and his/her family or friends recall that they saw, heard or said. The factual disputes may, for example, be as to:

- what a doctor said about the risks of the procedure or treatment, or about returning for further treatment or advice;
- what a claimant told a doctor about symptoms or about the timing of symptoms;
- what a doctor observed about how distressed or alert a patient was at a material time; or
- whether a doctor gave particular instructions or whether those instructions were actually carried out.

By this stage, you will be familiar with the medical expert's duty in dealing with conflicts in factual evidence[9]:

> Guidance   58   Where there are material facts in dispute experts should express separate opinions on each hypothesis put forward. They should not express a view in favour of one or other disputed version of the facts unless, as a result of particular expertise and experience, they consider one set of facts as being improbable or less probable, in which case they may express that view, and should give reasons for holding it.

Therefore, on each occasion where there is more than one possible factual scenario, the expert should consider:

- whether it is appropriate, based on his/her expertise, to express an opinion as to which set of facts is more probable; and
- what his/her opinion would be, based on each of the factual scenarios in turn.

---

9   See Section 4.2.7

The expert needs to be very confident of his/her opinion before expressing an opinion on only one of two (or more) competing factual scenarios. In the following example, the expert expresses an opinion on the basis of each of two factual scenarios. A lawyer would find the following evidence **helpful**:

> If the mother's statement about Y's drowsiness is accepted by the court, then I am of the opinion that all reasonably competent paediatricians would have administered Acyclovir to Y soon after her admission to hospital, because with the preceding history there was a significant chance that she had Herpes Simplex Encephalitis. If, however, the court accepts, in keeping with the contemporaneous medical records, that Y was not as drowsy as her mother describes, then I am of the opinion that it would have been reasonable for the clinicians to have diagnosed a self-limiting viral illness and to wait and see how the situation developed before deciding on treatment...

Many clinical negligence claims are in reality disputes about the factual situation at a particular time, rather than being disputes about the appropriate standard of care. Such factual disputes can only be resolved by reference to expert opinion, owing to the technical nature of the dispute. Where, for example, something went wrong in the course of an operation, the essential issue may be a factual issue as to the action by the surgeon that precipitated the operation 'going wrong' rather than any question of the surgeon's standard of operative skill and whether or not it was below the appropriate standard.

This distinction can be illustrated by *Swift v Bexley & Greenwich Health Authority*[10], in which the claimant was blinded in the course of an operation to clip an aneurysm in the brain. The issue was initially approached as being one of whether the operation was carried out negligently, that is, whether the neurosurgeon exercised the skill of a reasonably competent neurosurgeon. However, the experts in the case agreed that the blindness was caused either by a clip damaging the optic nerve or by an ischaemic effect causing catastrophic loss of blood to the optic nerve. If the clip had damaged the optic nerve, then there would have been a failure to exercise the ordinary skill of a neurosurgeon because the clip would not have been placed on the optic nerve had an appropriate level of skill been shown. If the blindness was caused by the ischaemic effect, this was an unavoidable side effect of the operation and not caused by an inadequate level of skill in performing the operation.

The judge was able to prefer the claimant's expert opinion on this point over that of the defendant's expert, as he was entitled to do when faced with conflicting opinions on a factual issue[11]. The judge found that it was the clip being placed on the optic nerve that caused the damage and therefore, as both of the experts agreed that this action would fall below an acceptable standard of care, the surgeon was found to be in breach of duty.

---

10   High Court 25th May 2000 (Lawtel 19/12/2001)

11   See Section 8.5

It is, therefore, essential for the medical expert to identify whether the principal issue in the case is one of fact, which (as we saw in the last chapter) the judge will resolve on the balance of probabilities or an issue of the standard of care, to which the judge must apply the Bolam test.

> The expert needs to be very confident of his/her opinion before express-ing an opinion on only one of two (or more) competing factual scenarios.

Approach to the Evidence

It is essential to accurately establish the facts before going on to consider issues relat-ing to standard of care or causation of damage. The role of the expert is, therefore, first to establish the relevant facts in relation to the dispute and to identify any points at which the factual basis is unclear or disputed. Where the factual basis is clear, the expert can then go on to consider the appropriate standard of care to which those facts give rise and the consequences of any failure in the standard of care.

Where the factual basis is unclear the expert must consider how that lack of factual clarity may be overcome (perhaps by obtaining further documents, further evidence or clarification of factual matters that are presently unclear). Where the factual basis remains unclear, the expert may be able to express an opinion, based on expertise, as to the more likely factual basis. However, if after further inquiry, it does not appear that any greater factual clarity can be obtained, then the expert should go on to consider the standard of care and/or causation on any alternative factual bases that the known facts might reasonably suggest as possible scenarios.

9.3.4   Series of Events

A particularly difficult opinion to express clearly is one where there are several medical events in the history (be these acts or omissions by medical staff) that may or may not have made a difference to the ultimate outcome. Such cases require the expert to project what the likely effect of each particular act or omis-sion would have been. Rather than being concerned with a single incident, many clinical negligence claims deal with a failure on the part of a number of clinicians to diagnose a condition or to treat appropriately over a period of time. Such claims may involve a multi-disciplinary or departmental failure, such as against several GPs and successive hospital departments in relation to a failure to diag-nose a possible life-threatening condition.

In all such cases, it will almost certainly be necessary to address the situation at a number of different stages in order to express an opinion on the standard of care to be expected (to address the duty that was owed) and on the consequences arising from any treatment that fell below the standard reasonably to be expected (to address causa-tion). At each significant stage of the history, the expert has to identify:

- what happened;
- what was a reasonable standard of care in the circumstances;
- whether or not the treatment given attained this reasonable standard of care (with reasons for the opinion);
- whether any failure in appropriate treatment caused any injury, damage or loss to the claimant; and
- whether any such failure actually made a difference to the outcome.

For example, if an expert criticises a junior doctor for failing to call a more senior colleague to examine a patient, then the expert also has to consider whether the more senior colleague would have acted differently to the junior doctor; if so, whether these actions would have made a difference to the ultimate outcome; and if so, what difference these actions would have made. The expert will then need to address the next stage of the history and follow the same assessment process.

I am of the opinion that in circumstances such as these where a previously well young man presented twice to an A&E department with persisting and worsening symptoms of vomiting in the presence of lower abdominal tenderness, no reasonably competent doctor would have failed to have referred him to a surgeon for review.

If he had been referred for a second review at the time of his second visit to the A&E Department, then I am of the opinion that on the balance of probabilities a diagnosis of acute appendicitis would have been considered, and in due course made, resulting in an operation taking place approximately 2 days earlier than in fact occurred.

Had surgery been performed at that earlier stage then the inflammatory process would have been arrested and, on the balance of probabilities, most of the sepsis, which was responsible for his complications and long critical stay in hospital, would have been avoided.

Standard of Care in Multi-Event Clinical Negligence Claims

The following example illustrates an expert's opinion when addressing the standard of care through a series of events and addressing both individual and departmental failures. A lawyer would find the following evidence **helpful**:

Standard of Care

The abnormality on the x-ray, the opacity on the left lung, was of such size and prominence that the failure to identify it by staff in the A&E Department fell below the standard reasonably to be expected of competent A&E clinicians. Once the abnormality was identified, no reasonably competent A&E clinician would have failed to have considered that it indicated that urgent action was needed.

Had the abnormality been identified, a reasonably competent A&E Department would have contacted the on-call medical team and handed Ms T's care over to them. Had Ms T been assessed by the on-call medical team then it is probable that she would have been admitted into hospital over the course of the next few days and undergone further appropriate investigations. These investigations would have established, typically within a week of undergoing the investigations, that she had carcinoma of the bronchus. She would then have been transferred to the chest physicians/surgeons who would have decided whether or not it was possible to undertake a surgical procedure.

It commonly takes a day or two for x-ray films taken in an A&E Department to be reviewed and an official report issued. In this case, it took 13 days for the x-ray to be reviewed. This delay in the A&E Department fell below the standard reasonably to be expected of reasonably competent A&E clinicians.

Having received a 'positive' x-ray report, the A&E Department made no attempt to contact Ms T for 4 weeks. This delay also fell below the standard reasonably to be expected of reasonably competent A&E clinicians. When the A&E Department tried to make contact, having failed to get through to Ms T on the phone, they left a single message on her voicemail. This was by now a very serious situation. The failure to take any further measures to attempt to contact Ms T, for example by contacting her GP or her parents whose details were on record, again fell below the standard reasonably to be expected of a reasonably competent A&E Department.

There was an absence of any initial or ongoing risk assessment for pressure ulcers. Although the hospital did not have in place written guidelines, such guidelines are commonly in use throughout the health service (as illustrated by the written guidelines in use at the neighbouring NHS Trust attached at Appendix 4). An initial assessment by the nursing team would have identified Mrs D's known mobility impairment as a risk factor and therefore would have identified her vulnerability to pressure ulcer development and the need for preventative measures to be taken and for close monitoring.

There is a total absence of reference to the risk of developing pressure ulcers in the care plans and in the daily nursing records prior to Mrs D being noted to have pressure sore on her heels and sacrum on 20 April 2011.

I am of the opinion that this failure to carry out any initial or subsequent risk assessment or to take any measures to eliminate or at least to reduce the risk of pressure ulcers and to monitor Mrs D for possible pressure sore development means that the care Mrs D received fell below the standard reasonably to be expected of any reasonably competent nursing team or hospital in 2011.

Causation in Multi-Event Clinical Negligence Claims

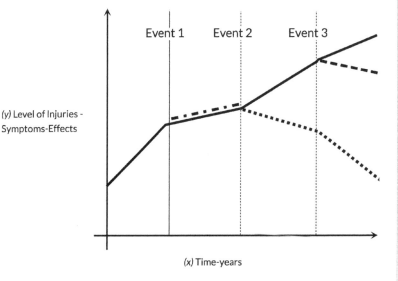

CAUSATION GRAPH #7: Multi-Event Clinical Negligence

Event 1   Event 2   Event 3

(y) Level of Injuries -
Symptoms-Effects

(x) Time-years

When dealing with causation in multi-event clinical negligence claims, the expert should follow the same basic approach used when reporting on multiple accident claims.

The facts represented by Causation Graph #7 show that there were three events in the treatment timeline where clinical negligence is alleged by the claimant.

Let us assume that the expert's opinion is that in all three instances the treatment decision made did not meet the Bolam test (i.e. on each occasion the clinicians acted in breach of their duty of care). The expert would then consider what difference each of the treatment decisions made. Here, the first event made no significant difference to the likely progression of the claimant's condition (compare to the dot-dashed line) even had the treatment been of the appropriate standard. The second treatment decision did affect the outcome markedly (compare to the dotted line) and the third decision at a much later stage also affected the outcome, but would have provided a less beneficial outcome than the earlier appropriate treatment decision (compare the dotted and the dashed line).

The expert should provide opinion on all three events, even though he/she may consider that the second event fell below the standard of care to be expected and caused damage. It is for the court to decide whether it accepts the expert's opinion evidence in the light of all the evidence before the court. This could mean that the expert's opinion on the second event is rejected by the court, but his/her opinion on the third event is accepted.

Factual situations can be further complicated by the need for experts in different disciplines to address causation based upon different treatment scenarios. Consider a case where on three occasions over a seven-day period a GP decides not to refer an increasingly lethargic child Y to hospital. When the child is admitted to hospital on day 7, she is found to have an acute viral infection from which with appropriate treatment she makes only a poor recovery. In this case, a GP expert would need to address the issue of breach of duty – the standard of care to be expected of a reasonably competent GP faced with a child exhibiting these symptoms and whether the child should have been referred to hospital sooner. The issue of causation would require that a paediatrician be instructed to address the question: without the delay in referral, what would the likely outcome have been for a child with that viral infection?

The GP expert giving an opinion in this case would need to consider whether on day 1, day 4 and day 5 the reasonably competent GP would have failed or declined to have referred Y to hospital. If the GP expert decides that on any one of these days the answer to this question is 'no' and that the child should have been referred, then the expert can give that opinion and move on to consider the next date. The GP expert would also need to consider on each occasion what the situation would have been had the hospital discharged the care of Y back to the GP without treatment because no infection had been identified.

A paediatrician would then need to address what would have been the likely situation had Y been referred on any of the dates when the GP would reasonably have been expected to refer the child, dealing with what symptoms Y would likely to have been suffering and the likely treatment that would have been offered and the probable outcome for the child.

If the paediatrician were to identify breach of duty on the part of the hospital once the child came into its hands which caused injury, the question will arise as to whether the negligence on the part of the hospital would be sufficient to 'break the chain of causation' of injury resulting from the GP's negligence. Such subsequent negligence would need to be sufficiently 'gross' to do so[12].

We now find ourselves facing the factual situation represented in Causation Graph #7 above. Once the paediatric opinion is that Y would have been started on antiviral medication as a precaution and that the viral infection would subsequently have been identified, the later failures to refer are only relevant to the extent that another paediatric expert disagrees with the first paediatric expert's opinion. The paediatric expert would therefore address what would the situation for Y have been without the failure to refer and contrast this with the situation as it is now following the referral on day 7. This comparison will be expressed as the difference in terms of the injury, symptoms, effects and consequences that Y now has over what she would have been likely to have had if an earlier referral had been made.

---

12   *Wright v Cambridge Medical Group* [2011] EWCA Civ 669 and see Sections 7.8 and 7.9

An essential approach to writing well-structured opinion in such cases is to set a clear agenda for each of the possible scenarios that the expert will address:

> In this section, I will give opinion, on the balance of probabilities, as to whether each of the decisions made by the GP not to refer the child to hospital was in accordance with medical practice that would be accepted as proper by a responsible body of GPs.
>
> Where I consider that the decision of the GP not to refer the child to hospital fell below an acceptable standard of care, I will also consider what the position would have been had the hospital failed to diagnose the child's condition and discharged her back into the care of the GP.

9.3.5   Complex Medical Issues

The expert report is the point of communication between the medical and legal experts (both the parties' lawyers and the judge). The report must be capable of being understood as a free-standing document regardless of the complexity of the medical issues it addresses. The expert report does not serve its purpose if it cannot be understood by the non-medically qualified reader, or the first-time reader, with little background knowledge of the case. If the medical issues are not fully understood, then the parties' lawyers cannot prepare the case and assess its prospects and certainly cannot prepare cross-examination of the opposing expert. Similarly, a judge cannot come to a reasoned and logical judgment.

The report must therefore explain the medical issues sufficiently for a non-medically qualified reader to have an understanding of the essential issues in the case. In this respect, the Introduction section to the report is very important. By succinctly setting the scene and identifying the key issues to be addressed, the task of the lawyers seeking to understand the evidence can be made a great deal more straightforward. It is difficult to write a clear introduction until the analysis of the evidence is complete and the key issues in the evidence have been identified. These key issues can also form an agenda for the opinions and conclusions that will follow later in the report.

Approach to the Evidence

It is often extremely helpful to include a subsection offering an overview of the case and the medical context at an early stage of the report. This introduces and where necessary explains the factual and the technical matters that will be addressed in the report. In some clinical negligence cases, the medical issues may be of such complexity that it is more appropriate to provide an appendix to explain the medical context, with a cross-reference to this appendix in the Introduction section of the report.

Case Overview

In March 2007, Y, aged 3 years old, developed an infection. She was seen by her GP on five occasions over the following 7 days, before being found by her mother stiff and unresponsive. She was admitted to Anywhere General Hospital. Tests were carried out in hospital, but the nature of the infection was not identified. Two days later, she was transferred to Somewhere Specialist Hospital where a diagnosis of Herpes Simplex Encephalitis (HSE) was made and treatment commenced. Two years on from the treatment, Y has been assessed as having neurological damage and developmental problems. A clinical negligence claim has been brought against the GP and the Anywhere General Hospital NHS Trust.

Medical Overview

HSE is an acute viral condition. Typically, it produces symptoms of fever, headache and increasing mental confusion but early symptoms and signs may be non-specific. If undiagnosed and untreated the mortality rate is over 70% and many survivors have serious disabilities. Antiviral therapy should be initiated promptly when the diagnosis is suspected and Acyclovir is the preferred therapy. Early antiviral treatment improves the prognosis of patients but even with such therapy just over half of children will have a degree of cognitive impairment. After appropriate treatment, many patients will be left with significant neuro-psychological and neuro-behavioural disorders.

This simple approach can alert the lawyers and the judge reading the report to the important factual and opinion matters that need to be assessed, making the report easier to understand and use. How far it is necessary to go in providing 'bite-size' explanations of the medical issues should be discussed with the instructing lawyers, though the lawyers themselves may initially need such explanations in order to assess what is necessary to prepare for the court.

Below, there is a further example of a technical summary that would be **helpful** to most lawyers:

The traditional 'open' approach to hernia repair necessitates a 10cm incision in the groin, removal of the hernia sac and repair of the posterior wall of the inguinal canal under direct vision. Laparoscopic repair is done from within the abdomen: under general anaesthesia, the abdomen is inflated with carbon dioxide and a 1cm diameter 'port' is introduced in the midline, through which a telescope is inserted. Two smaller ports allow the placement of long dissecting and cutting instruments. The internal orifices of the inguinal hernia or hernias can be visualised and a patch of woven plastic is stapled to the inner abdominal wall to cover all the defects, with care being needed to avoid damaging the adjacent blood vessels, vas deferens and spermatic cord.

A high-quality photograph or diagram (placed in an appendix and cross-referenced in the text) may be extremely useful in helping the lawyers and the court to understand technical issues and also limit the need to provide extended descriptions in the report.

> The expert report is the point of communication between the medical and legal experts (both the parties' lawyers and the judge). The report must be capable of being understood as a free-standing document regardless of the complexity of the medical issues it addresses.

Conclusion

In contrast to most personal injury claims, in clinical negligence the issue of breach of duty is an essential element for the appropriate medical expert to address. The law of negligence is straightforward, but its application to the facts of a particular case involves a careful and objective analysis of the actions of the clinicians involved. The phenomena of hindsight and focus bias make the task of the medical expert extremely challenging. The inherent complexity of dealing with causation in claimants who may already be ill at the time of the claimed negligent treatment only adds to the challenge. The approach of the expert has to be characterised by objectivity, accuracy and precision.

Key-Point Summary

1. One or more experts may be instructed to deal with the issues in a clinical negligence claim: breach of duty, causation of injury or damage, and condition and prognosis.

2. Hindsight and focus bias are important issues when assessing the evidence relating to clinical negligence cases. Experts reporting in clinical negligence claims need to pay close attention to the range of opinion when applying the Bolam test.

3. It is essential that the expert assesses the facts in a logical way, paying close attention to the knowledge that was available to the clinicians at the point in time clinical decisions were made.

4. Many clinical negligence cases turn on the court's decision in respect of factual issues on which experts disagree. Where experts are applying their expertise to give opinion on factual scenarios where direct or documentary evidence is not before the court, then it is essential that the expert

considers all potential factual scenarios that might reasonably have arisen and gives opinion on each of these scenarios.

5. Where the claimed negligence includes a series of events, the expert must establish the facts at each stage and consider issues of breach of duty and causation, or both, before moving on in the timeline to the next relevant event.

6. In many clinical negligence cases, the battleground is causation not the standard of care.

7. Expert reports in clinical negligence claims must contain sufficient explanation of the technical or medical issues to enable the lawyers to clearly understand the nature and basis of the claim.

Next Steps

In the next chapter, we will explore the reporting issues that concern experts who report on the quantum aspects of the claim and will explain how medical experts can assist these experts by including essential content in their reports.

10

Reporting On Care And Therapeutic And Other Needs

Introduction

In Chapter 6, we looked at the issues that the medical evidence should address in order to enable an assessment of the consequences of injury to be made. A care, therapeutic and other needs report, such as an accommodation needs report, (which we will refer to collectively as "a care and needs report") will be based on the medical reports and the opinions expressed in the medical reports relevant to such needs. It will also be based on the assessment made by the expert writing the report as the result of an interview, an examination or assessment and consideration of available records or other information. It is important that the principles addressed in Chapter 6 are understood and applied by anyone producing a care, therapeutic or other needs report.

A care and needs report will normally be required in a claim of substantial value. However, some care needs will arise in most other than very minor injury claims. As with all expert reports produced in injury claims, it is essential that such a report assists in the valuation of the claim, is readily comprehensible to the lawyer reading it, applies all of the applicable and relevant legal tests and provides justified and reasoned opinion.

As already explained in Chapter 6, damages are compensatory and are awarded, so far as is possible, to put the claimant in the position he or she would have been in but for the injury sustained. The purpose of the report is to assist in the assessment of that compensation. The court is concerned to establish what provision is reasonably required by the injured claimant to achieve that end. This should not be confused with the provision which might be made for the injured person who is reliant on state assistance in one form or another, although it is possible that one would inform the other[1].

Because damages are compensatory, it also follows that in appropriate cases there must be a set off (or deduction) in relation to any savings the claimant may experience by reason of having care provided, and the report should address this too.

Chapter Outline

In this chapter, we will consider rules about the content of the expert report and the joint statement, which are of particular relevance to care and needs experts. We will also consider the law in relation to care claims.

10.1 The Format of the Report

The requirements of an expert report which we have dealt with earlier in this book, and in particular in Chapter 4, in relation to medical experts are equally applicable to a care report. In producing a care and needs report, the proportionality principle applies and the expert must take care to produce a report that is proportionate to the value of the claim. There are several aspects of care and needs reporting that require particular attention, which we address in the following sections.

10.1.1 Sequential Reports

Care reports are often ordered by the court to be provided sequentially, that is the claimant will obtain and disclose to the other side its care report and the defendant's care expert will provide a report in response to that report. Paragraph 63 of the Guidance sets out the approach to this second report and we have provided further guidance at Section 4.2.13. The Guidance emphasises that:

- the second report should seek to identify where the first report is agreed, without repeating information adequately dealt with in the first report, and

---

1   See further Section 6.6.12

should focus on the material differences of opinion, and the reasons for the differences; and

- in providing an assessment of value of items in the report, the second report should 'contain a reconciliation between the claimant's expert's loss assessment and the defendant's, identifying for each assumption any different conclusion to the claimant's expert'.

While the wording of this last requirement may be less than clear, the presumed intention is that the second report should contain a schedule or table comparing the experts' respective valuations of aspects of the claim, and the reasons for a different conclusion on the part of the second expert. That way the areas of disagreement and the reasons for them should become apparent to the lawyers, and in due course, to the court. For example, if the difference in valuation is because of a difference of opinion as to appropriate hourly rates, or as to the degree of assistance for particular tasks which is required, or the number of certain items likely to be required, then this difference and a summary of the reasons for the different opinion must be set out in the schedule or table.

10.1.2 Joint Statements and Sequential Reports

Where care reports have been provided sequentially, then it is expected that this will assist in the approach to the joint discussion and joint statement. Paragraph 73 of the Guidance (see section 4.7.2) emphasises that the joint statement should focus on the areas of disagreement identified in the second (usually defendant's) report, although the first (usually claimant's) expert will need to consider and respond to what the second expert had to say about areas of disagreement. This may require consideration of factual material, the content of expert medical reports, the basis for the second expert's opinion, or any other material before the care and needs experts that is relevant to explaining the disagreement.

10.2 The Meaning of "Care"

A care report must address the provision of those services that replace that which the claimant is no longer able to do as a result of the injuries sustained and that are reasonably required to put the claimant back in the position he/ she would have been in in the absence of the injury (see Section 6.6.12). Those services should give back to the claimant the benefit of such activities and the measure of independence enjoyed before the accident so as to restore the claimant's autonomy so far as is reasonably possible. They must be services which the claimant will probably make use of and therefore a consideration of the claimant's actual or likely response to an offer of such assistance is relevant. If it would be refused if offered, its cost will not be recovered. Such services can include the provision of emotional support in a suitable case and where that is reasonable.

The question may arise as to whether a claimant is better cared for at home or within an institution. The test to be applied is whether the care and accommodation chosen and claimed for by the claimant is reasonable. The courts have rejected the argument (on behalf of the defendant) that the claimant must show that his best interests reasonably required the regime for which he was contending. It was held that paternalism did not replace the right of a claimant to make a reasonable choice[2]. Therefore, the claimant's own wishes must be taken into account. In such cases, the expert must therefore record the claimant's wishes as well as considering the reasonableness and practicality of those wishes.

Care must be assessed in the context of the particular claimant and his/her environment. Care needs may well be affected by the general suitability of the claimant's home. An unsuitable home will give rise to greater care needs unless or until the home can be made more suitable.

In some cases, prior to the award of any damages, it may be that the claimant's family is providing for all of the claimant's needs, but the proposals for the future do not therefore need to assume that care will continue to come from the claimant's family just because they are available or because they have been providing the care in the absence of any other provision. Restoring the claimant's independence includes the independence not to be dependent on his/her family. The claimant's partner may be providing for all of the claimant's care needs, and be prepared to continue doing so if necessary, but the claimant might prefer to regain something of the previous relationship as companions rather than continue the new relationship of client and carer.

In addition to the claimant's own care needs, the claimant is entitled to recover damages for the cost of providing services to others to whom the claimant would have provided those services but for the injuries. So, for example, a claimant may have been caring for, or providing other services to, a disabled relative prior to the accident but is no longer able to do so[3]. An award may be made for the cost of someone else providing that care or those services now, whether it is provided gratuitously or commercially.

10.3 Family Care (Gratuitous Services)

As already indicated, injuries do not need to be severe for a sum to be recovered for family care and assistance arising out of an injury. Even a period of symptoms following an accident of a few weeks may result in such a claim[4]. Damages may be awarded to compensate for the extra domestic services provided by family members, to fill in for that which the claimant would have done but for the effects of the injury. An award of damages for such gratuitous services is held by the claimant for the benefit of the person who performed the services and should therefore be passed on by the claimant to that person. However, if this care is provided by a tortfeasor (the wrong doer, i.e. the defendant), then it is not recoverable - the legal principle being that a wrongdoer cannot benefit from his/

---

2   *Sowden v Lodge* [2004] EWCA Civ 1370

3   *Lowe v Guise* [2002] EWCA Civ 197

4   See *Giambrone v Sunworld Holidays Ltd* [2004] 2 All ER 89 which confirmed the recoverability of an award for a parent's care for a child with gastroenteritis.

her wrongdoing. This situation might arise where the claimant was a passenger in a car driven by a spouse, which was involved in an accident. It also follows that if the claimant is unlikely to pass on the sum recovered to the service provider (for example, because of an acrimonious divorce so that the claimant may be unwilling to make a payment to a former wife or partner) then it is not recoverable. This would be an issue for the lawyers and not the care expert to address, though the care expert would be able to report any direct evidence observed as to the nature of the relationship or any information given by the claimant as to the nature of the relationship. Once again, careful note-taking is an essential element, because the care expert is at this point involved as a fact finder. (See Section 4.2.4 and 7.4.4).

If future care is to be such non-commercial care provided by family members, then provision should be considered for the contingency of a potential breakdown in that provision, perhaps because of a falling out within the family, perhaps because of the ageing of the care provider, or, if provided by an adult child, because that adult child may move away or seek greater independence.

In a case involving a very severely injured child, inevitably the parents will have some continuing involvement in looking after the child. However, the value of parental involvement may not necessarily be taken into account against, and in reduction of, the commercial care package in such cases, unless this parental input has the effect of removing the need for an element of the care package (such as what would otherwise be the need for a night sleeper or some emergency provision).

10.4 Calculating the Cost/Value of Non-Commercial Care

In valuing past care, only care actually provided and reasonably required is relevant – and that may therefore be less than what was in fact provided. Having assessed the amount of care provided by family members, in terms of hours per day or week, it is necessary for this to be converted into a cash sum as part of the damages to be awarded. The Local Authority spinal point 8 (the local authority home carer rate) is generally used[5]. However, it is important to remember that the assessment is still one of reasonable needs and that the care report is not a local authority assessment of what the minimum care required might be, but rather of what would be a reasonable provision[6].

Generally, the basic flat hourly rate will be used for such care, although the aggregate rate, which allows for weekend and night time care, may be used if the care is provided to a significant degree at weekends and at night, and also in cases involving very severe injury and exceptional care on the part of the family members. The court will decide the rate having considered the evidence as to the timing and extent of such care. The lawyers (and the court) will deduct a sum equivalent to

---

5   Usefully set out in "Facts & Figures: Tables for the Calculation of Damages" published by Sweet & Maxwell and the Professional Negligence Bar Association

6   See Section 6.6.12

any Carer's Allowance received by the family members and the value of any direct payments made to the claimant for care needs from any award and the existence of such allowance or payment should therefore be identified in the report where possible.

Although the care report will be expected to provide a mathematical calculation of reasonable care costs, the court may award a "round figure" lump sum rather than an amount calculated mathematically by multiplying the hours by an hourly rate. In part at least this is the inevitable result of the difficulty that there is in providing a reasonable assessment of the number of hours reasonably required as a result of the injury.

A discount on the cost/value of care will be made by the lawyers (or by the court), and not by the care expert, where services are provided gratuitously to reflect the notional tax and national insurance which would have been deducted if the carer were paid. Although 25% is commonly used as a discount, the appropriate discount can be between 20 and 33% and is one which the court considers produces a fair result on the facts of the particular case. In some cases, where the care provided is exceptional, the court may make no deduction at all. In assessing non–commercial care, the court's objective is to award the reasonable value of services provided.

In some cases, the family carer has given up work to provide the caring services. If that is considered to have been a reasonable course of action, a claim can then be made for those lost net earnings, up to the cost of the commercial cost of care which would otherwise have been incurred. The assessment of the care provided is still needed from the care expert as an alternative method of valuation and in so doing the expert is likely to be assisting with the question of whether it was financially reasonable to give up employment in order to provide the care.

10.5 Calculating the Cost of Commercial Care

A claimant can recover the cost reasonably to be incurred in purchasing commercial care, taking into account the type, extent and nature of the care required and taking into account all other relevant factors such as the degree of need for continuity in carers and the rates prevailing in the locality. It is necessary to consider whether on the particular facts it is appropriate to use agency carers (likely to be more expensive) or for carers to be directly employed (involving greater administration).

In calculating the cost of fulltime care by directly employed carers, provision will be made for the need to cover holidays, sick leave and training etc. – and therefore the number of notional weeks per year for which provision must be made for employed carers is likely to be 59 or 60 weeks a year[7]. In addition, a case manager is likely to be required (see below). Because the object is to provide for the claimant's reasonable needs, such items as the potential need for double-ups to cover

---

7   See *X v A Strategic Health Authority* [2008] EWHC 2727

unplanned transfers should be taken into account when assessing the required number of carers.

Consideration should also be given as to whether, in a team of carers, there should be a team leader (paid at a higher rate) thereby reducing the amount of, and therefore the cost of, case management involvement.

The possibility of the use of live-in carers might be considered in appropriate cases although issues such as the Working Time Directive will need to be addressed.

In addition to ensuring that there is an adequate number of carers, both on a daily basis and on an annual basis, provision must also be made for all of the other related potential expenses, such as Employers' National Insurance Contributions, employer's compulsory pension contributions and the cost of appropriate training. Of course, if agency care is considered appropriate on the facts of the case, while the hourly rate will probably be higher, these additional costs will not be incurred.

10.6 Causation

Causation, which we have considered in detail in Chapter 6, remains an important issue when providing a care and needs report as it does in all areas of assessing the consequences of injury and damages recoverable. The cost or value of care (or therapy or equipment) which would have been required anyway because of a pre-existing need cannot be recovered. It will, however, be necessary to consider, where that pre-existing care need is covered by family members, such as care provided by a younger or more able spouse or a child:

- whether that family care would in fact have continued or for how long it is likely to have continued;
- whether the nature of the care has so changed that it is now of a different character requiring for example substantial commercial care so that an offset would not be appropriate[8].

Except in clear cut cases the expert should provide assessments of pre-existing care and leave the lawyers to argue whether an off-set is appropriate on the particular facts. In a complicated case and depending on the consistency of the evidence, it may be necessary to cost more than one possible scenario (and leave the lawyers or the court to resolve which is the most appropriate scenario). As always the causation graph which we looked at in Chapter 6 may well assist in this process, in identifying the situation prior to and in the absence of the injury and comparing it with the situation as it now exists and will be in the future.

---

8   In *Sklair v Haycock* [2009] EWHC 3328 the judge declined to offset 4 hours a day provided by the claimant's father, now aged 80, and therefore likely to be provided in future at no cost to the claimant by his local authority, against his post injury need for 24 hour care. This approach has been criticised as failing to carry out an assessment of what additional care need the injury has resulted in.

10.7 The Need for Services Other than Care

The basic principle is that the claimant is entitled to recover damages for the loss of the ability to perform any tasks previously enjoyed or performed, where this can be assessed in money's worth. Each case will have its own particular needs which the care expert should seek to identify, and if outside the expert's area of expertise, then the expert should identify for the instructing lawyer the appropriate expert to report on it.

In a more serious injury claim, there may well be a requirement for a case manager to co-ordinate the necessary care, rehabilitation and support of the claimant. More generally there may be a need, because of the injury, for someone to provide DIY and home maintenance services, general housekeeping – such as cleaning, shopping, laundry and ironing, cooking, washing up – and gardening help.

The assessment will be based on the particular facts of the case and these facts must be ascertained by the expert and set out in the report. This will include consideration of the past history of such tasks being performed, the size and nature of the home and of the household, the skills of the claimant which were used in providing such services, and, for example, the size and type of garden – whether it is one acre of carefully maintained beds and vegetables, or a small paved urban patch. The ability of the claimant to have continued carrying out such services in the absence of the injury, whether through age or through other conditions (the causation issue), needs to be considered and addressed.

10.8 Aids and Equipment etc.

The expert will need to consider those articles or items of expenditure which might assist the claimant in achieving some independence or in restoring aspects of his or her life lost as a result of the injury. These should be items which would not otherwise be (or have been) required. For example, whereas a few years ago we might well have claimed for the cost of a microwave or mobile phone following injury, it would be difficult to argue now that they would not have been purchased in any event.

The list should include items already purchased, items needed now and items which will be needed at some future date. The items all need to be explained and justified in the context of the injury and the claimant's resulting condition, as assessed from the medical reports and from the expert's own assessment, along with the timing of the need for the items.

To value this aspect of the claim, the lawyer requires both the capital cost of the items and information as to when they will be required, their likely life and the frequency of likely replacement. Care experts frequently provide for this purpose an annual replacement cost calculated on the basis of the current capital cost being spread over the lifetime of the item.

In appropriate cases, consideration should be given to expenditure which will be saved, for example, the cost of a standard item of furniture which is needed might be offset against the cost of a specialised and more expensive item of similar furniture.

Regular additional items of expenditure – such as insurance, increased utility bills, increased laundry bills etc – should be detailed and justified. Additional mobility needs must be identified with the reasonable manner in which they can be met being addressed, for example by adaptations to a vehicle or by the use of taxis. For some injured claimant's, the future cost of holidays will be increased, because of the need for upgraded flights to provide adequate space or comfort or because of the reasonable need for a carer or support worker to assist the claimant to be able to take the holiday. The expert should try to provide a basis on which this additional expenditure can be assessed.

The expert should be careful to remain within his/her area of expertise and to indicate, when appropriate, the need for other input to assess any particular need or the costs of addressing those needs.

10.9 Therapy and Treatment

The claim should include the cost of past and future reasonable input by occupational therapists, physiotherapists, speech therapists, osteopaths and chiropractors, podiatrists, psychologists or any other recognised practitioners. The need, the timing and frequency (whether now, every year, in 5 years or whatever) and the cost (both per session and frequency) all must be addressed and justified.

A clear and reasoned opinion should be expressed as to the aims and anticipated outcome of such therapy or treatment.

As with aids and equipment, the fact that necessary therapy or treatment might be available on the NHS does not prevent a claimant recovering the cost of having the therapy or treatment privately, if that is what the claimant is likely to do if funds are provided[9].

10.10 Accommodation Cost

The need to incur additional costs on accommodation as a result of injury should be supported by the medical evidence and by the care report as well as having input as to costing from an architect or surveyor. The claimant may need to be re-housed, for example to a bungalow or have need of major adaptations to the home such as the building of an extension or need to move to a different area for a number of different reasons, including to be closer to supportive family members or for example (in an appropriate case) to avoid steep hills.

The final assessment of the amount recoverable is for the lawyers. For example, the law currently permits only the notional cost of funding the additional capital cost of a new property to be recovered[10].

---

9   Section 2(4) of the Law Reform (Personal Injuries) Act 1948

10   *Roberts v Johnstone* [1989] QB 878

Rather than a move, building works may be required to provide adequate provision in the current home – a downstairs bedroom and bathroom, provision for a wet room, a refitted kitchen, wider doors, ramps, hand rails, a stair lift etc. It may be necessary for the claimant and family to move out to rented accommodation while the works are carried out. The law permits the recovery of the reasonable building and related costs, less an allowance for any betterment value of the property.

10.11 Prosthetics

A claimant is entitled to recover expenses that are reasonably incurred as a result of the injury. The range of prosthetics now available and becoming available is increasing, and the sophistication of prosthetic devices is tending to increase the likely cost to be allowed for in the care package. The expert should put forward proposals based on the reasonable requirements of that particular claimant, with his or her particular interests (pre and post injury) and particular need. That may involve recommendations, with justification spelt out as it applies to that particular claimant, for a range of prosthetics for different activities, with different attributes or as spares.

It is not always clear how well the claimant will manage with a particular prosthesis and it may be reasonable for the claimant to purchase one even if it transpires (or were to transpire) that it does not in fact assist the claimant.

The expert may also be able to express an opinion as to the likely extent to which the claimant will be able to make use of the prosthesis and therefore indicate the likely need for alternative methods of dealing with the disability or for additional assistance at times when the prosthesis is not in use (and which the care expert will need to address, or may already have addressed, in the care report).

10.12 Assistive Technology

There is a growing range of technological solutions for injured persons to enable them to regain independence or enjoy activities which would otherwise be difficult or impossible. The test to be applied in assessing whether damages should include provision for any particular item of assistive technology is whether it is reasonable in all of the circumstances of the case to provide for it. The expert should therefore explain, unless it is patently obvious, how the need for the equipment arises from the nature of the injury and the benefit that the claimant is expected to gain. In appropriate cases, it will also be important to address the practicality of the claimant making use of, or learning to make use of, the technology.

In an increasingly technological world, it is necessary to be realistic as to whether certain items would in any event probably have been used or been present, such as a smart phone with voice recognition technology, or, if a more expensive model of some kind is needed, to explain the additional and necessary benefits that such additional expenditure will purchase. In some areas the report may be explaining how needs can reasonably be met by making use of what is now available without cost or at minimal cost, such as video calls through Skype or the use of certain Apps.

Conclusion

Care and other needs reports are required to support a variety of heads of claim arising from an injury. All of the legal principles that apply to medical expert reporting apply to care and needs experts. Any recommendations must be reasonable and the reasons for the inclusion of aspects of the care package must be included in the report. The proportionality principle applies and a care and needs expert needs to make sure that the cost of the work needed to generate the report is proportionate to the value of the claim.

Key-Point Summary

1. The principles that apply to opinion evidence for medical experts also apply to care and other needs reporting. The same standards of legal understanding apply in the provision of quantum reports.

2. The courts often order care and other needs reports to be produced sequentially. Where the basis of the assessment is agreed, the report of (usually) the defendant's expert should focus on the differences and the reasons for those differences, rather than reproducing information that is agreed. This also applies to the Joint Statement that will be produced as a case moves towards a court hearing.

3. Care and other needs must be assessed in the context of the particular claimant and the particular circumstances of his/her environment.

4. Any aspect of a care package must be considered in the light of the claimant's actual or likely response to them; if the claimant is likely to refuse the service, then the cost will not be recovered.

5. Where a claimant's family members are providing care, the care package need not assume that these arrangements will continue for the future and the claimant him/herself may want to create a greater sense of independence or return to a more normal sense of relationship.

6. The claimant is entitled to recover for the cost of providing services to others that he/she can no longer provide.

7. A tortfeasor (wrongdoer) cannot benefit from his/her wrongdoing.

8. Causation of damage is a key-consideration for care and other needs reports and in complex cases it may be necessary to provide the lawyers and the court with different care scenarios to assist in the valuation of the claim.

9. When dealing with aids and equipment, the report should deal with the

likely capital cost, maintenance and running cost and the likely period before replacement.

10. Accommodation costs, whether for moving or providing adequate provision in the claimant's current home will need to be supported by medical and care evidence and will likely require additional evidence from an architect or surveyor; an allowance will be made for any betterment of the property.

11. Prosthetics and adaptive technologies are developing fields – the care and other needs experts must address the need and use of such equipment and the likelihood that the claimant will make use of it.

Next Steps

In the next chapter, we will explore the report writing skills that are fundamental to producing high-quality expert reports.

11

Writing the Report

Introduction

Producing a high-quality expert report is fundamental to the expert's role in the litigation process. Whereas advisory reports provide an initial framework within which the viability of the claim is assessed, expert reports help the lawyers to make better quality decisions about whether to settle a claim or to pursue it to court. The level of damages at which a claim will settle will be heavily influenced by the totality of expert evidence in the case.

The quality of expert reports is fundamental to achieving settlements that accurately reflect the realities of the claim. When a case comes to trial, high-quality expert reports are also essential to the court, as judges place great weight upon expert evidence when deciding cases.

The writing skills set out in this chapter are applicable to all expert reports. It is an excellent investment for experts to spend whatever time is necessary to improve their report writing skills. This is an excellent way to build a good reputation amongst instructing solicitors and enhance the usefulness of their reports throughout the litigation process.

Chapter Outline

We will give guidance on how to produce an expert report, the required structure of the report as indicated by the CPR and how to develop expert report templates that effectively communicate the evidence to the court. We will discuss how to express supported opinions in both straightforward and complex cases and how to provide evidence in response to the new guidance on sequential reports. Finally, we will explore some practical writing skills and the presentation of reports, both of which are essential to producing high-quality evidence.

11.1 Essential Approach to Producing Expert Evidence

Expert reports need to address the relevant expert issues in a clear, concise and reliable way. Expert reports should set out the relevant factual matters on which the opinions in the report are based and provide clear and informed reasoning to support the opinions expressed[1].

An uncontested medical expert report is often the only expert evidence in a case[2]. As such, it is profoundly important that the expert report deals with all the issues that are relevant to the claim and that the report is written to an appropriate standard of accuracy and precision. In more complex cases, where medical expert reports become the basis for the assessment of care and rehabilitation, the experts dealing with these quantum issues will also be relying on the medical expert reports to get a clear understanding of all of the medical aspects of causation and the consequences of injury for the claimant.

Whenever the lawyers handling a claim or a judge at trial cannot clearly understand an expert report or the report has not covered all of the relevant issues, then that report will not have served its purpose in the litigation process.

The importance placed upon experts producing high-quality reports are a present concern of the courts. In a recent case[3], Turner J, while addressing issues relating to the care and rehabilitation of a seriously injured child, made the following remarks about the care reports before the court:

> 'I would make the following points, some general and some specific to this case:
>
> (i) There is a regrettable tendency for experts to produce reports which are simply far too long. The comments made by Sir James Munby in his article on this topic in [2013] Family Law 816 are as apposite to personal injury litigation as they are to care cases:

---

1   Unless the expert relies on the factual basis produced by another expert

2   See for example Section 3.3.2 and the Pre-Action Protocol for Personal Injury Claims and Section 3.4 above and the RTA Protocol and EL/PL Protocol

3   *Harman v East Kent Hospitals NHS Trust* [2015] EWHC 1662 at 32

*"...too many expert reports..., are simply too long, largely because they contain too much history and too much factual narrative... I want to send out a clear message: expert reports can in many cases be much shorter than hitherto, and they should be more focused on **analysis** and **opinion** than on history and narrative. In short, expert reports must be **succinct**, **focused** and **analytical**. But they must also of course be **evidence based.**" [Judge's emphasis]*

In the experience of this Court it is not unusual for care reports, for example, in catastrophic injury cases to exceed 100 pages in length. Very often the same narrative detail can be found repeated in report after report from different disciplines. The consequences are deleterious. All this involves the parties and the Court in spending a disproportionate time reading the reports which results in an increase in costs. Furthermore, the likelihood that important points are lost in the vastness of the context in which they appear is unhelpfully increased.

(ii) Against the background of longer and longer reports there is, however, little sign, in some cases at any rate, that the care and attention spent on analysis and opinion, as opposed to history and narrative, is being given commensurate attention and priority.

(iii) Experts should deal with the issues raised by the other side promptly. In this case, the defendant makes a legitimate point in emphasising that neither the claimant's care expert nor educational psychologist dealt with the option of continued residential care in their reports until the joint statements and even then the matter was dealt with in an over concise way. One inevitable consequence of this was that the reasoning of the experts was only finally fleshed out in oral evidence during the hearing. This should not happen.'

There are important insights to be taken from these remarks:

1. Many expert reports are simply too long. The point that Turner J (quoting Sir James Munby) wants to emphasise is that the excessive length of reports is a consequence of the unnecessary repetition of the factual basis – the history – at the expense of the analysis and opinion of the expert. The Guidance issued in Dec 2014 specifically addresses the issue of the repetition of the history in sequential reports[4], as follows:

Guidance   63   Where there is to be sequential exchange of reports then the defendant's expert's report usually will be produced in response to the claimant's. The defendant's report should then:

---

4   See also Section 4.2.14

(a) confirm whether the background set out in the claimant's expert report is agreed, or identify those parts that in the defendant's expert's view require revision, setting out the necessary revisions. The defendant's expert need not repeat information that is adequately dealt with in the claimant's expert report.

(b) focus only on those material areas of difference with the claimant's expert's opinion. The defendant's report should identify those assumptions of the claimant's expert that they consider reasonable (and agree with) and those that they do not; and

(c) in particular where the experts are addressing the financial value of heads of claim (for example, the costs of a care regime or loss of profits), the defendant's report should contain a reconciliation between the claimant's expert's loss assessment and the defendant's, identifying for each assumption any different conclusion to the claimant's expert.

It is, however, important to notice the caveat in the quote from Sir James Mumby that concludes his criticism: "But they [the reports] must also of course be evidence based". So experts, where it is relevant to the opinions they express, need to have checked the accuracy of any factual basis on which they choose to rely, and need to state that this work to check the factual basis has been carried out, before they then move on to give the analysis and opinion.

We would add to Turner J's criticism, in that many experts have not developed the medico-legal skill of expressing supported opinions and correctly applying the appropriate legal tests to their opinion. This often seems to be the underlying reason that the expert chooses to focus on reproducing an extensive history, where the skills of applying expertise to the evidence are not required.

It is essential that experts focus their attention on explaining the rationale that supports their opinions and apply to those opinions the appropriate legal test.

2. Repetition is costly and is unhelpful to the lawyers and the court. The courts are rightly concerned with time being spent reading the same information from different professionals for five reasons:

(a) it increases costs for the lawyers and the courts (and so ultimately the parties to the claim);

(b) important evidential points may be 'lost in the vastness' of the evidence produced;

(c) the failure of an expert to deal with an essential issue may be missed altogether by the experts and the lawyers;

(d) the expert's response to an essential issue raised by the other side may in consequence be delayed; and

(e) the response to an issue raised by the other side may be inadequate when the proportionality principle is taken into account.

In this case, the care experts would have needed simply to note that they had read the history in the medical reports prior to making their assessment[5]. Prior to the 'Jackson reforms'[6] the repetition of the history was seen as evidence that the expert had read the material in the case; now a simple statement of agreement (and with appropriate amendments where required) suffices.

11.1.1 Importance of the Proportionality Principle

There is little doubt that the increasing prominence of the proportionality principle is having impact on the litigation process. The criticism of the claimant experts is not only that they did not respond in the first instance to the defendant reports, but also that when they did address the issue in the Joint Statement, they failed to deal with the issue adequately and proportionately to the seriousness of the issue.

When the option of continued residential care was raised by the defendant's experts, the claimant's experts (a care expert and an educational psychologist) did not apparently deal with this additional issue by producing an addendum to their reports. The experts either did not recognise or did not pay attention to the importance of this issue in the defendant reports.

The court's criticism of the way in which the claimant experts dealt with the issue in the Joint Statement, 'the matter was dealt with in an over [sic] concise way', strongly suggests that the support for the opinions that the claimant experts ultimately expressed – i.e. their reasoning as applied to the relevant facts of the case – was not included in Joint Statement. We will address this point when we consider opinion writing technique below.

11.2 Expert Report Structures

Most of the difficulties that experts have writing expert reports arise from a lack of understanding of expert report structures. Experts, particularly those who are inexperienced in the type of case that is the subject of the report, will often reach for a 'model template', which are available from a variety of sources.

There is nothing wrong with using or producing model templates, so long as the expert has the level of skill required to know when a template is either inappropriate or needs to be modified to address the relevant issues effectively.

---

5   It is probable that the care reports were written prior to the issue of the Guidance, but the learning points for our purposes remain valid.

6   See Section 2.8

The required form and content of an expert report is set out in CPR 35, PD35 and the Guidance[7]. Experts must familiarise themselves with each of these documents before writing their first (or next!) expert report, as they declare they have done so in the declaration at the conclusion of every report[8]. The approach indicated by the CPR is consistent with the reporting principles that underlie scientific reports, requiring the report author to include:

1. clear report objectives;

2. a defined methodology;

3. an accurate factual basis for the opinions to be expressed; and

4. logical and supported opinions and conclusions.

11.2.1 Linear Report Structure

The linear report structure is used when all of the issues that the expert needs to address arise from a single factual basis. The essential elements of an expert report are:

1. an introduction to the report that identifies the qualifications (and relevant experience) of the expert, sets out the substance of all facts and instructions given to the expert by the instructing solicitor and makes clear where the expert is relying on the work of others in producing the evidence;

2. a statement setting out the methodology adopted by the expert and the information available to the expert when considering the facts of the case;

3. a factual basis for the report containing all facts relevant to the issues that the expert has been instructed to address, making clear the sources of those facts and where necessary cross-referencing a particular fact to its source;

4. where an examination or assessment is required, details of the examination or assessment findings[9];

5. a section detailing all the opinions and reasoning of the expert on all relevant issues, with a concise summary of all the expert's conclusions at the end of the report;

6. the Expert's Declaration and Statement of Truth as required by the CPR.

---

7   See Chapter 4 for a detailed discussion of these requirements

8   See Section 4.2.15

9   An expert gives opinion only within his or her area of expertise – when dealing with issues that fall outside the expert's area of expertise, best practice is to recommend a referral to an expert in the appropriate speciality.

We set out the linear structure below and then discuss the key-elements of the structure:

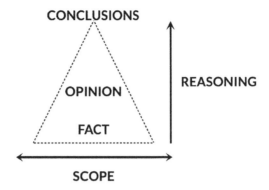

Instructions

The instructions received from the instructing solicitor by the expert define the scope of the report and from these the expert identifies all the expert issues that need to be addressed.

Expert should not go beyond the scope of the instructions without first agreeing amended instructions with the instructing solicitor. There are three reasons for this:

1. the issue that the expert considers to be important to report upon may not be part of the litigation – a typical issue is the concern that an expert may have about the standard of care provided to an accident victim in hospital - the legal ramifications of introducing a clinical negligence element into a personal injury claim are both practically and legally complex[10];

2. the issue may have been dealt with by another expert and the lawyer will not want, and will not want to pay for, another expert to deal with the same issue;

3. the issue may already have been agreed by the other side and there is no need for further evidence on the issue.

This is not to say that an expert who identifies an issue that falls outside his/her instructions should ignore the issue. Experts who raise issues with solicitors and seek instructions upon them are highly valued. Indeed, many solicitors include a "catch all" instruction at the end of their detailed instructions, such as:

> "Please identify and report on any other relevant issues."

---

10   See Section 7.9

The solicitor's instructions may be very concise, particularly in low-value cases:

"Please produce a condition and prognosis report on Mr Smith."

It is important for the report to state how the expert has interpreted the instruction:

I am instructed by Sue Quickly & Co to write a medical report on Mr Smith. I have interpreted this instruction as follows:

1. I am to interview Mr Smith and perform a medical examination;

2. I am to review Mr Smith's General Practitioner and Hospital records;

3. I am to identify any injuries Mr Smith has on presentation and give opinion, on the balance of probabilities, as to their causation;

4. I am to give a prognosis for any injuries that I consider are caused by the accident and where appropriate suggest further treatment to improve prognosis;

5. I am to give an opinion on the likely consequences arising from any such injuries and whether the consequences claimed by Mr Smith are reasonable and attributable to the accident; and

6. I am to set out my findings and conclusions in a report that complies with the requirements of CPR Part 35.

When the expert chooses to interpret a concise instruction, it is essential that the expert understands and can apply the legal tests relevant to the evidence, otherwise the expert needs to clarify the instructions with the instructing solicitor.

We set out below an example of an expert who is confused about the legal tests involved in reporting on an alleged breach of duty and who needed to clarify his instructions before writing the report:

I have been instructed to:

1. Give opinion on the standard of care reasonably to be expected of the treating clinicians;

2. Give opinion on whether the actions or omissions of the treating clinicians fell below the standard of care to be expected of reasonably competent clinicians;

3. Give opinion on whether the treating clinicians breached their duty of care to the claimant; and

4. Did any of the breaches of a duty of care cause damage to the claimant, and if so, what damage has resulted?

Clearly, the expert has misunderstood the legal issues in the case, with issues 2 & 3 dealing with the same legal issue in different language. This not only creates a lack of clarity by creating repetition in the evidence, but also encourages the expert to adopt the potentially dangerous drafting strategy of substituting words and phrases to make what is essentially the same information look as though it is saying something different. This kind of ambiguity is cross-examination heaven for a trial barrister and should be avoided by experts at all costs.

When the report deals with complex issues, it may help the reader to list the order of sections in the report, perhaps with a brief outline of what will be included in each section.

1.9   I have presented my evidence in the following sections:

    2. History of the Accident and Recovery
    3. Presenting Condition
    4. Medical History
    5. Examination
    6. Opinion and Prognosis
    7. Consequences of Injuries
    8. Summary of Conclusions

Factual Basis

The expert then presents the facts relevant to the issues that need to be addressed. The factual basis should not attempt to give added weight to particular facts, through the use of phrases such as, 'an important fact to note is…' and should not contain any fragmented expressions of opinion. The weight given to particular facts and analysis of the factual basis should form part of the opinion section in the report.

If there are facts that the expert considers to be significant, a more appropriate technique is to set out the issue to alert the lawyers to its importance and to give a cross-reference to where the expert deals with the issue in the report:

> The nursing staff did not carry out a second falls assessment when Mr Smith's mobility improved on 16 February 2014. I discuss the implications of this omission in Section 7.4.

Opinion

Each opinion in the report should be supported by reference to the factual matters relevant to the opinion and an explanation of how the expert has applied his/her mind to those facts to reach a conclusion. Each opinion expressed needs to apply the appropriate legal test.

In Appendix 1, we have set out five report templates for personal injury reports (physical/psychological), industrial disease, clinical negligence and care and other needs reports based on this linear structure. It may be helpful to look at these templates and the notes to the templates at this point, before moving on to the discussion of the modular report structure set out below.

11.2.2 Modular Report Structure

The linear structure of an expert report will work extremely well where the issues upon which the expert has been instructed to report share a common factual basis. However, where a report has to deal with issues that arise from separate factual bases or where the factual basis is extensive, the linear structure is often not the most efficient or effective way to present the evidence.

For example, consider a personal injury report that has to deal with a series of complex orthopaedic injuries, say to a claimant's spine, chest and right knee. It may be difficult for the lawyers to follow the evidence if the expert were to set out all of the facts for each of these specific injuries in turn, before returning to express opinions on the first, second and then the third injuries. This approach would mean that the factual account of the first injury to the spine and the opinion based on that factual account would be separated by the factual account relating to the second (chest) and third (right knee) injuries.

Beyond this, reporting on injuries to different structures in the body may involve different methodologies, in addition to having distinct factual sources for the expert's opinion evidence – for example, different radiology reports and scans. In attempting to deal with all these issues within a linear structure, the evidence may become difficult for both the lawyers who need to use the report prior to trial and for a judge at trial. We have already discussed the inherent danger of important issues being missed by the parties reading the report.

It is often more helpful to write a complex report using a modular structure:

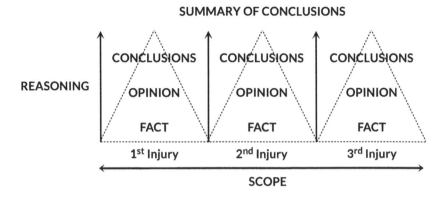

Using this structure, the three separate injuries can be dealt with in separate modules (one section for each module in the structure). The linear template would need to be modified to take account of the modular structure of the evidence:

1. **Introduction**

2. **History of the Accident and Recovery Period** (from the claimant)

3. **Presenting Condition** (from the claimant)

4. **Spinal Injuries**
   4.1 Methodology
      [...]
   4.2 Medical History (from medical records)
      [...]
   4.3 Examination
      [...]
   4.4 Opinion
      [...]

5. **Chest Injuries**
   5.1 Methodology
      [...]
   5.2 Medical History (from medical records)
      [...]
   5.3 Examination
      [...]
   5.4 Opinion
      [...]

6. **Right Knee Injury**
   6.1 Methodology

[...]
6.2 Medical History (from medical records)
[...]
6.3 Examination
[...]
6.4 Opinion
[...]

7. **Consequences of Injuries**

8. **Summary of Conclusions**

The only sections that remain outside the modular structure are: 'History of the Accident', 'Presenting Condition', 'Consequences of Injuries' and 'Summary of Conclusions'. These sections are common to all of the issues in the report. Note also the separation of fact and opinion within each module of the report.

The modular structure is often useful when dealing with clinical negligence cases. Many clinical negligence cases involve an extensive factual basis, perhaps involving separate episodes of treatment. It can be much more efficient to set out these separate treatment episodes as separate modules of the report, giving opinion and conclusions on each episode before moving on to the next. The advantage is, once again, keeping the factual basis and the opinion on each issue closer together in the report, thereby creating a logical flow and an ease of interpretation and use for the lawyers and the court. Care reports are also written using this modular structure.

11.2.3 Report Templates

Report templates should always facilitate the most efficient presentation of the expert's evidence to the court. As such, there is no model template that will deal with every case and it is essential that experts develop the necessary skill and confidence to create a new (or alter an existing) template, if the evidence in a case requires such.

Differentiation of Factual Sources

In creating a personal injury/industrial disease report template, a basic principle is to differentiate the different sources of the evidence that the expert is relying upon in producing the report. In a personal injury report, it is best to set out in separate sections those facts elicited from the claimant during the interview and examination, those facts from medical or other records, and the direct factual evidence from the expert's examination of the claimant. (In the case of mental state examinations, clearly there is no separation between interview and examination.) Care and therapeutic reports will be based upon the consequences of injury that the medical experts have identified combined with the direct evidence of the care and therapeutic experts when carrying out their own assessments of the claimant.

The differentiation of factual sources enables the expert to consider whether there are any factual conflicts between the different sources of factual information that the expert needs to address in the Opinion section of the report. The court is also able to assess the quality of an opinion by considering the credibility and reliability of the source(s) of the factual evidence on which the opinion is based, before moving on to consider how the expert has applied his/her mind and expertise to the facts drawn from these sources.

Narrative Approach

In a clinical negligence report template, rather than separating the different sources of information, the expert, by applying his/her expertise to the various sources of information, will set out his/her understanding of the chronology of events in the treatment history. Here, the principle is one of establishing a factual narrative of the likely chain of events, by bringing together facts from different sources of information – e.g. medical records, nursing notes, correspondence, treatment protocols and the witness statements of clinicians and family members. The expert should then reference the source of the information included in the narrative, either in the main text or by using footnotes.

11.2.4   Presenting Evidence in a Logical Order

A logical approach to presenting the factual basis of the evidence will increase the speed and quality of the lawyer's interpretation of the report. Much of the information in a medical expert report will be expressed using chronologies. In personal injury reports, the history of the accident and recovery will be a chronology given to the expert by the claimant, dealing with the period from the accident date to the examination date.   Similarly, the claimant's account of his/her medical history will also be presented as a chronology, as will the expert's review of the claimant's medical records. In addition to these chronologies, industrial disease claims may include chronologies of employment history and of the evidence relating to use of, or exposure to, the relevant agent(s). In care reports, the chronology from the accident date to the date of the assessment and for the future is usually broken into logical periods based on the type and extent of care needed in each period.

A past medical history or employment history that is not presented in chronological order is confusing, reflects poorly on the professionalism of the expert and is also very difficult to use should the report come to be used in court. It will be regarded by the lawyers and the judge as lazy, bad practice and possible evidence of a less than clear approach to the issues in the case. The use of tables or spreadsheets with automatic sort capabilities means that there is no excuse for a lack of a proper chronological order.

In cases with extensive records, where only a few records are of relevance to the issues in dispute, it may be easier to include copies of the relevant records in an appendix to the report and use the body of the report to provide a commentary on these entries, with appropriate cross-references and quotes from the records at key-moments in the chronology.

Care reports are often concerned with a wide-variety of issues required within the care package. The report will be easier to understand and use if the expert identifies the order in which evidence will be presented:

> In this report, I will assess the care package in the following sections:
>
> 2. Claimant's Pre-Injury Level of Function
> 3. Care and Assistance
> 4. Appliances, Aids and Equipment
> 5. Accommodation
> 6. Employment
> 7. Travel and Transportation
> 8 Extra-Household Expenditure
> 9. Holidays
> 10. Quantum

Relevance

The claimant's medical history need only detail issues relevant to the injuries and prognosis that are the subject of the claim, with other matters in the history being either omitted entirely or summarised very briefly:

> The following entries in the GP notes are relevant to my assessment of causation for the claimant's injuries:
>
> 1. 25 March 2004: presented with mild right sciatic pain. He was prescribed painkillers (Ibuprofen) and advised to rest for three days.
>
> 2. 4 Aug 2005: presented with lower backache following a weekend spent decorating. Advised to avoid any heavy lifting and to rest. No prescription given.

There is a benefit in providing an overview of other presentations in the medical history only where the expert intends to base opinions upon those presentations. For example, both orthopaedic experts and psychiatrists may wish to give details of a claimant's frequent attendance at his GP with minor health complaints - for the orthopaedic expert this may be a factor in his/her assessment of the likely period of recovery from an injury, while for the psychiatrist, this pattern of attendance may indicate pre-existing illness behaviour that is now expressing itself as a failure to recover from an injury. The context of the medical history in both of these examples may be important.

However, where entries in the records have no relevance to the claim, or where they merely confirm a negative (such as that there were no relevant attendances or indications of illness etc.) to save time and cost these should be omitted. The only benefit in including such details is to indicate that the expert has actually read the records. It is now sufficient to include in the methodology section of the report a description of the quantity of records considered in producing the report and how many hours the expert spent on considering the records. If there are problems with the quality of the records or the records are incomplete the expert should say so.

Using Chronologies in Clinical Negligence Reports

In clinical negligence, a chronology of events is the main component of the factual basis and central to the report. Omissions or inaccuracies in the chronology of events can have very serious consequences for a party as such mistakes speak to the professionalism of the expert and may undermine the basis for the opinions reached in the report.

Where there is little or no conflict between different sources of information, the chronology will be set out in date/time order within one section (here assuming a linear report structure/template). The sources of information – the clinical records and the witness statements – can be quoted at the key-moments in the chronology to illustrate the factual account.

Medical experts often have to deal with medical records that are incomplete or poorly written. When considering the case, the first task for the expert may be a laborious attempt to interpret each entry in the records. With extensive and poorly written records, this can be both time consuming and irritating, especially when many of the entries may be barely legible or even illegible. And having spent time on this task, there is an understandable temptation for experts to simply reproduce a summary of the entries in the records, rather than producing a concise account of the events that took place.

For the lawyers and the court, simply translating the records rather than providing a concise account of the events that were taking place is usually unhelpful. The lawyers and the court simply do not have the technical knowledge to be able to understand the importance or relevance of entries in the records, without guidance from the expert about what was actually happening and what these entries actually mean.

The best approach is to give a clear account of the chronology of events that would be accessible to a lawyer, quoting relevant entries from the records at the key moments in the treatment process. This account of the events must be accurate and when relating to contentious matters should include verbatim quotations from the records with explanations of the entries provided as required. It is very helpful to use the date (and where known and relevant to do so, the time) to begin paragraphs in the chronology of events or to use dates and times as subheadings. For ease of reference, it is also useful to include cross-references to the page numbers from the bundle of medical records where these page numbers exist. Important entries in the records should never be paraphrased and should always be quoted precisely.

In the example below, the expert chose to create a three-column presentation of the information. Although this is not a requirement (dates could be included as sub-headings with the chronology and page references included in brackets) this shows the expert is very aware of how the report will be used by the lawyers and the court and is responding to this with the layout of the report:

26.9.03	GP: Letter Mr W to GP: "Bypass continues to function well. She has once more resumed smoking."	Page 121
6.12.03	GP: Letter Mr W to GP: "Aorto-femoral bypass graft continues to function well. She is still smoking."	Page 122
15.3.05	GP: Letter Mr W to GP: "All pulses present. Doppler testing showed normal ankle/brachial pressure index. I am disappointed to find she is still smoking. Re-do arterial surgery or further more distal bypasses are always a problem in patients of this sort and may carry a life-threatening potential."	Page 164
	[A Doppler ultrasound test uses reflected sound waves to evaluate blood as it flows through a blood vessel. It helps doctors evaluate blood flow through the major arteries and veins of the arms, legs, and neck. It can show blocked or reduced blood flow caused by narrowing in the arteries.]	

When factual disputes about the chronology of events do occur, the expert has to consider whether these factual disputes can be set out clearly within one section dealing with the chronology of events or whether the sheer number of factual disputes means that evidence from the claimant and defendant witnesses needs to be addressed in separate sections – i.e. two sections dealing with the chronology of events, one each from the evidence of witnesses on each side. The expert's opinion on these factual conflicts should be dealt with in the Opinion section and not inserted in fragments throughout the factual basis of the report.

11.3 Expressing Opinions

Every opinion expressed in an expert report has to be based upon a detailed analysis of the available facts and must be supported by clear and informed reasoning. It is essential that experts develop the discipline of applying, and then setting out in the report, a logical thought process to support each opinion they express.

To ensure that each opinion is appropriately supported, it is essential for experts to develop the discipline of employing a structured approach to expressing opinions. This discipline also encourages the expert to adopt a careful and logical approach when considering the evidence in the first instance and is a useful way to avoid the temptation of jumping to a conclusion.

A 'rule of thumb' for opinion writing is that only one opinion should be expressed in each paragraph. A properly expressed opinion, including the relevant facts and an explanation of the underlying rationale will take at least a paragraph to write. A second opinion included in a paragraph is usually unsupported.

11.3.1 Owning an Opinion

The overriding duty of experts is to 'help the court on the matters within their expertise'[11]. Therefore, expert evidence is always the expression of an individual's opinion. This individual responsibility needs to be reflected in the grammar used when writing the opinion, which should be in the first-person singular - 'I' or 'my':

- In my opinion, Mr Jones suffered a ......
- I consider that the prior history of ... is not material to...
- My assessment of the claimant's situation is...
- On examination, my findings were...
- I conclude, therefore, that ...

Each of these phrases demonstrates in the grammatical use of the first person singular that the expert has applied his/her professional skill in expressing the opinion and is committed to it. When an expert chooses to use a less direct expression, lawyers often sense that the expert is unwilling to commit him/herself to the opinion.

Compare the following statements of opinion:

1. *It is considered* that the ongoing symptoms *are related* to the accident.

2. *I consider* that the ongoing symptoms *are caused* by the accident.

In the first example above, the use of the third person singular short passive construction 'it is considered' and the ambiguous phrase 'are related' when addressing causation indicates that the expert is either unwilling or unable to offer a firm opinion. This may or may not be the underlying reality, but it is on the words on the page that the parties and the court have ultimately to base their decisions. In the second example, using the first person singular active construction 'I consider' and addressing the legal test of causation correctly with the unambiguous verb phrase 'are caused by' creates a far stronger impression for the lawyers and the court.

---

11   See CPR 35.3(1) and Section 4.1.3

A more subtle way that experts communicate a lack of commitment to an opinion is with the use of the phrase 'In my view...' It is a phrase that often appears in expert reports as soon as difficult issues arise, where the phrase 'in my opinion' makes way for the less assertive phrase 'in my view'. This creates an impression that other views may also be valid and in an environment where the standard of proof is 'on the balance of probabilities' this can be very concerning for the party relying on the expert's evidence.

Another approach that suggests a lack of commitment is an opinion that emerges from negation:

> Therefore, it would *not be unreasonable* to conclude that *were it not* for the previous injury, his recovery would have been achieved more quickly.

Contrast this with a clear and positive expression of opinion:

> Therefore, I conclude that it is more likely than not that the previous injury extended the claimant's period of recovery by an additional 3-6 months.

11.3.2 Addressing the Standard of Proof and Relevant Legal Tests

In a civil case, a precise interpretation of an expert's opinion is only possible where the expert applies the civil standard of proof and the appropriate legal test to the opinion. From the lawyers' perspective, any opinion that does not lead to a clear conclusion – by the expert applying the appropriate legal test - is unusable in court unless or until it is correctly expressed.

Experts are expected to apply the civil standard of proof and the appropriate legal tests to each of their opinions. Experts should use the standard phrases from the source of the test[12] and should not vary these phrases, as this potentially causes confusion and delay or the need for the lawyers to seek clarification of the report from the expert.

---

12   See Chapters 5, 6 and 8 for a more detailed discussion of the legal principles and tests underlying medical expert reports

Standard Phrases for Civil Standard of Proof and Legal Tests

Standard of Proof	1. on the balance of probabilities…
	2. more probable than not…
	3. more likely than not…
Causation	1. the accident (incident or adverse event) caused the following injuries…
	2. in the absence of the accident the claimant would/would not have suffered…
	3. but for the accident the claimant would/would not have suffered…
Causation (material contribution test)	4. the contribution of the exposure was more than minimal
Consequences of Injuries	1. The following consequences are reasonable and are attributable to the accident…
	2. The following restrictions are medically supportable as resulting from injuries sustained in the accident…
Breach of Duty	1. No reasonably competent practitioner (define expertise/speciality) would have acted (or failed to act) in this manner at that time…
	2. The practitioner did not exercise a level of skill ordinarily to be expected of a… (define the practitioner) practising at that time…
	3. The actions of the doctor fell below the standard reasonably to be expected of a reasonably competent… (define the practitioner) at that time…

Some medical experts use the phrases 'index accident' or 'index event' in their reports. These are not legal terms, but lawyers understand that the expert is referring to the accident, incident or event that the expert has been instructed to consider. Often the term adds nothing, because there is no other non-index accident or non-index event.

In clinical negligence claims, the use of phrases such as 'sub-optimal' and 'substandard' is inherently difficult as these phrases have no legal meaning. Unfortunately, many instructing solicitors who do not appreciate the importance of giving clear and accurate instructions to experts use the phrase substandard as a short-hand description for the Bolam test. Experts should avoid the temptation to follow these less than competent instructions in this regard and should instead apply the Bolam test accurately[13].

Phrases for Expressing Opinion

ASSERTIVE PHRASES	WEAK PHRASES
In my opinion	In my view
I consider that	It is considered
I conclude	I think/feel
My findings were	I believe
My assessment is	I contend/submit[14]

Opinion Structures

An expert who does not justify an opinion with a clear rationale falls short of one of the basic requirements of expert evidence. The court needs to assess the basis of an opinion to test its soundness, before it can decide what weight to attach to the opinion in its consideration of the totality of evidence in the case.

When faced with such unsupported opinion, the consequence for the lawyers is that they are limited in their ability to properly assess the strengths and weaknesses of the case, which results either in additional correspondence with the expert to request clarification of the evidence or lower-quality decisions being made about progressing the case (i.e. making a Part 36 offer[15], settling the claim, or continuing to trial). We have also seen that such omissions may not come to light until cross-examination in court – a very uncomfortable place to discover an omission[16].

To improve the way opinion evidence is presented, we encourage experts to apply the same structure to every opinion they express. In this way, every opinion will be appropriately supported by the facts relevant to the opinion and by the expert's reasoning in moving from those relevant facts to reach the conclusion.

---

13   See Section 8.1

14   Bringing forward contentions and making submissions are the actions of counsel in court and these terms should not appear in an expert report.

15   See Section 2.8.5

16   See the discussion in Section 11.1

There are two basic structures available when expressing opinions:

11.3.3   Long-Form Opinion

- Topic

- Facts relevant to the opinion

- Reasoning process

- Conclusion (applying the appropriate legal test)

The long-form opinion structure is best suited to presenting any opinion that requires detailed analysis. It is the classic structure for presenting opinion in scientific writing and has the advantage of taking the lawyers and the court stage-by-stage through the reasoning process that the expert has used.

11.3.4   Short-Form Opinion

- Topic

- Statement of Opinion (applying the appropriate legal test)

- Justification of Opinion (reasons)

- Amplification (further explanation if required)

The short-form opinion structure is best suited to presenting straightforward opinions and is typically – though not entirely - found in low-value claims. It allows the expert to state the reasons for holding an opinion, rather than setting out the full reasoning. This allows the opinion and the basis for it to be written more concisely – which is extremely important given the proportionality principle which is seeking to limit the costs recoverable for expert evidence, particularly in low-value claims. The Short-Form Opinion is also extremely useful when producing advisory reports for a solicitor.

11.4 Expressing Opinions in Sequential Reports

The Guidance introduces new guidance on sequential reporting[17]. Sequential reporting is not new, being a feature of the pre-action protocol in industrial disease and illness claims, and its use has often been agreed between the parties or ordered by the court in a wide variety of personal injury claims.

---

17   See Section 4.2.13

The guidance essentially encourages the defendant's expert (in whichever discipline) to respond to the claimant expert's report[18]. This works well where there is common ground between the two experts as to the nature of the issues relevant to the case, even where there may be a wide-variation of opinion on these issues.

In one sense, the courts are encouraging the defendant expert to produce a report that takes on some of the features of a Joint Statement issued following a meeting of experts. This approach is clearly aimed at helping the lawyers to understand and concentrate upon the divergence of opinion between the experts at an earlier stage of the litigation process and so facilitate an early settlement of the case.

Problems arise, however, where the claimant and defendant experts disagree fundamentally on the nature of the issues or where the claimant expert's report is poorly produced and the defendant expert is left with the unenviable task of sorting out the mess. In this latter circumstance, there is a danger that experts who are faced with a poorly produced claimant's report simply choose to agree the report rather than spend time trying to untangle the mess.

Approach to Producing Sequential Reports

When responding to an order from the court for a sequential report to be produced, the first task of the defendant expert is to check that the factual basis of the report is agreed or to indicate where additional facts need to be taken into account or where facts included in the claimant's report are irrelevant.

The defendant expert should then identify and list all of the issues on which the claimant expert has expressed opinion and state agreement or disagreement with the claimant expert's opinion. Where there is disagreement the defendant expert needs to express his/her own opinion and the basis for the contrary opinion.

Although the Guidance requires the defendant expert to 'identify those assumptions … that they consider reasonable … and those they do not'[19] there is no requirement on the defendant expert to explain the difference, though it will clearly help the lawyers if such an explanation is offered. If the basis of the claimant expert's opinion is unclear to the defendant expert, it is appropriate to give this opinion without speculating as to the possible reasons for the divergence of opinion.

As the defendant has the opportunity to see the claimant expert's evidence before providing any of its own, there may be a temptation on the part of the defendant lawyers to invite the defendant's expert not to 'give away' anything in his/her report that has not been raised in the claimant's report. This issue seems to be most prevalent in quantum reports dealing with, for example, the care packages

---

18   Clearly, there are situations where a claimant expert may be instructed after reports have been obtained from both claimant and defendant experts and so may be producing a sequential report when instructed by the claimant. However, for ease of explanation, we will address the more common situation of a defendant responding to a claimant report.

19   Guidance para 63(b)

for severely injured claimants where the defendant expert may recommend more care than is being claimed by the claimant's care experts.

It is the duty of the defendant's expert to help the court on the matters within his or her expertise[20] and to write a report which is independent, a useful test of which is that the expert would express the same opinion if given the same instructions by another party[21]. It is, therefore, self-evident to say that the defendant expert's role is not to gold-plate the claimant's claim, but is rather to assess the claim to see whether it is reasonable (a legal test) and that the items claimed are attributable (a legal test) to the alleged breach of duty.

A reasonable approach is indicated in such situations. So long as the items claimed in the claimant's report fall within the range of reasonable opinions on the matter, then the defendant expert is entitled to agree the items without generating additional evidence – and expense for the parties - on the point. However, where the claimant's expert has included or omitted items that fall outside the range of reasonable opinions – whether this increases or decreases the quantum of the claim - it is the expert's duty to include opinion on these items, whether the solicitor is happy with the outcome or not.

The lawyers for a party may not always understand the expert's duty to the court and the implications of this duty in such situations. We have heard examples of inappropriate phone conversations between lawyers and the experts they have instructed, but an expert's duty to the court is a fundamental principle of being an expert witness and cannot be compromised when providing a report under the CPR for use in proceedings.

11.5 Expressing Opinions in Quantum Reports

A major criticism of quantum reports is that too much of the expert's time is spent producing schedules for the costs involved in the care of the claimant, while little time is spent explaining the basis for the expert's opinion of the care package.

The rationale that underlies the assessment of a claimant's care or therapeutic needs must be clearly explained to the court. If the matter comes to trial, it is highly likely that the differences between the parties are not related to the rate applied to items in the care package, but is in fact concerned with whether such items are necessary at all or whether some other approach to care would be more appropriate. The purpose of reports that deal with quantum issues is not simply to calculate costs, but to explain to the court why the care package indicated is necessary, appropriate and reasonable and, so far as is practicable, places the claimant back in the position that he/she would have been in 'but for' the accident.

This requires the expert to set out the basis for the opinion – the facts that have been taken into account and the assumptions that have been made in developing

---

20   CPR 35.3(1) and see Section 4.1.2

21   Guidance para 11 and see Section 4.1.3

the care package (or some aspect of it). There needs to be a much clearer description of the methodology adopted in establishing the factual basis for the care package which needs to include:

1. assessing the claimant's pre-injury level of function;

2. assessing the claimant's present level of function and the likely progression for the future (i.e. based on the witness statements/expert reports);

3. the practitioner's direct observations of the claimant's level of function (through practical testing and general observation);

4. the difference the accident has made and the evidence base on which the quantification of this difference is to be assessed; and

5. the rationale that supports the recommendation for care or incurring of costs.

In reports dealing with quantum issues, the expert instructed by the defendant should now conclude his/her report by producing a summary of the schedules of the claimant and defendant experts, indicating where items in the schedule are agreed and where there are differences, with a cross-reference to the relevant para graphs in each report so that the lawyers can analyse the differences[22].

Sequential Reports (Example)

Category	Claimant			Defendant			Reason for Difference
Personal Care Items	Ref	Cost (£)	Replacement Period	Ref	Cost (£)	Replacement Period	
Shower	7.44	3000	10 years	6.13	1750	10 years	A new wet room is not required, though adjustments to the shower are required
Body Dryer	7.54	700	5 years	6.27	0		In discussion with the Mr Smith, he said he would not use this system
Customised Storage Units	7.15	1000	10 years	6.65	1000	15 years	Agree cost. Disagree replacement period.

---

22 Depending on the complexity of the case, it may be necessary to break the summary table into sections dealing with different aspects of the care package, using different headings in the table to reflect the type of costs that need to be summarised.

11.6 Writing Skills

When producing expert evidence, it is essential that experts achieve accuracy and precision in their use of language. We identify five writing disciplines that all experts should seek to develop:

1. writing for the court;

2. providing technical explanation;

3. using descriptive language;

4. using modal auxiliary verbs; and

5. addressing the standard of proof and relevant legal tests.

11.6.1 Writing for the Court

Expert reports are written for a non-medically qualified legal readership of solicitors, barristers and judges. The claimant will also be shown the report (save in exceptional cases). The medical language that a doctor uses when talking to other doctors will generally be confusing or misleading to a legal readership, unless such language is defined and where necessary explained.

A medical expert may assume the level of expertise in the lawyers and the court of an 'informed layperson'. We would characterise this person as being a reasonably intelligent professional, with a good education and mental faculties, but who does not have detailed medical or technical knowledge on the issues on which the expert gives opinion. A typical lawyer is reasonably well-educated and intelligent (at least, most would like to think so), but cannot be expected to have any medical expertise save that gained from reading a variety of medical expert reports, personal experience of medical matters and from watching medical dramas on television. This limitation applies equally to therapeutic and care disciplines.

11.6.2 Providing Technical Explanations

Where technical issues move beyond the understanding to be expected of a layperson, explanations of such technical matters are usually required. It is essential that the instructing lawyers understand the words on the page, but more important is that they understand the significance of the words on the page in relation to the matters in dispute.

It is not the expert's role to attempt to provide an extensive technical education for the lawyers, but it is critical to the expert's role to delineate the technical issues relevant to the dispute and to make sure these issues are explained sufficiently that the lawyers can make appropriate settlement decisions or argue the case in court.

The basic approach to giving a medical explanation suitable for the lawyers is to adopt a four-stage structure:

1. introduce the topic;

2. explain the basic technical facts;

3. amplify with essential detail; and

4. explain the relevance of the issue to the facts of the case.

We set out three examples of medical explanations that lawyers would consider useful in an appropriate case:

Explanation: Glasgow Coma Scale

An expert may begin the explanation of the 'Glasgow Coma Scale' by introducing the issue with a 'headline sentence' - a reasonably short sentence that introduces the topic to be explained:

> The 'Glasgow Coma Scale' (GCS) is widely used by clinicians as an assessment tool to make an initial assessment of the severity of a patient's brain dysfunction.

The expert can then move on to explain the basic medical facts that the lawyer will need to grasp to understand the GCS, without introducing any unnecessary detail or complexity:

> A treating clinician when using the GCS will observe the level of responsiveness of the patient after initial resuscitation, by assessing the patient's ability to perform three basic functions:
>
> 1. eye opening
>
> 2. motor response (i.e. ability to move)
>
> 3. verbal response.
>
> The clinician then compares his/her observations of the patient against the criteria set for each of the three functions within the GCS and awards a score for each function. The minimum possible total score is 3 and the maximum is 15. A score below 10 suggests a serious dysfunction, with a score of 7 or lower indicating coma.

Once the basic medical facts have been presented, the expert can then decide whether it is necessary to move to a greater level of detail:

> The scales for scoring each function are as follows:
>
> 1. <u>eye opening</u>: a maximum of 4 points for spontaneous response and a minimum of 1 for none;
>
> 2. <u>motor response</u>: a maximum of 6 for obeying commands and a minimum of 1 for none;
>
> 3. <u>verbal response</u>: a maximum of 5 for being orientated and a minimum of 1 for no orientation.
>
> Using the GCS allows a rudimentary assessment of outcome to be made at an early stage and enables any improvement or deterioration in the patient's function over time to be monitored more closely by the clinical team.

The expert must then explain the relevance of the explanation to the facts in the case:

> 'In this case, the claimant was scored at 10. This indicates that...'

Explanation: Personality Disorder

The following explanation of 'personality disorder' follows the same approach as above:[23]

> Personality disorder is a deeply ingrained and maladaptive pattern of behaviour that persists through many years. [**Headline**]
>
> The diagnosis is made where the abnormality of behaviour is severe enough to cause mental and emotional suffering or anguish for the person suffering with the disorder and/or other people. The abnormality of behaviour is generally apparent by the adolescent years. Some people with a personality disorder are able to mature into happier adults, but most have to endure the disorder for years or even decades. [**Explanation**]
>
> Psychotherapy in a variety of forms is considered to be of therapeutic value for people with personality disorder, although there is no clear evidence that any psychotherapeutic intervention is of particular benefit. Given the variety of patterns of behaviour that the diagnosis can encompass, this lack of clear evidence is perhaps unsurprising. [**Amplification**]

---

23   In creating this explanation we have drawn on information in the *Oxford Concise Medical Dictionary* - 4th Edition (1994).

The impact of these patterns of behaviour on an injured person's ability to recover from an accident is difficult to assess. Each injured person responds differently to injury even in the absence of any psychiatric or psychological issues. However, the coping mechanisms of people with personality disorders are often far more brittle than those of most people and they find adjusting to their new reality more challenging. Also, their ability to come to terms with what has happened to them and so adjust successfully to a future with physical restrictions is often diminished by their patterns of abnormal behaviour. In this case... [**Relevance to case**]

Explanation: Ankylosing Spondylitis

Below, we set out a third example, again using the same approach:

'Ankylosing spondylitis' is an inflammatory and progressive degenerating condition of the spine. [**Headline**]

This condition manifests in two stages. The first stage involves inflammation of the synovial joints, which includes the joint capsules and their attached ligaments and tendons. This inflammatory process is known as 'spondylitis'. In the second stage, a degenerative process leading to the fusion of the vertebrae occurs. This degenerative process is termed 'ankylosis'. The condition can lead to severe deformities of the spine, loss of extension and a bent forward posture. [**Explanation**]

The condition predominantly affects young men. It usually commences in the sacroiliac joints in the lower spine, which are located beneath the lumbar vertebrae and above the coccyx. The condition results in pain and stiffness and treatment is by analgesics, anti-inflammatory drugs and regular daily exercises. In severe cases, where the bent forward posture becomes too great, it may be necessary to perform an 'osteotomy' of the spine, an operation to separate and realign fused joints. [**Amplification**]

In this case, the MRI scan of the claimant's spine indicates that he had a pre-existing condition of ankylosing spondylitis. This means that without the accident, he would in any event have been experiencing pain and stiffness. Since the accident, he reports ... [**Relevance to case**]

Notice that the explanations are sufficient to enable the lawyers to understand the significance of the issue in the case, without going too far into the detail of the condition. It may be that as a case develops, further explanation may be required, particularly where experts disagree as to the diagnosis or its relevance to the dispute. The instructing solicitor will advise the expert should this be required.

Accuracy and Precision

An essential discipline of writing evidence is to ensure that all the language in the report is used with accuracy and precision. This includes the use of technical language, quotations from sources, descriptive language and legal tests. The basic discipline is that the expert should write in a style that enables the lawyers and the court to establish an accurate and precise interpretation of the evidence.

Medical expert witnesses can assume that the lawyers reading their reports will be able to understand technical evidence where information is presented logically and with appropriate explanation. We have already quoted the GMC Guidance as to the use of language and terminology that will be readily understood by lawyers and the court[24].

When producing a report, care should be taken to facilitate the lawyers' ease of understanding by avoiding the use of undefined technical medical language. Such undefined technical language, in any area of expertise, will generally be too difficult for the lawyers unless it is clearly explained in lay terms. Experts often stray from this approach.

When using technical language, the best approach is to define the first use of a technical term in a footnote or a bracket. It is often helpful to italicise the first use of a term. If there is a large number of technical terms in the report, bringing these terms together in a glossary is often helpful. The report should identify in the Introduction section where the glossary is to be found - the glossary can either be placed in an appendix or placed directly after the contents page for ease of use by the lawyers and the court.

The examples below illustrate language that most lawyers would find **unhelpful** were no explanation of the terms to be given:

This treatment is likely to be associated with less morbidity.

The left eye had an uncorrected visual acuity of 6/9 part improving to 6/5 +2 or 6/4 part with -0.75/+0.25 x 160.

The patient was offered a sub-talar arthrodesis.

Her other problems include instability of her INR resulting sometimes in very high levels.

---

24   See Section 4.1.1

> ... Mr Q has post-traumatic cerebral arachnoiditis with formation of posttraumatic cysts in both frontal lobes and in the right parietal lobe of the encephalon with stable cephalic, vestibuloatactic, and asthenovegetative syndrome.

In personal injury reports, lawyers are familiar with terms like 'soft tissue injury' or 'muscular ligamentous injury', but defining 'cervical spine' is probably helpful. Some medical experts would simply substitute 'neck' for 'cervical spine'. In other less familiar disciplines, there is a greater need to define terms.

One exception from the general rule about defining terms is the use of technical language in the examination section of a report. In this section, the expert can simply set out the Examination findings, which can then be presented at the beginning of the Opinion section as a list of injuries that need to be addressed.

Most lawyers would find the following language **helpful** as terms are simply explained:

> The surgeon offered the patient an operation to fuse the bones in the foot, known as a sub-talar arthrodesis.

> Her other problems include unstable and sometimes very high readings of INR [International Normalised Ratio is a measurement for the effectiveness of anticoagulation of the blood], a high reading being indicative of a high chance of bleeding.

> Reviews of the scans and clinical examination showed a Le Fort I/II type pyramidal fracture of the mid-face [broken facial bones including the hard palate, maxilla and cheek bones]

Expert reports are technical reports written for a non-technical readership, so a balance has to be struck between simplifying technical language to aid comprehension of the report and using technical language to maintain accuracy. This is a matter of style and experts develop their own approach to reflect their individual writing style, the difficulty of the technical issues in the report and the likely familiarity of the lawyers with the technical issues.

Particularly in more serious or complex cases, the use of defined technical language is more helpful to the lawyers than attempts at substitution with simplified phrases. Defined technical language helps the lawyers to delineate the medical issues in dispute and facilitates the comparison of reports from different experts in the case. Defined technical language also helps the lawyers to communicate with each other about the medical issues, once they have grasped the essential concepts in the dispute. The key is for the expert to make sure that when using technical language, it is easy to understand by defining and where necessary explaining issues in the report.

Lawyers tend to develop a greater level of technical knowledge in the disciplines with which they are most familiar. Owing to their familiarity with road traffic accident claims, lawyers are generally more comfortable with orthopaedic reports on neck and back injuries than with reports in less common disciplines. Where appropriate, it is helpful for experts to provide good-quality visual elements in the appendices to their reports to help the lawyers to understand the evidence. A clear diagram of relevant anatomical structures or a photograph – perhaps dealing with scar tissue - will usually help the lawyers to grasp the importance of what the expert is attempting to communicate in the text.

Some lawyers do specialise in particular areas of injury – for example, brain injury or industrial diseases – where the specific requirements of the claim demand a greater level of medical knowledge and understanding on the part of the lawyers. Lawyers with a particular interest in clinical negligence claims are also likely to come within this category. However, in all disciplines, the standard of knowledge reasonably to be expected of instructing lawyers and the court remains that of 'an informed layperson'.

The lack of awareness amongst medical experts as to the technical abilities of their readership would perhaps be remedied if medical experts had to spend an afternoon interpreting legal text:[25]

> 31.—(1) Except where paragraph (2) applies, a payment of income to which regulation 29 (calculation of earnings derived from employed earner's employment and income other than earnings) applies shall be treated as paid—
>
> (a) in the case of a payment which is due to be paid before the first benefit week pursuant to the claim, on the date on which it is due to be paid;
>
> (b) in any other case, on the first day of the benefit week in which it is due to be paid or the first succeeding benefit week in which it is practicable to take it into account.
>
> (2) Income support, unemployment benefit, sickness or invalidity benefit, or severe disablement allowance under the Social Security Act shall be treated as paid on the day of the benefit week in respect of which it is paid.

---

25   In this case Regulation 31 of the Income Support (General) Regulations 1987

11.6.3 Using Descriptive Language

Any descriptive language in a medical expert report must be capable of being quantified by a lawyer, so that an accurate assessment of loss can be made:

> Mrs H experiences some discomfort in her right wrist.

It is impossible for the lawyer to interpret with any confidence the expert's use of the noun phrase 'some discomfort'. The expert must attempt to make the situation clear by dealing with both the severity and the frequency of the symptoms:

> Mrs H experiences discomfort in her right wrist. She describes this discomfort as "a dull aching sensation", which she experiences several times each day. She says that she particularly feels this sensation when she rotates her wrist rapidly or when she grips heavy items, such as her shopping bags.

Medical experts often adopt negation as a form of description. However, the example below illustrates the difficulties that arise:

> It is not uncommon for patients to experience pain and discomfort for several months following a bony injury to the wrist.

Here the adjective 'uncommon' (to denote the absence of this quality) is negated to form the adjective phrase 'not uncommon'. The lawyer's attempt at interpreting this phrase would likely be that the situation does not occur often enough to be described as common (def. occurring often) nor so rarely as to be uncommon (def. out of the ordinary) – leaving 'not uncommon' to fall someway between these two extremities.

In reality, the lawyer probably does not have the first idea what frequency of occurrence 'common' or 'uncommon' actually represents, leading to a ragged guess at the interpretation the expert actually intends the lawyer to make. Alternatively, the lawyer may simply draft a letter to the expert to seek clarification. Once again, the description should be quantified either by reference to literature or from professional experience:

In my clinical experience, following a bony injury to the wrist, approximately 10-15% of patients will continue to experience ongoing pain and discomfort for up to 12 months after the removal of the plaster cast. These patients use analgesics, such as Ibuprofen, to relieve their symptoms of pain. In the majority of these patients, symptoms settle with time and they make a full recovery. However, in approximately 5% of all cases, the pain and discomfort does not resolve.

The symptoms described by Mr P seem to me to be consistent with the type and severity of pain and symptoms described to me by patients in my clinical practice whose pain and symptoms do not resolve with time. I therefore consider that Mr P's ongoing complaints of pain are attributable to the accident and are unlikely to resolve.

The need to be specific is also undermined by overly brief descriptions that the medical expert may consider to be correct, but that may still mislead the lawyer:

Mr S will now go on to make a gradual recovery.

The lawyer may interpret this to mean that the recovery will be full, even though the word 'full' is omitted. The end point of recovery should also be defined or described. It is helpful for the expert to spell out, using simple and pragmatic language, the meaning he/she intends to communicate to the lawyers:

Mr S will go on to make a gradual recovery, but will not return to his pre-accident level of function. It is unlikely that he will be able to return to his former employment as a fitter, involving as it does frequent heavy lifting and walking over rough ground. However, he will be able to carry out most kinds of work of a lighter nature that do not require excessive lifting or repeated bending.

Similarly, the lawyer may have little appreciation of the normal effects of particular injuries or procedures on an individual. Medical expressions may not convey the reality of the condition or injury, meaning that the lawyers may not understand the impact or the potential impact on the claimant, thereby misjudging the value of the claim:

Mr T fractured 5 ribs and felt discomfort from the injury for a month.

This may be better and more fairly described as:

> Mr T fractured 5 ribs. Typically, this results in intense pain for several weeks and interferes with breathing and coughing, hence the need in his case for substantial pain relief. The consequent severe chest infection, for which he was briefly admitted to hospital, would almost certainly not have occurred or have been significant but for the impact of the fractures on his ability to breathe and cough.

The importance of providing a full explanation is also illustrated by the following opinion:

> Mrs J is left with a permanent tracheostomy.

This may be better and more usefully described as:

> Mrs J is left with a permanent tracheostomy. A tracheostomy provides direct access to the trachea [wind pipe] by surgically making an opening in the neck. Once an opening is made, it needs to be maintained by the insertion of a tracheostomy tube. This is a most unpleasant, embarrassing and sociably devastating complication. On a day-to-day basis, the effects that Mrs J will have to deal with are…

Where the expert uses technical scales or technical scoring to quantify the description of a state - such as Pain Rating Scales, Apgar Scoring or Reference Intervals – an explanation of the scale or scoring should be included in the report, either placed in the main text or appended to the report with an appropriate cross-reference.

11.6.4 Using Modal Auxiliary Verbs

In English, modal auxiliary verbs are used to express aspects of 'modality', such as: ability, duty, likelihood, necessity, obligation, permission and volition.

Most native speakers of English are familiar with the distinction between questions such as: "May I get up from the table?" and "Can I get up from the table?" Each question addresses a different aspect of modality: 'may' addresses permission ("Do I have permission to get up from the table?") while 'can' addresses ability ("Am I physically able to get up from the table?").

However, very few native speakers pay much attention to the use of the modal auxiliary verbs in respect of probability. This aspect of modality is fundamental in expert reports, especially so when expressing opinions.

In English, the modal auxiliary verbs are:

> May/Might
> Can/Could
> Will/Would
> Shall/Should
> Must
> Ought.

In respect of likelihood, the modal auxiliary verbs 'may' and 'can' along with the past tense and conditional 'might' and 'could' are used to express possible occurrences. The modal auxiliary verb 'will' is used to express a (highly) probable occurrence ('would' being the conditional form); 'shall' and 'must' deal with the modalities of duty and obligation.

It is essential that experts use the appropriate modal auxiliary verb to communicate clearly their opinion on likelihood – i.e. possibility and probability. Consider the following extract from a clinical negligence report on the actions of an ENT surgeon. Pay particular attention to the use of the modal auxiliary verbs:

> To proceed with a surgical procedure without access to such an investigation is negligent. Had the scans been scrutinised prior to the surgery it is possible that the surgeon would have identified the defect within the bony orbital wall. The surgical approach may therefore have been more cautious and the identification of orbital fat may have occurred earlier in the surgical procedure.

The expert describes the actions of the surgeon as 'negligent'. We have already addressed the potential difficulties of medical experts placing themselves in the judge's role, rather than simply applying the Bolam test[26] and this is an illustration of this error. However, it is the clause that begins 'it is possible' and the subsequent use in the next sentence of 'may' that creates an immediate contradiction in the evidence. For, if it is only possible that:

1. the defect within the bony orbital wall would have been identified prior to the surgery;

2. the surgical approach may have been more cautious; and

3. the identification of orbital fat may have occurred earlier;

then, on the balance of probabilities, looking at the CT scan prior to the operation would not have made any difference to the ultimate outcome.

---

26   See Section 8.1.1

Were a court to make its decision based on this expert evidence alone, there could be no finding of negligence (in law) against the surgeon, even though the expert has expressed an opinion that the treatment is in fact negligent. Note also that the expert does not deal fully with the 'but for' situation (i.e. what difference would there have been in the ultimate outcome without this omission on the part of the surgeon?).

Another aspect of modality that creates difficulty is 'obligation'. Consider the interpretative difficulties that arise for the lawyers in the following extract from a report on the death of a patient following an operation to realign a fractured femur:

> At this point, Mr B had a low-grade pyrexia, which should have indicated to the treating clinicians the possibility of an embolism and DVT prophylaxis should have been commenced immediately.

Simply using the modal auxiliary 'should' is never sufficient when an expert needs to apply the Bolam test. In medical practice, a lot of things 'should happen', but the court will seek to address the question as to whether the failure to begin DVT prophylaxis represented a standard of care that fell below the standard reasonably to be expected of the treating clinicians in those circumstances and at that time, such that no reasonably competent clinicians would have acted, or failed to act, in that manner. The Bolam test was not applied correctly in this report and so the expert's opinions would have needed to be clarified before it would have been useful to the lawyers and the court.

11.7 Presentation of the Report

Producing a well-presented expert report is extremely important. The lawyer's first impression of the report will be the initial frame through which the report is read and the primary aim of the expert should be to produce a report that is attractively presented and easy to read, assimilate and use.

Beyond the requirement in the CPR that expert evidence is to be presented in the form of a written report, there are no formal requirements in respect of report presentation. We offer basic guidance below for the presentation of an expert report.

We suggest that an expert report has the following elements included in its layout:

1. wide-margins (min 3cm);

2. appropriate font size (11-13pt depending on the font selected);

3. double-spaced text;

4. numbered paragraphs and pages;

5.   consistent presentation of section, main and sub-headings;

6.   numbered lists (rather than bullet points);

7.   appropriate page-header (claimant's name/case reference number/type of report/author/date); and

8.   single-sided text.

Each element of the layout increases the ease with which lawyers can use the report: wide margins mean that when the report is bound, the paragraph numbers are still visible and that there is space for the lawyer's notes; an appropriate font and size such as 'Times New Roman' 12pt is easy to read; double-spacing allows underlining and notes to be made on the text; numbered paragraphs make discussion of (and reference to) the report easier, as does the practice of numbering lists; page headers deal with the problem of pages that become detached from the report, while single-sided text allows extensive notes to be made on the facing blank page of the report and also avoids a myriad of photocopying problems.

Conclusion

The courts require expert reports to be written in a clear, concise and reliable manner. There is a clear trend for the courts to be seeking reports that are shorter and are more focussed on the issues relevant to the dispute, with the emphasis on explaining the basis of the expert's opinion and the precise application of the appropriate legal tests to the evidence.

Expert reports bring both factual and opinion evidence to the court. In personal injury and industrial disease claims, a report must address the key medico-legal aspects such as causation of injury, prognosis and the consequences that arise from the accident. In clinical negligence claims, the parties must also instruct experts to deal with the additional issue of breach of duty. Opinion evidence must be dealt with in its own section(s) and should not be fragmented by placing opinions within the factual basis of the report.

The new guidance in respect of sequential reports seems to be a sensible attempt to clarify expert issues earlier in the process and so avoid generating unnecessary additional issues and costs in the dispute. By giving opinion in the light of the claimant's report, the defendant expert is able to delineate where the experts agree and disagree and may be able to make clear to the lawyers the basis of any disagreement.

In quantum reports the rationale that underlies the assessment of a claimant's care or therapeutic needs must be clearly explained. The purpose of the quantum reports is not simply to calculate costs, but to explain to the court why the care package indicated is reasonable and places the claimant back in the position that he/she would have been in 'but for' the accident.

Key-Point Summary

1. The courts are seeking more concise and focussed reports that deal with all the issues in dispute, without resorting to the repetition of evidence contained in other expert reports previously produced in the case.

2. An essential skill of an expert witness is to ensure that the solicitor's instructions are clear and do not focus on irrelevant issues.

3. The required structure of an expert report separates the factual basis of the evidence from the opinions expressed by the expert - the factual basis should not contain opinion evidence and the facts set out in the report should be material to the issues on which the expert gives opinions.

4. Standard report templates are offered as a guide to help experts to present their evidence clearly and concisely; however, experts need to be alert to the reality that a particular case may require a specific template to be created to communicate the evidence more clearly.

5. Every opinion must be expressed with reference to the civil standard of proof and the appropriate legal test.

6. Sequential reports are an attempt to delineate differences in the expert opinions in a case at an earlier stage.

7. Experts producing quantum reports need to make sure that they are presenting a clear rationale for the opinions they express.

8. All language used in an expert report needs to be accurate and precise and be accessible to a non-medically qualified readership.

9. Experts need to take particular care when using descriptive language and modal auxiliary verbs to ensure that the intended meaning will be clear to the lawyers and the court.

10. High-quality report presentation is an important aspect of the report, enabling the lawyers and the court to use the report more easily and efficiently.

Next Steps

In the next chapter, we will discuss some of the important practical issues that arise in medico-legal work.

12

Practical Concerns in Expert Witness Practice

Introduction

The marketplace for medico-legal reports in civil claims is entering a period of fundamental change. Lord Justice Jackson's 'Review of Civil Litigation Costs' (see Section 3.1.2) was a response to the widespread concern over the high cost of civil litigation. This concern became aligned with the political controversy over rising car insurance premiums related to whiplash claims and the perception that fraudulent claims were being made on an industrial scale.

12.1 Financial Pressures on Lawyers

The Ministry of Justice has responded to the Jackson Report by transforming the way litigation costs are structured at the outset of a case and crucially, from the lawyers' perspective, by the extension of fixed fees regimes for processing Fast Track cases.

The fixed fees payable for injury claims in the Fast Track, which contains the more straightforward lower-value cases and therefore the greatest proportion of the medico-legal marketplace (i.e. claims valued at up to £25K), have undermined the business models of many legal firms who had established themselves as personal injury specialists. Many legal firms have seen a significant reduction of fee income resulting from the fixed fee regime and many firms have withdrawn from the marketplace for lower value claims (£1,000-10,000) and claims that require investigation or complex legal arguments.

The reduction in fees recoverable means that instructing solicitors are looking for ways to increase their margins. One approach has to been to push the work on to more junior lawyers, allowing legal firms to cut the costs involved in running the claims. Another approach has been to seek out higher value cases that have a higher percentage chance of a successful outcome. A third approach has been to seek to reduce the fees paid to experts, either before instructing the expert or after a settlement has been achieved.

Even as the personal injury marketplace is struggling to adapt to the changes to CPR post-Jackson, experts remain essential in the process. It is important to remember that without the support of experts for the claim being made, the court is highly unlikely to decide in the claimant's favour. Many medical experts have also developed an active role in helping instructing lawyers to identify viable higher value claims, through the provision of advisory (screening) reports.

12.2 Instructing Experts in Fast Track Cases (See also Sections 3.4.3 and 3.7.4)

The selection of experts in soft-tissue injury RTA claims is now handled through "MedCo", which intends to provide a panel of accredited[1] medical experts, specialising in the assessment of soft-tissue injuries. Using an online system, MedCo offers instructing solicitors a choice of randomly selected experts and a choice between instructing an expert directly or by selecting a "Medical Reporting Organisation" or "MRO" (essentially a Medico-Legal Agency) to provide a suitable expert to report on the claim.

---

1   The deadline for experts to be accredited under the MedCo accreditation scheme is January 2016, though at the time of writing (June 2015) there are few firm details as to what this accreditation will involve. It seems likely that the accreditation will in fact be limited to the expert successfully completing an online multiple-choice test.

Experts who are instructed via the MedCo portal – whether instructed directly by a solicitor or through an MRO – provide their reports for a fixed fee[2], with the vast majority of these claims being handled by GPs, junior doctors and latterly by physiotherapists.

A number of issues arise for experts involved in MedCo. Those who previously ran busy medico-legal practices producing a high volume of reports (whether by working through medico-legal agencies or by having established relationships with instructing solicitors, or both) are seeing a reduction in instructions as the available work is spread around a larger pool of experts. There is therefore less certainty as to the fees that will be earned by such experts and the provision of services to support the expert (medical secretaries, consulting rooms and marketing) becomes more difficult to plan.

At the same time, for those experts who are now gaining instructions directly from solicitors, there has been a substantial uplift in fees that the expert is earning per report, as in many cases the MROs have effectively been taken out of the intermediate position in the relationship between the solicitor and the expert. Additionally, experts are for the first time able to see the level of fee that the MRO is being paid and as a consequence of this transparency, what percentage of this fee is being paid to the expert and what percentage is being retained by the MRO.

Even for those experts who choose to work through MROs, the greater transparency regarding fees seems likely to allow experts to assert themselves more and rebalance the commercial relationship with the MRO. We would expect those experts who had in the recent past been paid very low fees for reporting – we have heard of fees as low as £25 per report being offered to some GP experts - would now be willing to seek better financial arrangements elsewhere in the marketplace or to establish their own medico-legal practice directly with instructing solicitors using MedCo as the interface.

Since the publication of the first edition, the authors of this text have consistently encouraged medico-legal agencies and lawyers to promote this book to the experts on their books, in order to raise the standards of medico-legal reports. The response, particularly from the medico-legal agencies whose focus is whiplash claims, has been underwhelming. As one senior executive of a medico-legal agency commented, "Quality is not on our agenda."

Although we have always found this attitude difficult to grasp, there is little if any doubt that the quality of reports from experts instructed through medico-legal agencies in the whiplash marketplace has remained stubbornly poor. The medico-legal agencies that have taken quality seriously have been those who are involved in higher value personal injury, industrial disease and clinical negligence claims, where the importance of a high-quality report has been an easier concept to grasp.

---

2   See Section 3.7.4

With the opening up of the market for low-value claims that MedCo has created, and particularly as instructions are now shared out amongst a larger pool of experts, we expect that over the coming months and years the quality of reporting will finally be on everyone's agenda – individual experts, MROs and instructing lawyers alike. It seems clear that there are now new opportunities for independent experts who want to establish viable medico-legal practices based on high-quality reporting and this competition is slowly releasing the hold that the MROs have had on the low-value claims marketplace.

12.3 Cost Budgeting
(See also Sections 2.8.9 and 4.1.5)

Beyond the Fast Track, the 'Jackson reforms' now require the instructing solicitor to produce a budget that will include the entire costs of running the case from issue through to trial. This budget includes all the work of the expert witnesses instructed in the case. One impact of Cost Budgeting is that the expert needs to know as accurately as possible what he/she will charge at each stage of the litigation in each case. Clearly, many cases will have similar levels of complexity and the expert will have a good sense of what commitment of time a case will entail, but the expert needs to be very alert for those cases that are beyond the ordinary and that may need to be priced specifically based on the complexity of the issues.

The future appears very much to be in the hands of the commercially and professionally competent expert. It is true to say that in many areas of expertise, and outside the limitations imposed by the Legal Aid Agency in those few areas where public funding continues, there has as yet been no downward pressure on expert fees. Such pressure presently appears to be limited to orthopaedic and psychiatric/psychological disciplines, where the MedCo system is creating a perception as to the value of expert reports in these disciplines. However, the stated aim of the Ministry of Justice is to control the cost of litigation and few would argue that the work of experts is a fundamental component and therefore a legitimate target for such cost control.

The allocation of reasonable costs, however, remains at the time of writing (June 2015) a somewhat haphazard process. The 'Jackson reforms' have created a situation where the court, often with little or no experience of the work that is actually required to generate expert evidence in a case, is limiting in an arbitrary manner the amount of expert fees recoverable from the defendant in case.

A recent example will serve as an illustration of this: an expert specialising in industrial disease investigations had to deal in a report with the duty of care relating to hearing loss in a factory worker in heavy industry. The expert had to investigate the safety standards in operation throughout the period of the factory worker's three decades of employment, as well as his employment history. The expert had agreed upfront with the instructing solicitor a fee of £2000+VAT for the work required. The work was carried out appropriately and the report written, which led to an offer to settle by the defendants in the case.

One might assume that the court would regard this as an appropriate use of expert evidence. However, the expert was later contacted by the instructing solicitor to discuss discounting his fees. This arose because the court had only allowed £500+VAT to be recovered from the defendants, even though the instructing lawyers had explained to the court the work that had been required of the expert and the importance of this work in settling the case.

The expert, justifiably, held the solicitor to the agreed amount, but it is easy to see how this type of situation and the lack of consistency in the way courts are addressing the fees recoverable is causing a downward pressure on fees or increasing the desire of instructing solicitors to attempt to renegotiate the fees payable after settlement of the case.

12.4 Terms of Appointment (see also Section 4.8)

In the new environment where experts are expected to be both professionally and commercially competent, it is essential that the expert's 'Terms of Appointment' are clearly set out by the expert and agreed by the instructing solicitors before work commences. The expert's terms of appointment can be provided in a letter or in a separate document attached to a letter sent to the instructing solicitors.

We set out below some sample terms of appointment with explanatory notes that we hope will be a useful starting point for an expert who wishes to produce comprehensive terms of appointment. These sample terms will need to be adapted to the particular requirements of the expert and adapted to reflect the charging basis of the expert and the nature of the relationship with the instructing entity. (Please note: these sample terms are provided here only as a guide and should be the subject of proper legal advice from your own professional advisors.)

Experts should be aware that if subsequent to providing their terms of appointment the instructing lawyer provides standard terms on which the lawyer will instruct the expert, this 'battle of the standard terms' is likely to result in the subsequent terms provided by the instructing solicitor applying, unless the expert responds in suitable terms and obtains a clear acceptance of the expert's terms from the instructing solicitor.

Where an expert is instructed through a Medical Reporting Organisation (MRO), then the MRO will probably impose its own terms on the expert, with little if any scope for the expert to vary them.

12.4.1 Providing Cost Certainty

The instructing solicitors will be looking for cost certainty (as far as is practicable) from the expert at the outset of the case. This enables a realistic budget of the costs for the expert's entire involvement in the case to be produced and will be an essential part of the court's cost management conference.

Once the cost budget is fixed, the court will only give permission to increase the budget in exceptional circumstances. In the absence of such permission, the solicitor may still instruct the expert to do additional work, but will do so in the knowledge that this extra work will not be recoverable from the other side.

An essential element of the terms of appointment, therefore, is being specific about the fee structure for the different types or complexity of cases that the expert is likely to address. For example, a simple case with relatively few medical records may be capable of a fixed price for reading records and writing the report, whereas a complex case with an extensive bundle of records may call for an hourly rate to be charged for the reading of records.

If the terms of appointment are clear and have an appropriate level of detail, then either the solicitor or the expert would be able to initiate a discussion as to how much time being spent on an aspect of the report would be seen as proportionate by the court.

Clear terms of appointment allow the expert to ascertain the solicitors' precise instructions on any matters that arise during the production of the report. Making sure that there is an agreed basis for all work to be carried out is now essential. Whereas in the past, the whole of an expert's fee would usually be recoverable from the defendants in the event of a settlement, this is not now the case. The level of fees that can be recovered from the other side relies on the judge in the case and many judges are simply not allowing a realistic level of recovery for the work that is carried out.

The natural tendency of the lawyer in a situation where the full fees have not been recovered is to go back to the expert to seek a cut in the fees charged. The decision about whether to discount the fee note is entirely a commercial decision by the expert and any refusal to pay a fee note would enable the expert to take appropriate legal action against the instructing solicitors.

There is no necessity for the expert to agree to a cut in his or her fees, so long as the terms of appointment are clear and the work charged for was agreed by the solicitor - either on the basis of the terms of appointment or the expert and the lawyer having clarified matters once the extent of the case had become clear. It is only in the grey area where experts carry out work in the expectation of being paid, without seeking the agreement of the instructing solicitor that matters become more difficult and disputes arise.

12.4.2 Sample Terms of Appointment

	Term:	Notes:
1	**Applicable terms:**	
	I agree to provide my services as an expert witness in accordance with the terms of appointment set out below and not on the basis of any other standard or other terms. You must return to me a copy of this letter signed by you, indicating your agreement with them. However in any event by continuing to instruct me to provide these services you are agreeing to accept these terms. These terms may only be varied by agreement in writing.	*It is desirable to have a signed copy of the terms on file, and essential to do so if there is a 'battle of the standard terms', as referred to above.* *Any variation or amendment should be recorded in writing and signed by both parties to avoid subsequent misunderstanding.*
2	**Capacity in which appointed:**	
	These terms are on the basis that I am appointed to report in this matter by you, the legal representative/insurer/professional indemnifier on behalf of the claimant/defendant, who is referred to below as 'the client'. Liability to pay my fees and expenses is yours and not that of the client, unless otherwise agreed in writing.	*It is important to be clear as to who is liable to pay in the event of non-payment – the lawyer, the lay client, the insurer, the healthcare provider etc. It is normally best to put this liability on the lawyer.*
	Alternatively	
	These terms are on the basis that I am appointed to report in this matter by you, as agent on behalf of the legal representative/insurer/professional indemnifier which acts on behalf of the claimant/defendant, who is referred to below as 'the client'. Liability to pay my fees and expenses is yours and the entity on whose behalf you act jointly and severally and not that of the client, unless otherwise agreed in writing.	*If instructions are through an agency and there is no agreement provided for (or imposed) as a consequence, the terms need to make clear whether it is the agency or the party who is liable to pay.*
	Alternatively	

	These terms are on the basis that I am appointed as a single joint expert on the instruction of ……….. and ……….. the legal representatives/insurers/professional indemnifiers on behalf of the claimant and defendant/First and Second Defendant, who is referred to below as 'the client'. Liability to pay my fees and expenses is yours on a joint and several basis and not that of the client, unless otherwise agreed in writing.	*As a SJE, payment should be the liability of each and both entities instructing the expert.*
3	References below to 'the case' or 'the litigation' include references to any matters on which I am instructed to provide my services whether or not court proceedings have been commenced or are intended.	
4	**Nature of report required:**	
	My instructions are to provide a full report (the 'initial report') to which the CPR apply on condition and prognosis/breach of duty/causation	*It is essential to set out clearly the nature of the report required, and in particular if the report is to be something other than a full CPR compliant report.*
	Alternatively	
	My instructions are to provide an advisory report/screening report/desktop report (the 'initial report'). In these circumstances should I subsequently be instructed to provide a full report to which the CPR apply, further time (and fees) will be incurred in order to comply with my duties under the CPR.	

5	If I am instructed to provide a report without considering or reading any or all of the medical, treatment or rehabilitation records, or where the fee agreed or time allowed is insufficient to permit of that consideration or reading and I notify you of the same in writing, you understand that any opinions expressed will be qualified on the basis of having considered no or only limited such records.	*The expert must make clear in the report itself any limitations on the evidence considered and therefore any qualification on the opinion provided.*
6	**Services included in appointment:**	
	Where my instructions are to provide a full CPR compliant report, my duties will include the answering of Part 35 questions, attendance on joint discussions, at conference and at court as requested of me.	*Once instructions are accepted to provide a CPR report, the expert is bound to continue to provide his/her services for the rest of the litigation, save in exceptional circumstances (Guidance para 26).*
7	**Timetable for initial report:**	
	The initial report will be provided by me within ... weeks of provision of all relevant documentation including medical records	*It is essential to know and to record the date by which the initial report can be provided and therefore to confirm that the instructions can be fulfilled (Guidance para 23)*
	Alternatively	
	The initial report will be provided by me by no later than .... on the basis that all relevant documentation including medical records have been made available to me by	
	Alternatively	
	The initial report will be provided by me by no later than .... To the extent that medical records have not been made available to me in time to complete the report, I will provide a supplementary report within ... days of receipt of those medical records.	

8	**Charges:**	
	I charge £… per hour for all time spent on the case including/ excluding travel [except for attendance at court hearings]	*The basis of charging must be set out clearly. If there is a fixed fee or a maximum fee agreed, the expert should make clear any assumptions on which that is agreed, such as time involved or documents to be considered.*
	Alternatively	
	I charge £… per hour for all time spent on the case and £… per hour for travel.	
	[Time is recorded in 6 minute units.]	
	Alternatively	
	The initial report will be charged at a fixed fee of £…. [including all expenses and disbursements] on the basis that the client will be interviewed at ……….. and documentation provided will not exceed:	*In some fast track work, the medical expert's fee is fixed.*
	• [1 lever arch file] of medical records, which are provided in chronological order and in legible form	
	• I typed witness statement not exceeding [10] pages in length [or alternatively not more than [10] pages of witness statements]	
	• Not more than [10] pages of expert reports from other experts instructed in this case	
9	Attendance at court hearings is charged at £… per day [including travel and waiting time] and in the absence of written confirmation to the contrary will be taken to be for the entirety of each of the hearing days or for each day within the warned period notified.	*Although in practice an expert may only be required to attend for part of a trial, until the dates for attendance are known, the expert may be provided with a period during which she is required to be available. (Guidance para 84-86)*

10	You will pay any fees charged by me in answering Part 35 Questions raised by the other party/parties in the litigation in accordance with PD35 para 6.2	*This is the rule for multi-track cases but not under the PAP for PI cases in fast track claims (PAP para 7.10)*
11	All rates set out above will be reviewed annually on 1st January and any changes will be notified to you in writing.	
12	**Cancellation charges – court attendances:**	
	Because of the need to cancel clinics up to 8 weeks in advance, in the event of cancellation of a requirement to attend court, fees will be charged for the entirety of the hearing dates notified on the following basis:	*This should be adapted to the particular situation of the expert. The expert is entitled not to be out of pocket as a result of cancelling work in order to be available for a hearing which is then cancelled.*
	Notice of cancellation less than 7 days before the first day of hearing – 100% of the fee	
	Notice of cancellation less than 14 days (but not less than 7 days) before the first day of hearing – 75% of the fee	
	Notice of cancellation less than 28 days (but not less than 14 days) before the first day of hearing – 100% of the fee	
13	**Cancellation charges – consultations etc**	
	If any consultation, conference or other appointment is cancelled less than … hours in advance you will pay me a fee representing the time spent in any preparation, the time which would have been spent in the appointment and any expenses actually incurred.	

14	**Expenses and disbursements:**	
	You will reimburse me for all reasonable travel expenses and disbursements incurred including reasonable quality overnight accommodation. Rail and air travel will be on the basis of first class and business class respectively. If driving, this will be on the basis of …p per mile plus parking and tolls.	
15	**Time for payment:**	
	Save as otherwise agreed in writing, all fees and reimbursement of expenses are payable within 30 days of invoice.	
	Alternatively	
	Save as otherwise agreed in writing, all fees and reimbursement of expenses are payable within 30 days of the conclusion of the case or litigation by settlement, judgment or discontinuance.	*And see section 20 below and the requirement to inform the expert of the conclusion (Guidance para 87). The lawyer may not however recover the expert's fees for a considerable time after settlement or judgment.*
16	**Interest:**	
	Interest together with debt recovery costs is payable on any late payment at the rate applicable under the Late Payment of Commercial Debts (Interest) Act 1998.	*Currently 8.5% per annum*
17	**VAT:**	
	VAT is [not] currently chargeable on my fees.	*Medico-legal reports are subject to VAT at the standard rate if you are registered for VAT. Currently you must register for VAT if your business VAT taxable turnover is more than £82,000. Get your accountant's advice on this issue if you are in any doubt.*
18	**Reduction in fees and expenses:**	
	The fees and expenses set out above and calculated as set out above are to be paid in full whether or not any lesser sum (or no sum) is recovered from any opposing party in the litigation or assessed by any court.	*This reflects the fact that the expert's fees may not be recovered in full from the other side at the successful conclusion of the case, but that is immaterial to the expert.*

19	**Property in written work provided:**	
	I will own the copyright in all reports and other materials produced by me. Further the title to all reports and materials provided by me will remain with me until full payment has been received.	
20	**Keeping me informed:**	
	You will provide me with an outline programme for the completion and delivery of each stage of my involvement in the case or litigation.	*Guidance 20(f)*
	You will keep me informed at all times about any deadlines relevant to the provision of my services.	*Guidance 19 and 20(g)*
	You will send me promptly copies of any court orders or direction that refer to the involvement of experts in the litigation or in any way relate to the provision of my services or the fulfilment of my duties within the litigation.	*Guidance 19 PD35 para 8*
	You will provide me with details of any specific budget for my services, whether ordered by the court or otherwise.	*Guidance 20(g)*
	You will inform me when the case is concluded either by a settlement or trial.	*Guidance 87*
21	**Estimates of fees:**	
	I will provide an estimate of fees for the litigation through to trial on request and on provision of sufficient information about the nature of the matters on which I am to provide expert opinion. An estimate will be provided on the basis of the charges set out above.	*Estimates of fees are necessary in order for the court to grant permission to rely on an expert and for the costs budgeting process.*

Alternatively		
The following estimate of fees is provided on the basis of the nature of the matters on which I am instructed to provide an expert opinion and on the assumptions indicated. • Initial CPR compliant report: not more than … minutes consultation/interview, […] lever arch files/pages of ordered and legible medical records and … pages of witness statements - £…..		
• Re-examination and supplementary report: not more than … minutes consultation/interview, […] lever arch files/pages of ordered and legible medical records and … pages of witness statements - £…..		
• Reviewing other side's reports and providing written comments: not more than […] reports and not more than […] pages in total - £		
• Reviewing further documentation and surveillance evidence: not more than … minutes - £		
• Replying to Part 35 questions: not more than … minutes - £		
• Attending conference with counsel: not more than … minutes preparation, …. minutes n conference and … minutes travel - £…. plus travel costs		
• Attending joint discussion by phone/in person and preparing and agreeing joint statement: not more than … minutes - £…. [plus travel costs]		
• Attending trial – see charging rates above		

12.5 Establishing a Good Reputation with Lawyers

The quickest and easiest way to establish a good reputation with instructing solicitors is to write high-quality reports that are focussed on the issues that the lawyers require to be addressed. Whatever the case, the expert report will deal with one (or more) of the following legal issues: the duty of care owed by the defendant to the claimant, the causation and extent of injury (both now and for the future) and the extent of the damage caused.

The content of the report must be focused on the relevant issues and irrelevant information should be omitted from the report. The importance of producing evidence that is directly relevant to the solicitor's instructions (and where necessary clarifying the solicitor's instructions to enable the expert to produce such evidence) cannot be overstated. An expert report that is 30% longer than is required not only takes more time to produce, it also takes more time to read and understand by the lawyers. Clarifying instructions before starting work on more complex cases is often the best way to shorten the time spent producing the evidence.

The expert also needs to look carefully at how much evidence needs to be produced to meet the solicitor's instructions. Recent changes introduced in the Guidance allow for an expert to check and agree the chronology of another expert (or other experts where more than one expert has been instructed in the case), without having to reproduce the chronology in his or her own report.

Clearly, the relevant records/witness statements will still need to be checked to agree, expand or amend the chronology of another expert, but particularly where the history is set out across several expert reports, it is now unnecessary to recreate the chronology another time. Similarly, where the court orders the sequential exchange of reports, there are approaches to saving time that can cut the cost of the report (see also Sections 4.2.13 and 11.4).

All expert witnesses need to understand that there is little or no appetite from lawyers or the court for long reports that do not address effectively the relevant issues, do not justify opinions with a clear rationale and fail to apply the appropriate legal tests to the evidence.

12.5.1 Keeping to Deadlines

The importance of deadlines has increased markedly since the 'Jackson reforms' and the Mitchell case[3]. When the instructing solicitor gives an expert a date by which the work needs to be done, then in accepting the instruction the expert also accepts the deadline for the work to be completed. There will have to be a very good reason before the court will allow for an extension of a deadline, usually based around new evidence emerging or unforeseen additional work being required. There is very little, if any, flexibility for altering court orders.

---

3   See Section 3.6

PD35 para 8 states the following:

> Where an order requires an act to be done by an expert, or otherwise affects an expert, the party instructing that expert must serve a copy of the order on the expert. The claimant must serve the order on a single joint expert.

It is essential that experts have terms of appointment relating to being kept informed of timetables and deadlines by the instructing solicitor. If a solicitor does not inform the expert of a deadline, then it is once more a matter for negotiation about what can be achieved in the time available.

12.5.2   Conduct of Your Practice

It is extremely important that experts maintain a professional approach to their medico-legal practice. Clearly stated contact hours and timely responses to emails will be expected and appreciated by instructing solicitors. Where experts are working with MROs or medico-legal agencies, making sure that any contract terms regarding response times are acceptable and achievable in the light of an expert's often substantial clinical commitments is fundamental to the role of the expert witness.

12.5.3   Retention of Records (See also Section 4.1.7)

It is essential that the expert retains working papers and copies of records provided for a period of at least 10 years. This period is made up of the six year limitation period for any claim against the expert relating to professional negligence and a further three years in which a claimant is permitted to bring an action and additional time for service of proceedings. Where the claimant is under 18 years old, this limitation period does not start to run until the age of 18. If the claimant lacks capacity, then the limitation period will not start to run unless and until capacity is regained. In those cases, the papers should be retained for a longer period and in some cases arguably indefinitely.

Experts should keep regular backups of their data files and store one copy of their backups off site to avoid a total loss of data in the event of fire or theft.

12.5.4   Data Protection

An individual undertaking medico-legal work will be a data processing organisation under the Data Protection Act 1998 and must be registered with the Information Commissioner unless one of the exemptions under the Act applies. Notification with the Information Commission can be carried out online at the Information Commission website (https://ico.org.uk/) and involves payment of a statutory annual fee of £35.

All experts should be technologically aware. Firewalls and virus scanners that update on a daily basis are a basic requirement. Technologies to encrypt reports are also used by some experts.

12.6 Promoting an Expert Witness Practice

An important first step when considering how to promote a medico-legal practice is first to define what the focus of the practice actually is. This seems to be an ongoing issue for many experts, who tend to respond to the instructions that they are sent rather than seeking out the instructions that they actually want.

An expert can run an individual practice or join with other experts in an "experts' chambers" (modelled on the idea of a barristers' chambers, which are formed essentially to share administration and marketing costs) or can choose to work through medico-legal agencies – or indeed a mix of these approaches.

The essential steps to marketing an expert practice are to:

1. produce well-written and attractively presented reports;

2. write reports with clear and succinct opinions, supported by a clear rationale, and demonstrating an understanding of the legal framework of the claim;

3. have a professional presence on the web;

4. obtain full membership of one or more of the expert witness bodies (such as the Expert Witness Institute or the Academy of Experts);

5. join special interest groups to generate networking opportunities;

6. list the expert's professional details in one of the expert witness registers or directories;

7. contact firms of solicitors (by location or by market focus);

8. publish articles on medical or medico-legal topics;

9. present CPD workshops to firms of solicitors; and

10. develop professional relationships with other experts to generate referrals.

12.6.1 Maintaining the Integrity of Your Practice

Many of the disaster stories the authors of this text hear from experts begin when experts do something beyond their instructions or responsibilities in an attempt to be helpful. Helpfulness that goes beyond the usual boundaries of making a recommendation that the instructing solicitor obtains a report from an expert in another discipline is prone to land experts in more difficulty than they ever imagined possible. Be particularly careful when asked for help or advice from a claimant, as this can often be the open door through which problems arrive. Being courteous and professional are essential qualities of a good expert, but acting out of a sense of sympathy for the claimant is ill-advised. Nor is it useful to become an unpaid researcher for the instructing solicitor.

While writing and providing a report may feel a very private activity, giving evidence in court is not, with judgments being widely available on the internet and shared amongst lawyers. Mistakes once made can be difficult to explain and justify to a critical professional audience and can have a profound effect on how the expert is viewed in the marketplace.

Final Thoughts

Writing high-quality expert reports is a professional challenge. It is also an intellectual and professional discipline that requires a rigorous approach to analysing the available evidence, an objective approach to applying legal tests to the evidence and a clear understanding of the legal framework within which expert opinions are sought.

Adopting the approach to the evidence and the writing disciplines that we have explained throughout this book will enable experts to produce expert reports that are more accurate and precise and also more understandable for the lawyers and the court. This approach will also help the expert to produce evidence that fits into the commercial constraints within which the legal process now operates.

The benefit for experts who take on the discipline of writing high-quality expert reports is that a well-written and well-structured report is essential to the overriding objective of the court – 'to deal with cases justly and at proportionate cost'. It is also the best possible illustration of the skills of the expert and is an essential aid to providing effective and high-quality oral evidence in court - and withstanding rigorous cross-examination with the minimum of stress.

Producing high–quality expert reports is perhaps the best way to build a good reputation amongst the lawyers who will ultimately enable the expert to build a successful medico-legal practice.

Appendices

1(a)	Personal Injury Report Template – Physical Injuries
1(b)	Personal Injury Report Template – Psychological/Psychiatric Injuries
1(c)	Personal Injury Report Template – Industrial Disease
1(d)	Clinical Negligence Report Template
1 (e)	Care and Other Needs Report Template
2	Report Checklist
3	CPR Part 35
4	Practice Direction to Part 35
5	Guidance for the Instruction of Experts in Civil Claims 2014
6	GMC Guidance – Acting as a witness in legal proceedings (April 2013)
7	Example of a Schedule of Loss

Appendix 1

Appendix 1(a)

Personal Injury Report Template (Physical Injuries)

1. **Introduction**
   - Author: name, qualifications and relevant experience
   - Instructions
   - Background to the dispute (as necessary)
   - Sources of information
   - Methodology
   - Structure of the report

2. **History of the Accident and Recovery Period** (from the claimant)
   - Incident/accident details and subsequent events
   - Injuries/symptoms/effects following the accident
   - Initial treatment and progression of injuries/symptoms/effects
   - Subsequent treatment and progression of injuries/symptoms/effects
   - Consequences of injuries (from accident to present)

3. **Presenting Condition** (from the claimant)
   - Present injuries/symptoms/effects
   - Present treatment
   - Past medical history

4. **Medical History** (from medical records)
   - Relevant medical history

5. **Examination**
   - Details of examination and findings

6. **Opinion and Prognosis**
   - Summary of examination findings
   - Opinion as to present condition (if not already defined by examination findings)
   - Causation of injuries
   - Relevant pre-existing conditions (if any)
   - Prognosis of injuries
   - Future treatment (if relevant)

7. **Consequences of Injuries**
   - Opinion on the consequences resulting from physical injuries/symptoms/effects

8. **Summary of Conclusions**
    - List of conclusions
    - Declaration and Statement of Truth
    - Sign and Date

Explanatory notes on this template are provided below.

Appendix 1(b)

Personal Injury Report Template: (Psychiatric/Psychological Injuries)

1. **Introduction**
    - Author: name, qualifications and relevant experience
    - Instructions
    - Background to the dispute (as necessary)
    - Sources of information
    - Methodology
    - Structure of the report

2. **History of the Accident and Recovery Period** (from claimant)
    - Incident/accident details and subsequent events
    - Injuries/symptoms/effects following the accident
    - Initial treatment and progression of injuries/symptoms/effects
    - Subsequent treatment and progression of injuries/symptoms/effects
    - Consequences of injuries (from accident to present)

3. **Presenting Condition** (from claimant)
    - Present symptoms/effects
    - Present treatment
    - Psychiatric history

4. **Psychiatric/Psychological History** (from medical records)
    - Relevant psychiatric history
        • Personal
        • Family
        • Marital
        • Drugs/Alcohol
        • Employment
        • Personality

5. **Mental State Examination**
    - Details of mental-state examination and findings

6. **Opinion and Prognosis**
   - Summary of mental state examination findings
   - Opinion as to present condition: ICD-10 or DSM-V classification (if not already defined by examination findings)
   - Causation of injuries
   - Relevant pre-existing conditions (if any)
   - Prognosis
   - Future treatment

7. **Consequences of Injuries**
   - Opinion on the consequences arising from psychiatric/psychological condition/symptoms/effects

8. **Summary of Conclusions**
   - List of conclusions
   - Declaration and Statement of Truth
   - Sign and Date

Explanatory notes on this template are provided below.

Appendix 1(c)

Industrial Disease Report Template

1. **Introduction**
   - Author: name, qualifications and relevant experience
   - Instructions
   - Background to the dispute (as necessary)
   - Sources of information
   - Methodology
   - Structure of the report

2. **Employment History** (from employment records)
   - Positions held, when, and type of work
   - Type(s) and degree of exposure and history of exposure
   - Systems of work and safety precautions taken

3. **Medical History** (from medical/occupational health records)
   - Relevant medical history from:
     - Occupational health nursing notes
     - Occupational physician records
     - GP and hospital records
     - Previous medical reports

4. **Presenting Condition** (from claimant)
   - Present conditions/symptoms/effects
   - Present treatment
   - Past medical history
     - Treatment and progression of condition/symptoms/effects
     - Consequences arising from presenting condition

5. **Examination**
   - Details of examination and findings

6. **Opinion and Prognosis**
   - Summary of examination findings
   - Opinion as to present condition (if not already defined by examination findings)
   - Causation of injuries ('but for'/'material contribution')
   - Relevant pre-existing conditions (if any)
   - Prognosis
   - Future treatment (if relevant)

7. **Consequences of Injuries**
   - Opinion on the consequences resulting from condition/symptoms/effects

8. **Summary of Conclusions**
   - List of conclusions
   - Declaration and Statement of Truth
   - Sign and Date

Explanatory notes on this template are provided below.

Notes: Personal Injury Report Templates (1a-c)

The following notes are primarily based on the personal injury template for physical injuries (1a), with the vast majority of these notes applying equally to psychiatric/psychological template (1b) and the industrial disease template (1c).

Additional notes specific to templates (1b) and (1c) are included at the end of the notes on the personal injury template (1a).

1. Introduction

The Introduction establishes the expertise of the author and the issues he/she has been instructed to address in the report.

Author

- Write 2 or 3 paragraphs that establish the expert's qualifications and relevant experience.

Instructions

- Set out the substance of all material instructions from the solicitor or where the instructions to the expert are only briefly stated by the solicitor, set out the expert's understanding of his/her instructions.

Background to the Dispute

- Particularly in more complex cases, it is helpful for the expert to begin by briefly summarising the facts of the case so that the reader understands the basic outline of the issues in dispute.

Sources of Information

- List the information made available to the expert. This may include GP and hospital records, scans, X-rays, witness statements and photographs. If there is an extensive list of sources, it is preferable to place this list in an appendix with a cross-reference in the main text.
- Give the dates of documents or in the case of medical records, the range of dates. This ensures that should the case reach court months or even years later, the specific documents that the expert has seen when producing the report can be identified.
- Where the expert is instructed specifically to report without having had sight of the medical records, this should be clearly stated so that the basis of the report is clear.

Methodology

- For a typical personal injury report (car accident/slip and trip), there is no particular demand from the lawyers for a detailed methodology section, as the process is familiar. However, the expert should set out the basic approach adopted, and where time has been spent in carrying out a particular task (such as reading detailed records) state that time so that the basis for the expert's fee is clear to the parties and the court.
- More technically demanding investigations will require that a Methodology section/sub-section be included, either in the Introduction section or in complex cases requiring detailed investigations, as Section 2 of the report.

Structure of the Report

- Set out the structure of the report as a list of sections.

2. History of the Accident and Recovery Period

In this section, give details of the history taken from the claimant, reporting those facts relevant to the medical issues and quoting the claimant's own words where relevant.

Incident/accident details and subsequent events

- Report only on accident details relevant to medical issues (e.g. in a car accident case, experts would be likely to record the type and severity of the collision, whether the claimant was wearing a seat belt, whether the car had headrests fitted, whether the claimant was able to brace before the collision).
- Give details of any immediate or subsequent medical treatment (e.g. did the claimant get out of the car unaided and was he/she taken to casualty).

Injuries/symptoms/effects following the accident

- Include details of the claimant's injuries, symptoms and the effects immediately following and for the first several days/weeks (depending on the severity) following the accident.

Initial treatment and progression of injuries/symptoms/effects

- Include the claimant's account of any initial treatment and the progression of injuries/symptoms/effects.

Subsequent treatment and progression of injuries/symptoms/effects

- Where treatment is extended over several weeks or months, give the claimant's account of the treatment received and the progress made.

Consequences of injuries (from accident to present)

- Give details of all claimed consequential loss since the accident to the date of the examination.

3. Presenting Condition

In this section, give details of the present complaints of the claimant, reporting those facts relevant to the medical issues and quoting the claimant's own words where relevant.

Present injuries/symptoms/effects

- Give details of the claimant's account of present medical complaints and the claimed restrictions arising from these complaints.

Present treatment

- Give details of the claimant's account of present treatment (both conventional and alternative modalities, as necessary).

Past medical history

- Give details of the claimant's account of his/her medical history.
- Give details of the claimant's explanation of any inconsistencies in his/her medical history which arise from a comparison with the claimant's medical records.

4. Medical History

In this section, include relevant details from the claimant's medical records. Where the expert is instructed not to read the claimant's medical records, make clear this instruction here as well as in the instructions received sub-section in the Introduction section.

Relevant medical history

- Identify relevant medical issues in the records[1].
- Check that the copy of the records you have been sent is complete.

5. Examination

In this section, the information can be written technically and without detailed explanation, as any issue that needs to be explained will be dealt with fully in the Opinion section that follows. However, brief explanatory notes will generally assist the reader to understand medical aspects of the report and therefore, where this explanation can be provided without overwhelming the reader with too much technical information, it is good practice to do so.

---

[1] The expert should receive from the instructing solicitor (or agency) medical notes that have been sorted into chronological order. If these records are received unsorted, the expert should contact the instructing solicitor to negotiate a fee for sorting the records. Any fee agreed for sorting the records should be in addition to the fee for writing the report. The terms of appointment agreed between the expert and the solicitor or agency at the outset of the relationship should also set out the expert's terms in respect of sorting medical notes to avoid any misunderstandings.

Details of examination and findings

- Report fully on the examination as this is direct evidence and is essential to the opinion expressed.
- Report NAD findings to establish that the test or assessment was actually carried out.
- Report findings on examination that are not consistent or are in some way surprising or out of the ordinary.

6. Opinion and Prognosis

This is the most important section of the report from the lawyers' perspective and requires the expert to give clearly stated opinions supported by reasons/reasoning.

Summary of examination findings

- List the injuries to be addressed based on the examination findings and analysis of the records.

Opinion as to present condition

- If not already defined by examination findings, give opinion as to the injuries the claimant has suffered as a result of the accident.
- Address each injury in turn making clear the relevant facts and the reasoning based on those facts.
- The expert may have been instructed not to examine the medical records. Having examined the claimant, if the expert considers that a review of the medical records is necessary or would be helpful, this should be stated.

Causation of injuries

- Give clear opinion on what caused the injury.
- Support all opinion with reasons.
- Give opinion on what the claimant's medical situation would have been without the accident ('but for').

Relevant pre-existing conditions (if any)

- Where the claimant has a pre-existing condition, explain how the progression of this condition would have affected the claimant and contrast this with the situation since the accident and for the future.

Prognosis of injuries

- Give a prognosis for each injury (or all the injuries together) dealing with deterioration/improvement with the likelihood of this occurring and over what time period.

Future treatment (if relevant)

- Give opinion on any future medical treatment that the claimant may need, what is the likelihood (as a percentage) of needing the treatment and when is it likely to be needed.
- Give opinion on any treatment that may improve the claimant's medical situation.
- Where the expert knows the cost of such treatment if carried out privately, this can usefully be included.

7. Consequences of Injuries

Opinion on the consequences resulting from injuries/symptoms/effects

- Use mundane language to describe the restrictions that the claimant faces in his/her activities of daily living.
- Avoid using percentages when describing what difference the injuries have made to the claimant's level of restriction.
- Do not stray into giving evidence beyond the area of expertise.

8. Summary of Conclusions

List of conclusions

- List the conclusions reached in sections 6 and 7. Where specific questions from the solicitor have been addressed, these can be set out in italics with the relevant conclusion set out beneath.

Declaration and Statement of Truth

- Make sure the Expert's Declaration and Statement of Truth comply with PD 35 and the Guidance.

Sign and Date

- It is unnecessary to sign every page of expert evidence in civil claims

Psychiatric/Psychological Reports

- Psychiatric/psychological reports are commonly criticised by lawyers for being too long for the complexity of the issues being addressed. There are two reasons for this criticism:

1. irrelevant information is included in the report; and

2. relevant information is included, but its relevance to the expert's reasoning in forming an opinion is not explained in the report.

- A psychiatric/psychological injury is often an integral part of the physical injuries a claimant has suffered. It is important that the psychiatric or psychological expert does not misquote a claimant who is discussing physical injuries, as there is a danger of creating inconsistencies in the evidence and therefore further opportunities for dispute between the parties.
- Wherever possible, the expert should read relevant reports on physical injuries prior to conducting the mental state examination.
- In the Opinion section, it is extremely helpful to set out the details of the relevant DSM-V or ICD-10 classifications, as the court is unlikely to be familiar with the specific features of and distinctions between different classifications.
- As with a report on physical injuries, it is essential that the report covers the likely situation in the absence of the accident ('but for') and specifically, in the case of long term conditions, whether other events in the claimant's life would, at some future time, have brought on the condition that is the subject of the dispute or some other condition. The likely onset and impact of any condition that would have been likely to develop in any event should be contrasted with the situation since the accident.

Industrial Disease Reports

- The employment history should be presented as a chronology. It is extremely important to be as accurate as possible when constructing this chronology as periods of exposure and when these occurred are fundamental to the opinions that will be expressed in the report. The history may also be a focus for challenge should the matter come to court.
- The type and degree of exposure should be detailed for each job and details should be given of the occupational health and safety precautions that were in place at the time of the exposure.
- Given the volume of records that are often available in such cases, it makes sense to set out the medical history after the employment history. The claimant's account of his/her medical history can be included as part of the Presenting Condition section.
- Causation may need to be addressed using the 'but for' test or the 'material contribution' test (or both) depending upon the solicitor's instructions and the facts of the case. If unsure, the expert should discuss the matter with the instructing solicitor.

Appendix 1(d)

Clinical Negligence Report Template

1. **Introduction**
   - Author: name, qualifications and relevant experience
   - Instructions
   - Background to the dispute
   - Overview of medical issues (as necessary)
   - Sources of information
   - Methodology
   - Structure of the report

2. **Chronology of Events**
   - Factual account of events from records/witness statements
   - Explanations of technical matters (as required)

3. **Past Medical History**
   - Overview of claimant's PMH with details of relevant history

4. **Opinion**
   - Breach of Duty
   - Causation

5. **Summary of Conclusions**
   - List of conclusions
   - Declaration and Statement of Truth
   - Sign and Date

Notes: Clinical Negligence Report Template

See also notes to the templates above.

1. Introduction

Clinical negligence disputes are generally more complex than personal injury cases, in terms of the facts of the case, conflicts in the evidence, the technical issues to be addressed and the range of medical opinion on the matters to be decided. Ensuring that the report adequately explains the medical issues in the evidence is of great importance.

Instructions Received

- Make clear whether the report will deal with liability (breach of duty), causation or both of these aspects of the claim.

- Occasionally, the expert will deal with condition and prognosis as well as liability and causation. If so, it is important that the liability and causation report is separate from the condition and prognosis report. The condition and prognosis report should follow the Personal Injury Report template.

<u>Overview of Medical Issues</u>

- It is often extremely helpful for the expert to introduce the medical issues that are central to the issues in the case. This should be a non-contentious explanation of these issues, drawing attention to the medical issues that need to be considered when deciding the issues in dispute.
- As a rough guide, 3 to 5 paragraphs will often be sufficient to give an introduction to the key medical issues. However, if a longer explanation is required, it may be useful to add this explanation as an appendix, giving a cross-reference in the main text.

<u>Sources of information</u>

- Information supplied to the expert is often extensive – if so, use an appendix to set out sources of information. It is also important to note any information that has not been supplied to the expert (e.g. missing pages of notes at important moments in the treatment process).

2. Chronology of Events

Provide a narrative (accessible to lawyers) of the treatment history, referenced to the sources of information from which it has been derived.

- Quote verbatim any important entries in the clinical record and explain what each entry means.
- Use sub-headings to indicate the date and time that the specific events occurred.
- Explain technical issues but avoid giving opinion on these issues when setting out the chronology. Such opinions should be given in the Opinion section of the report.

3. Past Medical History

- The past medical history in a clinical negligence report may need to be more detailed than in a personal injury report. This is because an underlying health condition is often the reason that the claimant was receiving medical treatment in the first instance.
- An underlying health issue may be an important component of the causation question.
- As in personal injury reports, the expert should still focus on the relevant medical history and summarise very briefly (or exclude) non-relevant medical issues.
- Make sure that medical records are quoted accurately.

- Where the past medical history will help to make clear the treatment process the claimant was undergoing, it may be clearer to place the Past Medical History section before the Chronology of Events section.

4. Opinion and Prognosis

- Opinion on breach of duty will be based on the test in *Bolam* or, in rare cases, the test in *Bolitho,* or for cases dealing with consent, *Montgomery.* Essentially, except in cases involving issues of consent, the analysis breaks down into the following stages:
    1. What would a reasonably competent clinician have done (or not done) in these circumstances?
    2. What did the clinician do or omit to do?
    3. Is there a range of professional opinion within which a responsible body of clinicians would have acted (or omitted to act) in the same manner?
    4. (and in cases where *Bolitho* is relevant) Can the treatment decisions made be logically supported in the light of the benefits and risks inherent in those decisions?

- Opinion in relation to breach of duty in consent cases essentially breaks down into the following stages:
    1. What material risks were there in the proposed treatment which would have been significant to this claimant and of which he/she should have been informed?
    2. What reasonable alternative or variant treatments were there, and what material risks would the alternative/variant have involved which would have been significant to this claimant and of which he/she should have been informed?"

- Opinion on causation, unless otherwise instructed, will apply the 'but for' test. When dealing with the actions or inactions of the clinicians involved in the claimant's care, the analysis breaks down into three stages:
    1. What did the clinician do or omit to do?
    2. What damage resulted from this action or inaction?
    3. Had the clinician acted differently, what would the outcome have been and what difference would this have made?

5. Summary of Conclusions

See notes for the Personal Injury Report template above.

Appendix 1(e)

Care and Other Needs Report Template

1. **Introduction**
   - Author: name, qualifications and relevant experience
   - Instructions
   - Assumptions
   - Information provided by instructing solicitor (or list in an appendix)
   - Sources of information (literature or other resources)

2. **Key-Events in Treatment and Recovery**
   - Pre-Injury condition and relevant Past Medical History
   - Overview of key events in the treatment and recovery
   - Rely on history in expert reports
   - Identify specific relevant entries
   - Delineate periods in the history

3. **Approach to Assessment**
   - Legal principle for the assessment of care and other needs
   - Methodology
     • Assessment tests
     • Formal observation of capabilities
     • Other material observations

4. **Assessment and Findings**
   - Summary of claimant's pre- and post-accident situation
   - Disabilities
     • Assessment test results
     • Formal observation of capabilities
     • Other material observations
   - Activities of daily living
     • Assessment test results
     • Formal observation of capabilities
     • Other material observations
   - Existing sources of help and support

5. **Opinion and Recommendations (with Breakdown of Costs)**
   - Restrictions and limitations relevant to the assessment of loss:
     I. Care Needs (Past & Future)
        • Period – Type – Hours – Hourly Rate
     II. Aids, Appliances, Equipment
        • Type – Supplier - Period – Capital – Costs
     III. Therapeutic Needs
        • Type – Number of Sessions – Cost
     IV. Other Needs (such as: Travel/Transport, Holidays, Extra Household Expenditure, Accommodation, Employment etc.)

V. Case Management
- Hours/Period – Hourly Rate – Travel Costs
- Provide a rationale to support each aspect of the care package

6. **Summary of Conclusions and Recommendations**
- List Conclusions and Recommendations
- Summary Total Costs by Category (Capital, Annual and Ongoing)
- Declaration and Statement of Truth
- Sign and Date

Notes: Care and Other Needs Report Template

1. Introduction

One common aspect of the instructions given to Occupational Therapy, Care and Other Needs experts is the assumptions that the instructing solicitor wants the expert to adopt. This is usually based on the findings of particular medical/psychological experts in the case. The solicitor's intention is to enable the evidence to be useful in valuing the case.

It is important that any such assumptions are clearly stated in the report, so that the court understands the basis on which the report was produced.

2. Key-Events in Treatment and Recovery

The courts have made abundantly clear (see section 11.1) that they do not want another iteration of all of the history of the claimant's injury and treatment. It is essential that the Occupational Therapy, Care and Other Needs reports select from other evidence only those elements that are essential to their own opinion evidence.

It is also essential to be very clear on how the history is to be divided into periods, which form the basis for the assessment of past loss and enable the court to follow the rationale of the expert when dealing with the future.

3. Approach to Assessment

Setting out the approach to the assessment is vital to supporting the rationale for the recommendations in respect of the care package that will be set out in section 5 – Opinion and Recommendations. Notice that the first element is setting out the legal principle (100% Recovery Principle) that is the basis for the assessment. There are then three types of observation (tests, formal and informal observations) that become the basis for the assessment.

4. Assessment and Findings

The summary of the claimant's pre- and post-accident situation would more logically be placed at the end of this section, rather than at the beginning. However, the template recognises how the report will often be used by the lawyers – not reading from beginning to end, but rather focussing on the Assessment and Findings and Opinion and Recommendations sections.

This element therefore summarises the expert's assessment of causation in pragmatic terms (the difference the accident has made) and it is upon this that the rest of the evidence is based. There is an argument to be made that this summary could be placed at the beginning of the Opinion and Recommendations section, but on balance, we place it here as it relates directly to the assessment of the claimant.

Notice the strong emphasis in this section on the direct observations of the expert. One of the important aspects of the expert's evidence is that he/she is in the claimant's home assessing directly the need. Other medical experts may be given a higher status in respect of their expertise, but it is those experts who are actually engaging with the claimant who have the strongest direct evidence based on observation of the claimant and his/her level of function.

5. Opinion and Recommendations (with Breakdown of Costs)

Essential to the opinion and recommendations of the expert is the rationale that explains why particular aspects of the care package are needed. Disputes between the parties on the way elements of the care package need to be valued are far easier to resolve than conflicts of opinion on what the need actually is. Therefore, every aspect of the opinion needs to be justified with clear reasons and appropriately explained. The level of provision needs to be explained and the costs included for each item. These can be brought into a schedule or schedules in the summary of conclusions.

6. Summary of Conclusions and Recommendations

As part of the Summary of Conclusions, the expert will produce a schedule (or schedules) of the summary total costs by category (i.e. capital costs, annual costs and ongoing costs).

In sequential reports, the opinions of both experts will be brought together with reasons explaining the differences between the experts. (See Section 11.4-5)

Appendix 2

Medico-Legal Report Checklist

Presentation of the Report

- ☐ Header: case name/reference; report author; speciality
- ☐ Footer: report date; page number
- ☐ Margins: 3cm
- ☐ Text: 11-13pt (depending on font)
- ☐ Spacing: Double line spacing
- ☐ Headings: **Section**, Main, *Subheadings* (headings should be easy to differentiate and consistently presented)
- ☐ Numbering: two level system - 1.1, 1.2, 1.3 / 2.1, 2.2, 2.3 etc.

Title Page

- ☐ Title of action and reference no.
- ☐ Title of report (Medical Report on Mr J Smith)
- ☐ Author (speciality)
- ☐ Date (of examination or report, or both)
- ☐ Claimant's contact details
- ☐ Instructions received from: (solicitor)
- ☐ Expert's contact details (include medico-legal practice contact hours)

Contents Page

- ☐ Section headings and page numbers

Body of the Report

Introduction

- ☐ CV appropriate for case (usually 2-3 paragraphs, with an appended CV as necessary)
- ☐ Include substance of all material instructions
- ☐ Refers to 'CPR Part 35 report' or 'report for the court'
- ☐ Include a background to the dispute (as necessary)
- ☐ Include sources of information
- ☐ Include outline methodology

Factual Basis

- ☐ Present factual basis clearly
- ☐ Define technical terms in a bracket or footnote
- ☐ Include appropriate level of technical explanation
- ☐ Maintain a clear separation of fact and opinion in report structure/template
- ☐ Reference sources of factual information
- ☐ Quantify descriptive language (where available, use scales of description - either set out in the report or the appendices)

Opinion

- ☐ Summary of injuries (Condition and Prognosis reports only)
- ☐ Give clear diagnosis of injury
- ☐ Express each opinion in a structured manner (Long-Form/Short-Form)
- ☐ Deal with causation fully (as appropriate) addressing the 'but for' situation
- ☐ Apply the standard of proof and appropriate legal tests, using the correct phrases
- ☐ Support all opinions with reasons/reasoning
- ☐ Give prognosis: likelihood of deterioration/recovery, giving a range of probabilities/ time period
- ☐ Address consequences by dealing with restrictions reasonable and attributable to the injuries, symptoms and effects

Summary of Conclusions

- ☐ Summarise all conclusions
- ☐ Address all relevant issues (with reference to the solicitor's instructions)
- ☐ Ensure the Expert's Declaration and Statement of Truth comply with PD35
- ☐ Sign and date report

Appendix 3

CPR Part 35 Experts and Assessors (as at June 2015)

Duty to restrict expert evidence

35.1

Expert evidence shall be restricted to that which is reasonably required to resolve the proceedings.

Interpretation and definitions

35.2

(1) A reference to an 'expert' in this Part is a reference to a person who has been instructed to give or prepare expert evidence for the purpose of proceedings.

(2) 'Single joint expert' means an expert instructed to prepare a report for the court on behalf of two or more of the parties (including the claimant) to the proceedings.

Experts – overriding duty to the court

35.3

(1) It is the duty of experts to help the court on matters within their expertise.

(2) This duty overrides any obligation to the person from whom experts have received instructions or by whom they are paid.

Court's power to restrict expert evidence

35.4

(1) No party may call an expert or put in evidence an expert's report without the court's permission.

(2) When parties apply for permission they must provide an estimate of the costs of the proposed expert evidence and identify –

    (a) the field in which expert evidence is required and the issues which the expert evidence will address; and

    (b) where practicable, the name of the proposed expert.

(3) If permission is granted it shall be in relation only to the expert named or the field

identified under paragraph (2). The order granting permission may specify the issues which the expert evidence should address.

(3A) Where a claim has been allocated to the small claims track or the fast track, if permission is given for expert evidence, it will normally be given for evidence from only one expert on a particular issue.

(3B) In a soft tissue injury claim, permission—

(a) may normally only be given for one expert medical report;

(b) may not be given initially unless the medical report is a fixed cost medical report. Where the claimant seeks permission to obtain a further medical report, if the report is from a medical expert in any of the following disciplines—

(i) Consultant Orthopaedic Surgeon;

(ii) Consultant in Accident and Emergency Medicine;

(iii) General Practitioner registered with the General Medical Council; or

(iv) Physiotherapist registered with the Health and Care Professions Council

the report must be a fixed cost medical report.

(3C) In this rule, 'fixed cost medical report' and 'soft tissue injury claim' have the same meaning as in paragraph 1.1(10A) and (16A), respectively, of the RTA Protocol.

(Paragraph 7 of Practice Direction 35 sets out some of the circumstances the court will consider when deciding whether expert evidence should be given by a single joint expert.)

(4) The court may limit the amount of a party's expert's fees and expenses that may be recovered from any other party.

General requirement for expert evidence to be given in a written report

35.5

(1) Expert evidence is to be given in a written report unless the court directs otherwise.

(2) If a claim is on the small claims track or the fast track, the court will not direct an expert to attend a hearing unless it is necessary to do so in the interests of justice.

Written questions to experts

35.6

(1) A party may put written questions about an expert's report (which must be proportionate) to –

    (a) an expert instructed by another party; or

    (b) a single joint expert appointed under rule 35.7.

(2) Written questions under paragraph (1) –

    (a) may be put once only;

    (b) must be put within 28 days of service of the expert's report; and

    (c) must be for the purpose only of clarification of the report,

    unless in any case –

        (i) the court gives permission; or

        (ii) the other party agrees.

(3) An expert's answers to questions put in accordance with paragraph (1) shall be treated as part of the expert's report.

(4) Where –

    (a) a party has put a written question to an expert instructed by another party; and

    (b) the expert does not answer that question,

    the court may make one or both of the following orders in relation to the party who instructed the expert –

        (i) that the party may not rely on the evidence of that expert; or

        (ii) that the party may not recover the fees and expenses of that expert from any other party.

Court's power to direct that evidence is to be given by a single joint expert

35.7

(1) Where two or more parties wish to submit expert evidence on a particular issue, the court may direct that the evidence on that issue is to be given by a single joint expert.

(2) Where the parties who wish to submit the evidence ('the relevant parties') cannot agree who should be the single joint expert, the court may –

    (a) select the expert from a list prepared or identified by the relevant parties; or

    (b) direct that the expert be selected in such other manner as the court may direct.

Instructions to a single joint expert

35.8

(1) Where the court gives a direction under rule 35.7 for a single joint expert to be used, any relevant party may give instructions to the expert.

(2) When a party gives instructions to the expert that party must, at the same time, send a copy to the other relevant parties.

(3) The court may give directions about –

    (a) the payment of the expert's fees and expenses; and

    (b) any inspection, examination or experiments which the expert wishes to carry out.

(4) The court may, before an expert is instructed –

    (a) limit the amount that can be paid by way of fees and expenses to the expert; and

    (b) direct that some or all of the relevant parties pay that amount into court.

(5) Unless the court otherwise directs, the relevant parties are jointly and severally liable for the payment of the expert's fees and expenses.

Power of court to direct a party to provide information

35.9

Where a party has access to information which is not reasonably available to another party, the court may direct the party who has access to the information to –

(a) prepare and file a document recording the information; and

(b) serve a copy of that document on the other party.

Contents of report

35.10

(1) An expert's report must comply with the requirements set out in Practice Direction 35.

(2) At the end of an expert's report there must be a statement that the expert understands and has complied with their duty to the court.

(3) The expert's report must state the substance of all material instructions, whether written or oral, on the basis of which the report was written.

(4) The instructions referred to in paragraph (3) shall not be privileged against disclosure but the court will not, in relation to those instructions –

    (a) order disclosure of any specific document; or

    (b) permit any questioning in court, other than by the party who instructed the expert,

unless it is satisfied that there are reasonable grounds to consider the statement of instructions given under paragraph (3) to be inaccurate or incomplete.

Use by one party of expert's report disclosed by another

35.11

Where a party has disclosed an expert's report, any party may use that expert's report as evidence at the trial.

Discussions between experts

35.12

(1) The court may, at any stage, direct a discussion between experts for the purpose of requiring the experts to –

    (a) identify and discuss the expert issues in the proceedings; and

    (b) where possible, reach an agreed opinion on those issues.

(2) The court may specify the issues which the experts must discuss.

(3) The court may direct that following a discussion between the experts they must prepare a statement for the court setting out those issues on which –

    (a) they agree; and

(b) they disagree, with a summary of their reasons for disagreeing.

(4) The content of the discussion between the experts shall not be referred to at the trial unless the parties agree.

(5) Where experts reach agreement on an issue during their discussions, the agreement shall not bind the parties unless the parties expressly agree to be bound by the agreement.

Consequence of failure to disclose expert's report

35.13

A party who fails to disclose an expert's report may not use the report at the trial or call the expert to give evidence orally unless the court gives permission.

Expert's right to ask court for directions

35.14

(1) Experts may file written requests for directions for the purpose of assisting them in carrying out their functions.

(2) Experts must, unless the court orders otherwise, provide copies of the proposed requests for directions under paragraph (1) –

(a) to the party instructing them, at least 7 days before they file the requests; and

(b) to all other parties, at least 4 days before they file them.

(3) The court, when it gives directions, may also direct that a party be served with a copy of the directions.

Assessors

35.15

(1) This rule applies where the court appoints one or more persons under section 70 of the Senior Courts Act 1981 or section 63 of the County Courts Act 1984 as an assessor.

(2) An assessor will assist the court in dealing with a matter in which the assessor has skill and experience.

(3) An assessor will take such part in the proceedings as the court may direct and in particular the court may direct an assessor to –

(a) prepare a report for the court on any matter at issue in the proceedings; and

(b) attend the whole or any part of the trial to advise the court on any such matter.

(4) If an assessor prepares a report for the court before the trial has begun –

(a) the court will send a copy to each of the parties; and

(b) the parties may use it at trial.

(5) The remuneration to be paid to an assessor is to be determined by the court and will form part of the costs of the proceedings.

(6) The court may order any party to deposit in the court office a specified sum in respect of an assessor's fees and, where it does so, the assessor will not be asked to act until the sum has been deposited.

(7) Paragraphs (5) and (6) do not apply where the remuneration of the assessor is to be paid out of money provided by Parliament.

Appendix 4

Practice Direction to Part 35 (as at June 2015)

Introduction

1

Part 35 is intended to limit the use of oral expert evidence to that which is reasonably required. In addition, where possible, matters requiring expert evidence should be dealt with by only one expert. Experts and those instructing them are expected to have regard to the guidance contained in the Guidance for the Instruction of Experts in Civil Claims 2014 at www.judiciary.gov.uk. (Further guidance on experts is contained in Annex C to the Practice Direction (Pre-Action Conduct)).

Expert Evidence – General Requirements

2.1

Expert evidence should be the independent product of the expert uninfluenced by the pressures of litigation.

2.2

Experts should assist the court by providing objective, unbiased opinions on matters within their expertise, and should not assume the role of an advocate.

2.3

Experts should consider all material facts, including those which might detract from their opinions.

2.4

Experts should make it clear –

(a) when a question or issue falls outside their expertise; and

(b) when they are not able to reach a definite opinion, for example because they have insufficient information.

2.5

If, after producing a report, an expert's view changes on any material matter, such change of view should be communicated to all the parties without delay, and when appropriate to the court.

2.6

1. In a soft tissue injury claim, where permission is given for a fixed cost medical report, the first report must be obtained from an accredited medical expert selected via the MedCo Portal (website at: www.medco.org.uk).

2. The cost of obtaining a further report from an expert not listed in rule 35.4(3C)(a) to (d) is not subject to rules 45.19(2A)(b) or 45.29I(2A)(b), but the use of that expert and the cost must be justified.

3. 'Accredited medical expert', 'fixed cost medical report', 'MedCo', and 'soft tissue injury claim' have the same meaning as in paragraph 1.1(A1), (10A), (12A) and (16A), respectively, of the RTA Protocol.

Form and Content of an Expert's Report

3.1

An expert's report should be addressed to the court and not to the party from whom the expert has received instructions.

3.2

An expert's report must:

(1) give details of the expert's qualifications;

(2) give details of any literature or other material which has been relied on in making the report;

(3) contain a statement setting out the substance of all facts and instructions which are material to the opinions expressed in the report or upon which those opinions are based;

(4) make clear which of the facts stated in the report are within the expert's own knowledge;

(5) say who carried out any examination, measurement, test or experiment which the expert has used for the report, give the qualifications of that person, and say whether or not the test or experiment has been carried out under the expert's supervision;

(6) where there is a range of opinion on the matters dealt with in the report –

    (a) summarise the range of opinions; and

    (b) give reasons for the expert's own opinion;

(7) contain a summary of the conclusions reached;

(8) if the expert is not able to give an opinion without qualification, state the qualification; and

(9) contain a statement that the expert –

    (a) understands their duty to the court, and has complied with that duty; and

    (b) is aware of the requirements of Part 35, this practice direction and the Guidance for the Instruction of Experts in Civil Claims 2014.

3.3

An expert's report must be verified by a statement of truth in the following form –

I confirm that I have made clear which facts and matters referred to in this report are within my own knowledge and which are not. Those that are within my own knowledge I confirm to be true. The opinions I have expressed represent my true and complete professional opinions on the matters to which they refer.

Part 22 deals with statements of truth. Rule 32.14 sets out the consequences of verifying a document containing a false statement without an honest belief in its truth.

Information

4

Under rule 35.9 the court may direct a party with access to information, which is not reasonably available to another party to serve on that other party a document, which records the information. The document served must include sufficient details of all the facts, tests, experiments and assumptions which underlie any part of the information to enable the party on whom it is served to make, or to obtain, a proper interpretation of the information and an assessment of its significance.

Instructions

5

Cross-examination of experts on the contents of their instructions will not be allowed unless the court permits it (or unless the party who gave the instructions consents). Before it gives permission the court must be satisfied that there are reasonable grounds to consider that the statement in the report of the substance of the instructions is inaccurate or incomplete. If the court is so satisfied, it will allow the cross-examination where it appears to be in the interests of justice.

Questions to Experts

6.1

Where a party sends a written question or questions under rule 35.6 direct to an expert, a copy of the questions must, at the same time, be sent to the other party or parties.

6.2

The party or parties instructing the expert must pay any fees charged by that expert for answering questions put under rule 35.6. This does not affect any decision of the court as to the party who is ultimately to bear the expert's fees.

Single joint expert

7

When considering whether to give permission for the parties to rely on expert evidence and whether that evidence should be from a single joint expert the court will take into account all the circumstances in particular, whether:

(a) it is proportionate to have separate experts for each party on a particular issue with reference to –

    (i) the amount in dispute;

    (ii) the importance to the parties; and

    (iii) the complexity of the issue;

(b) the instruction of a single joint expert is likely to assist the parties and the court to resolve the issue more speedily and in a more cost-effective way than separately instructed experts;

(c) expert evidence is to be given on the issue of liability, causation or quantum;

(d) the expert evidence falls within a substantially established area of knowledge which is unlikely to be in dispute or there is likely to be a range of expert opinion;

(e) a party has already instructed an expert on the issue in question and whether or not that was done in compliance with any practice direction or relevant pre-action protocol;

(f) questions put in accordance with rule 35.6 are likely to remove the need for the other party to instruct an expert if one party has already instructed an expert;

(g) questions put to a single joint expert may not conclusively deal with all issues that may require testing prior to trial;

(h) a conference may be required with the legal representatives, experts and other witnesses which may make instruction of a single joint expert impractical; and

(i) a claim to privilege makes the instruction of any expert as a single joint expert inappropriate.

Orders

8

Where an order requires an act to be done by an expert, or otherwise affects an expert, the party instructing that expert must serve a copy of the order on the expert. The claimant must serve the order on a single joint expert.

Discussions between experts

9.1

Unless directed by the court discussions between experts are not mandatory. Parties must consider, with their experts, at an early stage, whether there is likely to be any useful purpose in holding an experts' discussion and if so when.

9.2

The purpose of discussions between experts is not for experts to settle cases but to agree and narrow issues and in particular to identify:

(i) the extent of the agreement between them;

(ii) the points of and short reasons for any disagreement;

(iii) action, if any, which may be taken to resolve any outstanding points of disagreement; and

(iv) any further material issues not raised and the extent to which these issues are agreed.

9.3

Where the experts are to meet, the parties must discuss and if possible agree whether an agenda is necessary, and if so attempt to agree one that helps the experts to focus on the issues which need to be discussed. The agenda must not be in the form of leading questions or hostile in tone.

9.4

Unless ordered by the court, or agreed by all parties, and the experts, neither the parties nor their legal representatives may attend experts discussions.

9.5

If the legal representatives do attend –

(i) they should not normally intervene in the discussion, except to answer questions put to them by the experts or to advise on the law; and

(ii) the experts may if they so wish hold part of their discussions in the absence of the legal representatives.

9.6

A statement must be prepared by the experts dealing with paragraphs 9.2(i) - (iv) above. Individual copies of the statements must be signed by the experts at the conclusion of the discussion, or as soon thereafter as practicable, and in any event within 7 days. Copies of the statements must be provided to the parties no later than 14 days after signing.

9.7

Experts must give their own opinions to assist the court and do not require the authority of the parties to sign a joint statement.

9.8

If an expert significantly alters an opinion, the joint statement must include a note or addendum by that expert explaining the change of opinion.

Assessors

10.1

An assessor may be appointed to assist the court under rule 35.15. Not less than 21 days before making any such appointment, the court will notify each party in writing of the name of the proposed assessor, of the matter in respect of which the assistance of the assessor will be sought and of the qualifications of the assessor to give that assistance.

10.2

Where any person has been proposed for appointment as an assessor, any party may object to that person either personally or in respect of that person's qualification.

10.3

Any such objection must be made in writing and filed with the court within 7 days of receipt of the notification referred to in paragraph 10.1 and will be taken into account by the court in deciding whether or not to make the appointment.

10.4

Copies of any report prepared by the assessor will be sent to each of the parties but the assessor will not give oral evidence or be open to cross-examination or questioning.

Concurrent expert evidence

11.1

At any stage in the proceedings the court may direct that some or all of the experts from like disciplines shall give their evidence concurrently. The following procedure shall then apply.

11.2

The court may direct that the parties agree an agenda for the taking of concurrent evidence, based upon the areas of disagreement identified in the experts' joint statements made pursuant to rule 35.12.

11.3

At the appropriate time the relevant experts will each take the oath or affirm. Unless the court orders otherwise, the experts will then address the items on the agenda in the manner set out in paragraph 11.4.

11.4

In relation to each issue on the agenda, and subject to the judge's discretion to modify the procedure –

1. the judge may initiate the discussion by asking the experts, in turn, for their views. Once an expert has expressed a view the judge may ask questions about it. At one or more appropriate stages when questioning a particular expert, the judge may invite the other expert to comment or to ask that expert's own questions of the first expert;

2. after the process set out in (1) has been completed for all the experts, the parties' representatives may ask questions of them. While such questioning may be designed to test the correctness of an expert's view, or seek clarification of it, it should not cover ground which has been fully explored already. In general a full cross-examination or re-examination is neither necessary nor appropriate; and

3. after the process set out in (2) has been completed, the judge may summarise the experts' different positions on the issue and ask them to confirm or correct that summary.

Appendix 5

Guidance for the instruction of experts in civil claims

Introduction

1. The purpose of this guidance is to assist litigants, those instructing experts and experts to understand best practice in complying with Part 35 of the Civil Procedure Rules (CPR) and court orders. Experts and those who instruct them should ensure they are familiar with CPR 35 and the Practice Direction (PD35). This guidance replaces the Protocol for the instruction of experts in civil claims (2005, amended 2009).

2. Those instructing experts, and the experts, must also have regard to the objectives underpinning the Pre-Action Protocols to:-

    a. encourage the exchange of early and full information about the expert issues involved in the prospective claim;

    b. enable the parties to avoid or reduce the scope of the litigation by agreeing the whole or part of an expert issue before proceedings are started; and

    c. support the efficient management of proceedings where litigation cannot be avoided.

3. Additionally, experts and those instructing them should be aware that some cases will be governed by the specific pre-action protocols and some may be "specialist proceedings" (CPR 49) where specific rules may apply.

Selecting and Instructing experts

The need for experts

4. Those intending to instruct experts to give or prepare evidence for the purpose of civil proceedings should consider whether expert evidence is necessary, taking account of the principles set out in CPR Parts 1 and 35, and in particular whether "it is required to resolve the proceedings" (CPR 35.1).

5. Although the court's permission is not generally required to instruct an expert, the court's permission is required before an expert's report can be relied upon or an expert can be called to give oral evidence (CPR 35.4).

6. Advice from an expert before proceedings are started which the parties do not intend to rely upon in litigation is likely to be confidential; this guidance does not apply then. The same applies where, after the commencement of proceedings,

experts are instructed only to advise (e.g. to comment upon a single joint expert's report) and not to prepare evidence for the proceedings. The expert's role then is that of an expert advisor.

7. However this guidance does apply if experts who were formerly instructed only to advise, are later instructed as an expert witness to prepare or give evidence in the proceedings.

8. In the remainder of this guidance, a reference to an expert means an expert witness to whom Part 35 applies.

Duties and obligations of experts

9. Experts always owe a duty to exercise reasonable skill and care to those instructing them, and to comply with any relevant professional code. However when they are instructed to give or prepare evidence for civil proceedings they have an overriding duty to help the court on matters within their expertise (CPR 35.3). This duty overrides any obligation to the person instructing or paying them. Experts must not serve the exclusive interest of those who retain them.

10. Experts should be aware of the overriding objective that courts deal with cases justly and that they are under an obligation to assist the court in this respect. This includes dealing with cases proportionately (keeping the work and costs in proportion to the value and importance of the case to the parties), expeditiously and fairly (CPR 1.1).

11. Experts must provide opinions that are independent, regardless of the pressures of litigation. A useful test of 'independence' is that the expert would express the same opinion if given the same instructions by another party. Experts should not take it upon themselves to promote the point of view of the party instructing them or engage in the role of advocates or mediators.

12. Experts should confine their opinions to matters which are material to the disputes and provide opinions only in relation to matters which lie within their expertise. Experts should indicate without delay where particular questions or issues fall outside their expertise.

13. Experts should take into account all material facts before them. Their reports should set out those facts and any literature or material on which they have relied in forming their opinions. They should indicate if an opinion is provisional, or qualified, or where they consider that further information is required or if, for any other reason, they are not satisfied that an opinion can be expressed finally and without qualification.

14. Experts should inform those instructing them without delay of any change in their opinions on any material matter and the reasons for this (see also paragraphs 64-66).

15. Experts should be aware that any failure to comply with the rules or court orders, or any excessive delay for which they are responsible, may result in the parties who instructed them being penalised in costs, or debarred from relying upon the expert evidence (see also paragraphs 89-92).

The appointment of experts

16. Before experts are instructed or the court's permission to appoint named experts is sought, it should be established whether the experts:

    a. have the appropriate expertise and experience for the particular instruction;

    b. are familiar with the general duties of an expert;

    c. can produce a report, deal with questions and have discussions with other experts within a reasonable time, and at a cost proportionate to the matters in issue;

    d. are available to attend the trial, if attendance is required; and

    e. have no potential conflict of interest.

17. Terms of appointment should be agreed at the outset and should normally include:

    a. the capacity in which the expert is to be appointed (e.g. party appointed expert or single joint expert);

    b. the services required of the expert (e.g. provision of an expert's report, answering questions in writing, attendance at meetings and attendance at court);

    c. time for delivery of the report;

    d. the basis of the expert's charges (e.g. daily or hourly rates and an estimate of the time likely to be required, or a fixed fee for the services). Parties must provide an estimate to the court of the costs of the proposed expert evidence and for each stage of the proceedings (CPR.35.4(2);

    e. travelling expenses and disbursements;

    f. cancellation charges;

    g. any fees for attending court;

    h. time for making the payment;

    i. whether fees are to be paid by a third party;

j.   if a party is publicly funded, whether the expert's charges will be subject to assessment; and

k.   guidance that the expert's fees and expenses may be limited by the court (note expert's recoverable fees in the small claims track cannot exceed £750: see PD 27 paragraph 7).

18.   When necessary, arrangements should be made for dealing with questions to experts and discussions between experts, including any directions given by the court.

19.   Experts should be kept informed about deadlines for all matters concerning them. Those instructing experts should send them promptly copies of all court orders and directions that may affect the preparation of their reports or any other matters concerning their obligations.

Instructions

20.   Those instructing experts should ensure that they give clear instructions (and attach relevant documents), including the following:

a.   basic information, such as names, addresses, telephone numbers, dates of incidents and any relevant claim reference numbers;

b.   the nature of the expertise required;

c.   the purpose of the advice or report, a description of the matter(s) to be investigated, the issues to be addressed and the identity of all parties;

d.   the statement(s) of case (if any), those documents which form part of disclosure and witness statements and expert reports that are relevant to the advice or report, making clear which have been served and which are drafts and when the latter are likely to be served;

e.   where proceedings have not been started, whether they are contemplated and, if so, whether the expert is being asked only for advice;

f.   an outline programme, consistent with good case management and the expert's availability, for the completion and delivery of each stage of the expert's work; and

g.   where proceedings have been started, the dates of any hearings (including any case/costs management conferences and/or pre-trial reviews), the dates fixed by the court or agreed between the parties for the exchange of experts' reports and any other relevant deadlines to be adhered to, the name of the court, the claim number, the track to which the claim has been allocated and whether there is a specific budget for the experts' fees.

21. Those instructing experts should seek to agree, where practicable, the instructions for the experts, and that they receive the same factual material.

Acceptance of instructions

22. Experts should confirm without delay whether they accept their instructions.

23. They should also inform those instructing them (whether on initial instruction or at any later stage) without delay if:

    a. instructions are not acceptable because, for example, they require work that falls outside their expertise, impose unrealistic deadlines, or are insufficiently clear. Experts who do not receive clear instructions should request clarification and may indicate that they are not prepared to act unless and until such clear instructions are received;

    b. they consider that instructions are insufficient to complete the work;

    c. they become aware that they may not be able to fulfil any of the terms of appointment;

    d. the instructions and/or work have, for any reason, placed them in conflict with their duties as an expert. Where an expert advisor is approached to act as an expert witness they will need to consider carefully whether they can accept a role as expert witness; or

    e. they are not satisfied that they can comply with any orders that have been made.

24. Experts must neither express an opinion outside the scope of their field of expertise, nor accept any instructions to do so.

25. Where an expert identifies that the basis of his instruction differs from that of another expert, he should inform those instructing him.

26. Experts should agree the terms on which they are to be paid with those instructing them. Experts should be aware that they will be required to provide estimates for the court and that the court may limit the amount to be paid as part of any order for budgeted costs (CPR 35.4(2) and (4) and 3.15).

Experts' Withdrawal

27. Where experts' instructions are incompatible with their duties, through incompleteness, a conflict between their duty to the court and their instructions, or for any other reason, the experts may consider withdrawing from the case. However, experts should not do so without first discussing the position with those who instruct them and considering whether it would be more appropriate to make a written request for directions from the court. If experts do withdraw, they must give formal written notice to those instructing them.

Experts' right to ask court for directions

28. Experts may request directions from the court to assist them in carrying out their functions (CPR 35.14), for example, if experts consider that they have not been provided with information they require. Experts should normally discuss this with those who instruct them before making a request. Unless the court otherwise orders, any proposed request for directions should be sent to the party instructing the expert at least seven days before filing any request with the court, and to all other parties at least four days before filing it.

29. Requests to the court for directions should be made by letter clearly marked "expert's request for directions" containing:

    a. the title of the claim;

    b. the claim number;

    c. the name of the expert;

    d. why directions are sought; and

    e. copies of any relevant documentation.

Experts' access to information held by the parties

30. Experts should try to ensure that they have access to all relevant information held by the parties, and that the same information has been disclosed to each expert in the same discipline. Experts should seek to confirm this soon after accepting instructions, notifying instructing solicitors of any omissions.

31. If a solicitor sends an expert additional documents before the report is finalised the solicitor must tell the expert whether any witness statements or expert reports are updated versions of those previously sent and whether they have been filed and served.

32. Experts should be specifically aware of CPR 35.9. This provides that, where one party has access to information that is not readily available to the other party, the court may direct the party who has access to the information to prepare, file and copy to the other party a document recording the information. If experts require such information which has not been disclosed, they should discuss the position with those instructing them without delay, so that a request for the information can be made, and, if not forthcoming, an application can be made to the court.

33. Any request for further information from the other party made by an expert should be in a letter to the expert's instructing party and should state why the information is necessary and the significance in relation to the expert issues in the case.

Single joint experts

34. CPR 35.7-8 and PD 35 paragraph 7 deal with the instruction and use of joint experts by the parties and the powers of the court to order their use. The CPR encourage the use of joint experts. Wherever possible a joint report should be obtained. Single joint experts are the norm in cases allocated to the small claims track and the fast track.

35. In the early stages of a dispute, when investigations, tests, site inspections, photographs, plans or other similar preliminary expert tasks are necessary, consideration should be given to the instruction of a single joint expert, especially where such matters are not expected to be contentious. The objective should be to agree or to narrow issues.

36. Experts who have previously advised a party (whether in the same case or otherwise) should only be proposed as single joint experts if the other parties are given all relevant information about the previous involvement.

37. The appointment of a single joint expert does not prevent parties from instructing their own experts to advise (but the cost of such expert advisors will not be recoverable from another party).

Joint instructions

38. The parties should try to agree joint instructions to single joint experts, but in default of agreement, each party may give instructions. In particular, all parties should try to agree what documents should be included with instructions and what assumptions single joint experts should make.

39. Where the parties fail to agree joint instructions, they should try to agree where the areas of disagreement lie and their instructions should make this clear. If separate instructions are given, they should be copied to the other instructing parties.

40. Where experts are instructed by two or more parties, the terms of appointment should, unless the court has directed otherwise, or the parties have agreed otherwise, include:

    a. a statement that all the instructing parties are jointly and severally liable to pay the experts' fees and, accordingly, that experts' invoices should be sent simultaneously to all instructing parties or their solicitors (as appropriate); and

    b. a copy of any order limiting experts' fees and expenses (CPR 35.8(4)(a)).

41. Where instructions have not been received by the expert from one or more of the instructing parties, the expert should give notice (normally at least 7 days) of a deadline for their receipt. Unless the instructions are received within the deadline the expert may begin work. If instructions are received after the deadline but before

the completion of the report the expert should consider whether it is practicable to comply without adversely affecting the timetable for delivery of the report and without greatly increasing the costs and exceeding any court approved budget. An expert who decides to issue a report without taking into account instructions received after the deadline must inform the parties, who may apply to the court for directions. In either event the report must show clearly that the expert did not receive instructions within the deadline, or, as the case may be, at all.

Conduct of the single joint expert

42. Single joint experts should keep all instructing parties informed of any material steps that they may be taking by, for example, copying all correspondence to those instructing them.

43. Single joint experts are Part 35 experts and so have an overriding duty to the court. They are the parties' appointed experts and therefore owe an equal duty to all parties. They should maintain independence, impartiality and transparency at all times.

44. Single joint experts should not attend a meeting or conference that is not a joint one, unless all the parties have agreed in writing or the court has directed that such a meeting may be held. There also needs to be agreement about who is to pay the experts' fees for the meeting.

45. Single joint experts may request directions from the court (see paragraphs 28-29).

46. Single joint experts should serve their reports simultaneously on all instructing parties. They should provide a single report even though they may have received instructions that contain conflicts. If conflicting instructions lead to different opinions (for example, because the instructions require the expert to make different assumptions of fact), reports may need to contain more than one set of opinions on any issue. It is for the court to determine the facts.

Cross-examination of the single joint expert

47. Single joint experts do not normally give oral evidence at trial but if they do, all parties may ask questions. In general, written questions (CPR 35.6) should be put to single joint experts before requests are made for them to attend court for the purpose of cross-examination.

Experts' reports

48. The content of experts' reports should be governed by their instructions and general obligations, any court directions, CPR 35 and PD35, and the experts' overriding duty to the court.

49. In preparing reports, experts should maintain professional objectivity and impartiality at all times.

50. PD 35, paragraph 3.1 provides that experts' reports should be addressed to the court and gives detailed directions about their form and content. All experts and those who instruct them should ensure that they are familiar with these requirements.

51. Model forms of experts' reports are available from bodies such as the Academy of Experts and the Expert Witness Institute and a template for medical reports has been created by the Ministry of Justice.

52. Experts' reports must contain statements that they:

    a. understand their duty to the court and have complied and will continue to comply with it; and

    b. are aware of and have complied with the requirements of CPR 35 and PD 35 and this guidance.

53. Experts' reports must also be verified by a statement of truth. The form of the statement of truth is:

    "I confirm that I have made clear which facts and matters referred to in this report are within my own knowledge and which are not. Those that are within my own knowledge I confirm to be true. The opinions I have expressed represent my true and complete professional opinions on the matters to which they refer."

54. The details of experts' qualifications in reports should be commensurate with the nature and complexity of the case. It may be sufficient to state any academic and professional qualifications. However, where highly specialised expertise is called for, experts should include the detail of particular training and/or experience that qualifies them to provide that specialised evidence.

55. The mandatory statement of the substance of all material instructions should not be incomplete or otherwise tend to mislead. The imperative is transparency. The term "instructions" includes all material that solicitors send to experts. These should be listed, with dates, in the report or an appendix. The omission from the statement of 'off-the-record' oral instructions is not permitted. Courts may allow cross-examination about the instructions if there are reasonable grounds to consider that the statement may be inaccurate or incomplete.

56. Where tests of a scientific or technical nature have been carried out, experts should state:

    a. the methodology used; and

    b. by whom the tests were undertaken and under whose supervision, summarising their respective qualifications and experience.

57. When addressing questions of fact and opinion, experts should keep the two

separate. Experts must state those facts (whether assumed or otherwise) upon which their opinions are based; experts should have primary regard to their instructions (paragraphs 20-25 above). Experts must distinguish clearly between those facts that they know to be true and those facts which they assume.

58. Where there are material facts in dispute experts should express separate opinions on each hypothesis put forward. They should not express a view in favour of one or other disputed version of the facts unless, as a result of particular expertise and experience, they consider one set of facts as being improbable or less probable, in which case they may express that view and should give reasons for holding it.

59. If the mandatory summary of the range of opinion is based on published sources, experts should explain those sources and, where appropriate, state the qualifications of the originator(s) of the opinions from which they differ, particularly if such opinions represent a well-established school of thought.

60. Where there is no available source for the range of opinion, experts may need to express opinions on what they believe to be the range that other experts would arrive at if asked. In those circumstances, experts should make it clear that the range that they summarise is based on their own judgement and explain the basis of that judgement.

Prior to service of reports

61. Before filing and serving an expert's report solicitors must check that any witness statements and other experts' reports relied upon by the expert are the final served versions.

Conclusions of reports

62. A summary of conclusions is mandatory. Generally the summary should be at the end of the report after the reasoning. There may be cases, however, where the court would find it helpful to have a short summary at the beginning, with the full conclusions at the end. For example, in cases involving highly complex matters which fall outside the general knowledge of the court the judge may be assisted in the comprehension of the facts and analysis if the report explains at the outset the basis of the reasoning.

Sequential exchange of experts' reports

63. Where there is to be sequential exchange of reports then the defendant's expert's report usually will be produced in response to the claimant's. The defendant's report should then :

   a. confirm whether the background set out in the claimant's expert report is agreed, or identify those parts that in the defendant's expert's view require revision, setting out the necessary revisions. The defendant's expert need not repeat information that is adequately dealt with in the claimant's expert report;

b.   focus only on those material areas of difference with the claimant's expert's opinion. The defendant's report should identify those assumptions of the claimant's expert that they consider reasonable (and agree with) and those that they do not; and

c.   in particular where the experts are addressing the financial value of heads of claim (for example, the costs of a care regime or loss of profits), the defendant's report should contain a reconciliation between the claimant's expert's loss assessment and the defendant's, identifying for each assumption any different conclusion to the claimant's expert.

Amendment of reports

64.   It may become necessary for experts to amend their reports:

a.   as a result of an exchange of questions and answers;

b.   following agreements reached at meetings between experts; or

c.   where further evidence or documentation is disclosed.

65.   Experts should not be asked to amend, expand or alter any parts of reports in a manner which distorts their true opinion, but may be invited to do so to ensure accuracy, clarity, internal consistency, completeness and relevance to the issues. Although experts should generally follow the recommendations of solicitors with regard to the form of reports, they should form their own independent views on the opinions and contents of their reports and not include any suggestions that do not accord with their views.

66.   Where experts change their opinion following a meeting of experts, a signed and dated note to that effect is generally sufficient. Where experts significantly alter their opinion, as a result of new evidence or for any other reason, they must inform those who instruct them and amend their reports explaining the reasons. Those instructing experts should inform other parties as soon as possible of any change of opinion.

Written questions to experts

67.   Experts have a duty to provide answers to questions properly put. Where they fail to do so, the court may impose sanctions against the party instructing the expert, and, if there is continued non-compliance, debar a party from relying on the report. Experts should copy their answers to those instructing them.

68.   Experts' answers to questions become part of their reports. They are covered by the statement of truth, and form part of the expert evidence.

69.   Where experts believe that questions put are not properly directed to the clarification of the report, or have been asked out of time, they should discuss

the questions with those instructing them and, if appropriate, those asking the questions. Attempts should be made to resolve such problems without the need for an application to the court for directions, but in the absence of agreement or application for directions by the party or parties, experts may themselves file a written request to court for directions (see paragraphs 28-29).

Discussions between experts

70. The court has the power to direct discussions between experts for the purposes set out in the Rules (CPR 35.12). Parties may also agree that discussions take place between their experts at any stage. Discussions are not mandatory unless ordered by the court.

71. The purpose of discussions between experts should be, wherever possible, to:

    a.   identify and discuss the expert issues in the proceedings;

    b.   reach agreed opinions on those issues, and, if that is not possible, narrow the issues;

    c.   identify those issues on which they agree and disagree and summarise their reasons for disagreement on any issue; and

    d.   identify what action, if any, may be taken to resolve any of the outstanding issues between the parties.

They are not to seek to settle the proceedings.

72. Where single joint experts have been instructed but parties have, with the permission of the court, instructed their own additional Part 35 experts, there may, if the court so orders or the parties agree, be discussions between the single joint experts and the additional Part 35 experts. Such discussions should be confined to those matters within the remit of the additional Part 35 experts or as ordered by the court.

73. Where there is sequential exchange of expert reports, with the defendant's expert's report prepared in accordance with the guidance at paragraph 63 above, the joint statement should focus upon the areas of disagreement, save for the need for the claimant's expert to consider and respond to material, information and commentary included within the defendant's expert's report.

74. Arrangements for discussions between experts should be proportionate to the value of cases. In small claims and fast-tracks cases there should not normally be face to face meetings between experts: telephone discussion or an exchange of letters should usually suffice. In multi-track cases discussion may be face to face but the practicalities or the proportionality principle may require discussions to be by telephone or video-conference.

75. In multi-track cases the parties, their lawyers and experts should co-operate to produce an agenda for any discussion between experts, although primary responsibility for preparation of the agenda should normally lie with the parties' solicitors.

76. The agenda should indicate what has been agreed and summarise concisely matters that are in dispute. It is often helpful to include questions to be answered by the experts. If agreement cannot be reached promptly or a party is unrepresented, the court may give directions for the drawing up of the agenda. The agenda should be circulated to experts and those instructing them to allow sufficient time for the experts to prepare for the discussion.

77. Those instructing experts must not instruct experts to avoid reaching agreement (or to defer doing so) on any matter within the experts' competence. Experts are not permitted to accept such instructions.

78. The content of discussions between experts should not be referred to at trial unless the parties agree (CPR 35.12(4)). It is good practice for any such agreement to be in writing.

79. At the conclusion of any discussion between experts, a joint statement should be prepared setting out:

    a. issues that have been agreed and the basis of that agreement;

    b. issues that have not been agreed and the basis of the disagreement;

    c. any further issues that have arisen that were not included in the original agenda for discussion; and

    d. a record of further action, if any, to be taken or recommended, including if appropriate a further discussion between experts.

80. The joint statement should include a brief re-statement that the experts recognise their duties (or a cross-reference to the relevant statements in their respective reports). The joint statement should also include an express statement that the experts have not been instructed to avoid reaching agreement (or otherwise defer from doing so) on any matter within the experts' competence.

81. The joint statement should be agreed and signed by all the parties to the discussion as soon as practicable.

82. Agreements between experts during discussions do not bind the parties unless the parties expressly agree to be bound (CPR 35.12(5)). However, parties should give careful consideration before refusing to be bound by such an agreement and be able to explain their refusal should it become relevant to the issue of costs.

83. Since April 2013 the court has had the power to order at any stage that experts of

like disciplines give their evidence at trial concurrently, not sequentially with their party's evidence as has been the norm hitherto: PD 35 paragraphs 11.1-11.4 (this is often known as "hot–tubbing"). The experts will then be questioned together, firstly by the judge based upon disagreements in the joint statement, and then by the parties' advocates. Concurrent evidence can save time and costs, and assist the judge in assessing the difference of views between experts. Experts need to be told in advance of the trial if the court has made an order for concurrent evidence.

Attendance of experts at court

84. Those instructing experts should ascertain the availability of experts before trial dates are fixed; keep experts updated with timetables (including the dates and times experts are to attend), the location of the court and court orders; consider, where appropriate, whether experts might give evidence via video-link; and inform experts immediately if trial dates are vacated or adjourned.

85. Experts have an obligation to attend court and should ensure that those instructing them are aware of their dates to avoid and that they take all reasonable steps to be available.

86. Experts should normally attend court without the need for a witness summons, but on occasion they may be served to require their attendance (CPR 34). The use of witness summonses does not affect the contractual or other obligations of the parties to pay experts' fees.

87. When a case has been concluded either by a settlement or trial the solicitor should inform the experts they have instructed.

Experts and conditional and contingency fees

88. Payment of experts' fees contingent upon the nature of the expert evidence or upon the outcome of the case is strongly discouraged. In *ex parte Factortame (no8)* [2003] QB 381 at [73], the court said ' we consider that it will be a rare case indeed that the court will be prepared to consent to an expert being instructed under a contingency fee agreement'.

Sanctions

89. Solicitors and experts should be aware that sanctions might apply because of a failure to comply with CPR 35, the PD or court orders.

90. Whether or not court proceedings have been commenced a professional instructing an expert, or an expert, may be subject to sanction for misconduct by their professional body/regulator.

91. If proceedings have been started the court has the power under CPR 44 to impose sanctions:

    a.   cost penalties against those instructing the expert (including a wasted costs order) or the expert (such as disallowance or reduction of the expert" fee) (CPR 35.4(4) and CPR 44).

    b.   that an expert's report/evidence be inadmissible.

92. Experts should also be aware of other possible sanctions

    a.   In more extreme cases, if the court has been misled it may invoke general powers for contempt in the face of the court. The court would then have the power to fine or imprison the wrongdoer.

    b.   If an expert commits perjury, criminal sanctions may follow.

    c.   If an expert has been negligent there may be a claim on their professional indemnity insurance.

Civil Justice Council
August 2014

Appendix 6

GMC Guidance — Acting as a witness in legal proceedings (April 2013)

1. In *Good medical practice*[1] we say:

    - 11 You must be familiar with guidelines and developments that affect your work.

    - 12 You must keep up to date with, and follow, the law, our guidance and other regulations relevant to your work.

    - 14 You must recognise and work within the limits of your competence.

    - 72 You must be honest and trustworthy when giving evidence to courts or tribunals. You must make sure that any evidence you give or documents you write or sign are not false or misleading.

        a. You must take reasonable steps to check the information.

        b. You must not deliberately leave out relevant information.

    - 73 You must cooperate with formal inquiries and complaints procedures and must offer all relevant information while following the guidance in *Confidentiality*.

    - 74 You must make clear the limits of your competence and knowledge when giving evidence or acting as a witness.

2. In this guidance, we explain how doctors can put these principles into practice when acting as a professional witness or as an expert witness. If you give evidence as a witness of fact in a non-professional capacity (for example, as a witness to a traffic accident) you must follow the guidance in paragraph 72 of *Good medical practice*. Serious or persistent failure to follow this guidance will put your registration at risk.

---

1   General Medical Council (2013) *Good medical practice* London, GMC.

Duties of all witnesses

3.   Doctors play an important role in the justice system by contributing evidence both as expert witnesses and as witnesses of fact.

4.   Whether you are acting as a witness of fact or an expert witness, you have a duty to the court[2] and this overrides any obligation to the person who is instructing or paying you[3].

   This means you have a duty to act independently and to be honest, trustworthy, objective and impartial. You must not allow your views[4] about a person to affect the evidence or advice you give.

5.   You must understand your role as a witness throughout the court process. You must cooperate with case management, making sure you meet the timescales for producing reports and going to conferences, meetings or court hearings.

6.   You must make sure that any report you write, or evidence you give, is accurate and not misleading. This means you must take reasonable steps to check the accuracy of any information you give, and to make sure that you include all relevant information.

7.   People who do not have a medical background may rely on your advice and evidence to help them make decisions. Where it is possible to do so without misleading anyone, you should use language and terminology that people who are not medically qualified will understand. You should explain any abbreviations and medical or other technical terminology you use. Diagrams with explanatory labels can be useful.

Giving evidence as a witness of fact (professional witness)

8.   Witnesses of fact (also known as professional witnesses) provide professional evidence of their clinical findings, observations and actions, and the reasons for them.

9.   As a witness of fact, your written and oral evidence should be clear and concise, and must be based as far as possible on clinical records and notes made at the relevant period of time. You may include some opinion about the findings but you should make clear what is factual evidence and what is your opinion based on your professional judgement and experience.

---

2   Also tribunals and other public inquiries such as coroners' inquests.

3   *Civil Procedure Rules*, rule 35.3, *Criminal Procedure Rules*, rule 33.2, *Family Procedure Rules*, rule 25.3, *Children's Hearings (Scotland) Rules 1996, Act of Adjournal (Criminal Procedure Rules) 1996, Criminal Justice (Evidence) (Northern Ireland) Order 2004*.

4   This includes your views about a patient's lifestyle, culture or their social or economic status, as well as the characteristics protected by legislation: age, disability, gender reassignment, race, marriage and civil partnership, pregnancy and maternity, religion or belief, sex and sexual orientation.

Giving evidence as an expert witness

10. The role of an expert witness is to help the court on specialist or technical matters that are within the witness's expertise. An expert witness is able to consider all the evidence available, including statements and reports from the other parties to the proceedings, before forming and providing an opinion to the court.

11. You must make sure you understand exactly what questions you are being asked to answer. If your instructions are unclear, you should ask those instructing you to explain. If the instructions are still not clear, you should not provide expert advice or opinion.

12. You must only give expert testimony and opinions about issues that are within your professional competence or about which you have relevant knowledge including, for example, knowledge of the standards and nature of practice at the time of the incident or events that are the subject of the proceedings[5]. If a particular question or issue falls outside your area of expertise, you should either refuse to answer or answer to the best of your ability but make it clear that you consider the matter to be outside your competence[6].

13. You must give an objective, unbiased opinion and be able to state the facts or assumptions on which it is based. If there is a range of opinion on an issue, you should summarise the range of opinion and explain how you arrived at your own view. If you do not have enough information on which to reach a conclusion on a particular point, or if your opinion is qualified (for example, as a result of conflicting evidence), you must make this clear[7].

14. If you are asked to give an opinion about a person without the opportunity to consult with or examine them, you should explain any limits this may place on your opinion. You should be able to justify the decision to provide your opinion.

15. If, at any stage, you change your view on any relevant matter, you have a duty to make sure those instructing you, the other party and the judge are made aware of this without delay. You should tell your instructing solicitor, who should tell the other people who need to know. If the solicitor fails to do this, you should tell the court about your change of view. If you are not sure about what to do, you should ask the court or get legal advice.

16. You must respect the skills and contributions of other professionals giving expert evidence, and not allow their behaviour to affect your professional opinion.

---

5   The same principle applies where a doctor acts in a role other than as a witness – for example, as an adviser in a case

6   The Right Honourable Justice Wall (2007) *A handbook for expert witnesses in Children Act cases* Bristol: Jordans, 2nd edition.

7   See *Oldham MBC v GW & Ors* [2007] EWHC 136 (Fam). The judgment is available at www.bailii.org/ew/cases/EWHC/Fam/2007/136.html.

Notes and records

17. You must make full and accurate notes of meetings or interviews with the people involved in the case at the time an event happens or as soon as possible afterwards. Any notes or reports you make must be written fairly and impartially.

Understanding your role

18. You must understand and follow the law and codes of practice that affect your role as an expert witness. You should consider undertaking training for the role, where available (for example, from your medical defence body or your employer's legal department). In particular, you should make sure you understand:

    a. how to write a report that follows the procedures set out by the courts

    b. how to give oral evidence.

19. If you have expertise and experience in acting as an expert witness, you should be willing to share your knowledge with colleagues who might be called to give evidence in court, to help build their confidence and willingness to give evidence in the future.

Information security and disclosure

20. You must take all reasonable steps to read all relevant papers and keep them secure while in your possession.

21. If you receive information about a person and have reason to believe that they have not given consent for the information to be shared, you should return the information to the person instructing you and seek confirmation that consent has been given.

22. You should not disclose confidential information to anyone who is not involved in the court proceedings, unless:

    a. the person the information relates to gives their consent (and there are no other restrictions or limits on sharing the information)

    b. you must do so by law

    c. you are ordered to do so by a court or tribunal

    d. your overriding duty to the court and the administration of justice means that you must disclose the information.

Conflicts of interest

23. If there is a possible conflict of interest – for example, you have been professionally

or personally involved with one of the people involved in the case in the past, or you have a personal interest in the case – you must follow our guidance on conflicts of interest[8]. You must also make sure the people instructing you, the other party and the judge are made aware of this without delay. You may continue to act as an expert witness only if the court decides the conflict of interest will not affect the case.

Other sources of information

British Medical Association (2008) *Expert witness guidance* London, British Medical Association

The medical defence bodies publish resources to support their members who act as witnesses of fact and expert witnesses.

The Right Honourable Justice Wall (2007) *A handbook for expert witnesses in Children Act cases* Bristol, Jordans, 2nd edition

General Medical Council (2009) *Confidentiality London*, GMC, available at www.gmc-uk.org/confidentiality

The Academy of Medical Royal Colleges
www.aomrc.org.uk

The Civil Justice Council
www.judiciary.gov.uk/about-the-judiciary/advisory-bodies/cjc

Family Justice Council
www.judiciary.gov.uk/about-the-judiciary/advisory-bodies/fjc

The Crown Prosecution Service (Disclosure manual)
www.cps.gov.uk/legal/d_to_g/disclosure_manual

The Law Society of England and Wales
www.lawsociety.org.uk

The Law Society of Scotland
www.lawscot.org.uk

The Scottish Children's Reporter Administration
www.scra.gov.uk

---

8   General Medical Council (2013) *Financial and commercial arrangements and conflicts of interest* London, GMC.

Rules and legislation

England and Wales

The Criminal Justice Act 2003
www.legislation.gov.uk/ukpga/2003/44/contents

The Civil Evidence Act 1995
www.legislation.gov.uk/ukpga/1995/38/contents

The Civil Evidence Act 1995
The Civil Procedure Rules
The Criminal Procedure Rules
The Family Procedure Rules
Practice Direction on Experts in Family Proceedings Relating to Children

Access these documents using the search on the Ministry of Justice website
www.justice.gov.uk

Scotland

The Criminal Procedure Rules and Court Rules
www.scotcourts.gov.uk/library/rules/index.asp

Northern Ireland

The Rules of the Supreme Court
This document is not available online – contact the Office of Public Sector Information
(www.opsi.gov.uk) to find out how to get a copy.

Criminal Justice (Evidence) (Northern Ireland) Order 2004
www.legislation.gov.uk/nisi/2004/1501/contents

Appendix 7 - Schedule of Loss (Example)

C.T. -V- EVER-SO-QUICK DELIVERIES LTD

SCHEDULE OF LOSS

Date of birth of Claimant   15th February 1968
Date of accident   1st April 2011
Calculation date   1st April 2013

SUMMARY

PAST LOSSES

1	LOSS OF EARNINGS	8,180.97
2	CARE AND ASSISTANCE	10,276.71
3	COST OF MEDICAL TREATMENT	15,525.00
4	MEDICAL EQUIPMENT	205.99
5	LOSS OF INCOME AS FOOTBALL REFEREE	936.00
6	INTEREST	1,148.58

TOTAL OF PAST LOSSES AND INTEREST   36,273.25

FUTURE LOSSES

7	LOSS OF EARNINGS/EARNINGS CAPACITY	65,000.00
8	LOSS OF PROFIT FROM HOME IMPROVEMENTS	To be assessed
9	CARE AND ASSISTANCE	41,785.22
10	FUTURE EQUIPMENT AND TREATMENT COSTS	3,044.70
11	LOSS OF INCOME AS FOOTBALL REFEREE	2,199.60

Plus damages for pain, suffering and loss of amenity To be assessed

See medical reports of Mr Sawbones, Consultant Orthopaedic
and Spinal Surgeon, dated 1st April 2012 and 28th February 2013

PAST LOSSES

1 LOSS OF EARNINGS

The Claimant is employed as a maintenance
electrician by Pan-World Call Centre on a

short term contract. Prior to the accident
his average weekly net wage was -   261.70

The Claimant was off work for an initial
period of 3 months and then following the
discectomy on 30th June 2012 for 6 months.

The Claimant has arranged his work so
that he can avoid all but the lightest of
work and has managed to remain at
work since the operation.

1)	**Period 1st April to 30th June 2011**	
	Paid	275.00
	At pre accident rate would have earned	3,402.10
	Loss for period	3,127.10
2)	**Period 30th June 2012 to 29th December 2012**	
	Paid	1,750.33
	At pre-accident rate	6,804.20
	Loss for period	5,053.87

TOTAL LOSS OF EARNINGS   8,180.97

2   CARE AND ASSISTANCE

All care and assistance is claimed at the
aggregate rates for National Joint
Council pay rates Spinal Point 8
discounted by 25% to reflect the
gratuitous nature of the care and
assistance provided, an hourly rate of -   6.73 per hour

1)   The Claimant spent 4 days in hospital.
His wife visited each day to provide
support and comfort, and to provide
some care needs when hospital staff
were too busy to care for the Claimant.

His wife spent an average of 5 hours
per day providing this care for the
Claimant

5 hours x 4 days =   134.60

2)   For 3 weeks after discharge from hospital the Claimant was in great pain and dependant on his wife to provide him with all his needs, including drinks and food and assisting him with washing and toilet needs, and providing him with support and comfort.

His wife spent an average of 6 hours per day providing this care for the Claimant

6 hours x 3 weeks x 7 days =   847.98

3)   The Claimant gradually became more independent until in July he was able to return to work on light duties and no longer had care needs. His wife's care and assistance during that period reduced. Care is claimed on the basis of an average of 3 hours per day throughout the period of 9 weeks

3 hours x 9 weeks x 7 days =   1,271.97

4)   The Claimant has been unable to carry out any domestic or household tasks since the accident. Prior to the accident he used to carry out all vacuum cleaning and heavy cleaning tasks, maintain the garden and do the weekly supermarket shop. These tasks are now performed by his wife

These tasks are assessed at 5 hours per week

5 hours x 104 =   3,499.60

5)   Following the operation the Claimant required a great deal of assistance. This was provided for by his wife and is assessed as being 12 hours per day for 4 weeks, 6 hours per day for 4 weeks and 2 hours per day for 12 weeks

(12 hours x 4 weeks x 7 days) +
(6 hours x 4 weeks x 7 days) +

(2 hours x 12 weeks x 7 days) =   4,522.56

TOTAL CARE AND ASSISTANCE   10,276.71

3   COST OF MEDICAL TREATMENT

1)   Cost of discectomy operation   15,000.00

2)   Cost of post-operative physiotherapy

      15 sessions at £35   525.00

TOTAL COST OF MEDICAL TREATMENT   15,525.00

4   MEDICAL EQUIPMENT

1)   Support belts   75.00

2)   Heat pads   21.00

3)   TENS machine   19.99

4)   Batteries for TENS machine
      @£5 per month - to date 18 months   90.00

TOTAL COST OF EQUIPMENT   205.99

5   LOSS OF INCOME AS FOOTBALL REFEREE

The Claimant was a Football
Association referee class 5, and
regularly refereed matches at weekends,
for which he received a payment of £30
per match. A claim is made on the
basis of 1 match every other week from
September to May (39 weeks) and
allowing for tax at 20%

Period 1st April 2011 to 1st April
2013

78/2 matches = 39 x £30 x 0.8 =   936.00

TOTAL NET LOSS OF INCOME AS REFEREE   936.00

6   INTEREST

Interest is claimed at one half the
Special Account rate from 1st April

2011 to the date at which this schedule
is calculated namely 1st April 2013
namely at 3.27%
on losses to date, namely   35,124.67

TOTAL INTEREST   1,148.58

TOTAL OF PAST LOSSES AND INTEREST   36,273.25

FUTURE LOSSES

Age of Claimant at calculation date   45
Life time multiplier (Ogden Table 1)   23.88
Multiplier for loss of earnings to age 65
(Ogden Table 9)   15.19

7 **LOSS OF EARNINGS/EARNINGS CAPACITY**

The Claimant is not suffering any loss
of earnings at present. However he is at
risk of having to take periods of time
off because of the continuing back
symptoms. He has sustained an
impairment of his earning capacity and
is at risk of suffering loss of earnings.
Ogden calculation:
Annual net earnings -   13,608.40

1) Multiplier not disabled, in employment,
   no qualifications
   Adjustment Table A   0.86
   Apply to multiplier to age 65 15.19
   Adjusted multiplier   <u>13.06</u>
   Apply to net earnings   177,725.70

2) Multiplier disabled, in employment, no
   qualifications
   Adjustment Table B   0.55
   Apply to multiplier to age 65 15.19
   Adjusted multiplier   <u>8.35</u>
   Apply to net earnings   113,630.14

   Probable future loss of earnings
   (Ogden)   64,095.56

   Therefore a reasonable sum to

compensate the Claimant for his risk of
unemployment in the future as a result
of the effect of his injury on him would
be of the order of -   65,000.00

8   LOSS OF PROFIT FROM HOME IMPROVEMENTS

The Claimant had bought, done up and
sold houses in which he lived for over
10 years. He bought his current home in
September 2006 and had carried out
some improvements. However because
of the accident and the continuing
symptoms the Claimant is unable to
carry out the works of re-wiring,
re-plumbing, improvements and
decorating which he had planned and
which the house required. He will have
to employ labour to carry out this work
for him. The Claimant claims the cost
of such labour. Full particulars will be
provided in due course.

The Claimant has lost the opportunity
to make profits on future properties
which he would have purchased and
done up for sale. The Claimant is
obtaining accountancy evidence to
demonstrate the likely profit he would
have made on each such property.   To be assessed

9   **CARE AND ASSISTANCE**

Continuing at 5 hours per week - see
2(4) above - value per year -   1,749.80
Multiplier (life time)   <u>23.88</u>

TOTAL VALUE   41,785.22

10   **FUTURE EQUIPMENT AND TREATMENT COSTS**

1)   Batteries for TENS machine @ £5 per
        month - per year   60.00
        Multiplier (life time)   23.88

        Total value   1,432.80

2)	Physiotherapy - allow 3 sessions per year during periods of exacerbation @ £45 each - per year	135.00
	Multiplier (say 50% of life time)	11.94
	Total value	1,611.90

TOTAL VALUE		3,044.70

11 LOSS OF INCOME AS FOOTBALL REFEREE

The Claimant would have continued to act as referee until aged 50 on 15th February 2018.

Annual net loss = 39/2 x £30 x 0.8 =	468.00	
Period of loss 5 years - multiplier (Ogden Table 28)	4.70	

TOTAL VALUE		2,199.60

Dated 1st April 2013

Statement of Truth

[I believe] [The claimant believes] that the facts stated in this schedule are true.

I am duly authorised by the Claimant to sign this statement

Full name

Signed

Sue Quickly & Co
Claims House
Nowin Nofee Boulevard
Goldchester
Solicitors for the Claimant

Index

References are to Section numbers

Lightning Source UK Ltd.
Milton Keynes UK
UKOW06f1933081015

260126UK00001B/1/P